iWrite Math

Pre-Calculus Mathematics 12 Book

- *Functions and Relations*
- *Transformations*
- *Exponential and Logarithmic Functions*
- *Applications of Exponential and Logarithmic Functions*
- *Polynomial Functions and Equations*
- *Permutations & Combinations*
- *Analyzing Radical and Rational Functions*
- *Trigonometry - Functions and Graphs*
- *Trigonometry - Equations and Identities*

Publisher: Absolute Value Publications

Authors: Alan Appleby, Greg Ranieri

Reviewers and Contributors: Victoria Lozinski, Susan Appleby,
                              Nickolas Rollick, Danny Glin, Tony Audia

Printed in Canada.

ISBN 978-1-926979-06-9

For information contact:

Absolute Value Publications Inc.
P.O. Box 71096
8060 Silver Springs Blvd. N.W.
Calgary, Alberta
T3B 5K1

Bus: (403) 313-1442
Fax: (403) 313-2042

e-mail: avp@avpbooks.com
           avp@absolutevaluepublications.com

web site: www.avpbooks.com
           www.absolutevaluepublications.com

iWrite Math Pre-Calculus Mathematics 12 Book

The iWrite Math Pre-Calculus Grade 12 book is a complete resource and a 100% fit for the combined Western and Northern Canadian mathematics curriculum.

There are nine curricular units. Each curricular unit is subdivided into individual lessons. The last lesson in each unit is a practice test containing 20 multiple choice questions, 6 numeric response questions, and an extended response question.

Most lessons can be covered in one hour (plus homework time), but some may require more time to complete. Most lessons are composed of four parts:

- ### Investigations, Explorations, or Review
   which include inquiry based learning that can be teacher led, student led, or a combination of both.

- ### Class Examples
   which are applications of the investigations, explorations, or review.

- ### Assignments
   which include short response, extended response, multiple choice, and numeric response questions provided for student practice.

- ### Answer Key
   which contains the answers to the assignment questions.

The **Teacher Solution Manual** is a complete copy of the book with detailed solutions to all the investigations/explorations/review, class examples, and assignments.

The **Student Solution Manual** provides detailed solutions to all the investigations/explorations/review, class examples, and assignment questions. It does not include the actual questions.

Advantages for Students

- Students write **in** the book so that the math theory, worked examples, and assignments are all in one place for easy review.

- Students can write on the diagrams and graphs.

- Provides class examples and assignments so that students can use their time more efficiently. By focusing on solving problems and making their own notes, students improve their study skills.

- For independent learners, the book plus solution manual fosters self-paced learning.

- Encourages inquiry-based learning, group learning, and peer tutoring.

- The design of the book ensures that students are fully aware of the course expectations.

- The iWrite Math book is also available as an app at the Apple iTunes Store.

- We hope you enjoy using this book and that with the help of your teacher you realize the success that thousands of students each year are achieving using the book series.

Advantages for Teachers

- Written by teachers experienced in preparing students for success in high school and diploma examinations.

- Comprehensively covers the Western and Northern Canadian curriculum.

- Can be used as the main resource, or in conjunction with a textbook, or for extra assignments, or review.

- Reduces school photocopying costs and time.

- Allows for easy lesson planning in the case of teacher or student absence.

- The iWrite Math series is available in the following fromats:
  - Book
  - App form for tablets
  - Promethean Flipchart
  - Smart Notebook

Student, teacher, and parent responses to the iWrite Math book series have been very positive. We welcome your feedback. It enables us to produce a high quality resource meeting our goal of success for both students and teachers.

iWrite Math Pre-Calculus Mathematics 12 Book - Table of Contents

Functions and Relations Lesson #1:
Functions Review and Preview

Overview

In this unit we will develop an understanding of operations on functions and composition of functions. In this lesson we will review some of the properties of polynomial functions, absolute value functions, and radical functions. First we will introduce the concept of **interval notation**.

Interval Notation

The solution to an inequality in x has been graphed below.

Using **set builder notation**, the solution can be written as $\{x \mid 2 \le x < 5, x \in R\}$.

Interval Notation is a more concise way of describing the solution. The above solution can be expressed using interval notation as $[2, 5)$. The closed bracket, [, indicates that the 2 is included, and the open bracket,), indicates that the 5 is not included.

Interval notation can be used to describe domain and range.
Consider the function whose graph is $y = x^2$.
The range, $\{y \mid y \ge 0, y \in R\}$, can be written as $[0, \infty)$, and the domain, $\{x \mid x \in R\}$, can be written as $(-\infty, \infty)$.

In this course, domain and range will be expressed in both **set builder notation** and in **interval notation**. Unless otherwise specified, use set builder notation.

Polynomial Functions

A polynomial function in x is a function in the form

$$f(x) = a_n x^n + a_{n-1} x^{n-1} + a_{n-2} x^{n-2} + \dots + a_2 x^2 + a_1 x + a_0,$$

where
- $a_0, a_1, a_2, \dots a_n$ are real numbers, $a_n \ne 0$,
- $n \in W$.

$a_1, a_2, \dots a_n$ are called <u>coefficients</u>. a_n, is called the <u>leading coefficient</u> and a_0 is the <u>constant term</u>. The value of n is the <u>degree</u> of the polynomial.

For example, the polynomial function $f(x) = 7x^3 + x^4 - 8x^2 + 5$ has

degree_____, leading coefficient _____, and constant term _____

Three common polynomial functions we will use for transformations are

- Linear Functions   • Quadratic Functions   • Cubic Functions

---

Linear Functions

A linear function is a polynomial function of degree 1 of the form $f(x) = ax + b$.
The graph of a linear function is a straight line.

Another function whose graph is a straight line is a **constant function** - a function whose value never changes. It is a polynomial function of degree zero, and can be written in the form $f(x) = ax^0 \Rightarrow f(x) = a$.

Class Ex. #1

Sketch the following functions and state the domain and range using set builder notation.

a) $y = 3x + 1$

b) $y = 5$

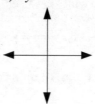

Quadratic Functions

A quadratic function is a polynomial function of degree 2 which can be written in <u>general</u> or <u>standard</u> form.

General Form:
$f(x) = ax^2 + bx + c$, where $a \neq 0$.

Standard Form
$f(x) = a(x - p)^2 + q$, where $a \neq 0$.

Class Ex. #2

a) Use a graphing calculator to sketch the graph of the function with equation $y = x^2 - 3x - 18$ and determine

   i)   the zeros of the function   **ii)** the y-intercept of the graph

   iii) the coordinates of the vertex

   iv) the domain and range using interval notation

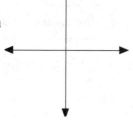

b) Use factoring to determine the zeros.

c) Rewrite the equation of the graph of the quadratic function in standard form. Explain how this form helps determine the coordinates of the vertex of the graph.

Class Ex. #3

Use a graphing calculator to sketch the graph of the quadratic function
$f(x) = -3x^2 + 4x + 1$.

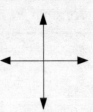

a) Use the features of a graphing calculator to determine the zeros of the
function to the nearest hundredth.

b) Use the quadratic formula to determine the exact values of the zeros
in simplest radical form.

Cubic Functions

A cubic function is a polynomial function of degree 3 of the form.
$f(x) = ax^3 + bx^2 + cx + d, \ a \neq 0.$

Class Ex. #4

Consider the cubic function with equation $y = x^3 - 8x^2 + 16x - 8$.

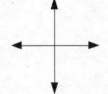

a) Use a graphing calculator to sketch the graph of the cubic function.

b) Use the features of a graphing calculator to determine the x-intercepts
of the graph to the nearest tenth.

c) Using interval notation, state the solution to the equation $y > 0$.

Absolute Value Function

An absolute value function is a function of the form $f(x) = |x|$, where

$$f(x) = |x| = \begin{cases} x & \text{if } x \geq 0 \\ -x & \text{if } x < 0 \end{cases}$$

Class Ex. #5

Sketch the graph of the absolute value function $f(x) = |x - 2|$ and
determine the domain and range.

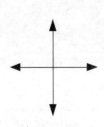

Radical Functions

A radical function is a function which contains a variable in the radicand such as $f(x) = \sqrt{x}$.

Class Ex. #6

a) Sketch the radical function $g(x) = \sqrt{2x - 1}$.

b) Determine the domain and range of the function using both set builder notation and interval notation.

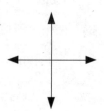

Complete Assignment Questions #1 - #8

Function Notation

Class Ex. #7

If $f(x) = x^2 + 4x + 5$, find the following in simplest form:

a) $f(2)$ **b)** $2f(x)$ **c)** $f(2x)$

d) $f(x) - 2$ **e)** $f(x - 2)$ **f)** $f(-x)$

Class Ex. #8

Consider the function $f(x) = x^3$. Match each function on the bottom row with an expression on the top row.

Expression   **A.** $x^3 + 5$ **B.** $(x + 5)^3$ **C.** 5^3 **D.** $(5x)^3$

Function   **1.** $f(x + 5)$ **2.** $f(5x)$ **3.** $f(x) + 5$ **4.** $f(5)$

Class Ex. #9

If $f(x) = |x|$, write the following in terms of the function f.

a) $|x| - 4$ **b)** $|x + 3| - 2$ **c)** $2|x|$ **d)** $|2x|$

Complete Assignment Questions #9 - #14

Assignment

1. The equations of the graphs of five functions are given below. In each case, sketch the graph and determine

   i) the zeros (to the nearest tenth if necessary)

   ii) the domain and range

   a) $y = -2x + 4$ **b)** $y = 5x - 10$ **c)** $y = x^2 - 2x - 15$

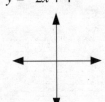   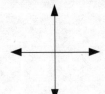   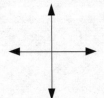

   zeros

   domain

   range

   d) $y = -x^2 - 3x - 4$ **e)** $y = (x + 1)(x + 2)(x - 5)$

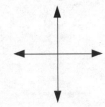   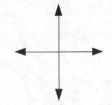

   zeros

   domain

   range

2. The linear function with equation $y = ax + b$ is in slope y-intercept form.

   a) Which parameter represents the slope of the line?

   b) Which parameter represents the y-intercept?

   c) If $a > 0$, describe the slope.

   d) If $a < 0$, describe the slope.

3. How can you tell from the quadratic function $f(x) = ax^2 + bx + c$ whether the graph of the function will open up or open down?

4. Consider the quadratic function $f(x) = 2x^2 - 5x - 6$.

   a) Sketch the graph of the function on the grid.

   b) Use the features of a graphing calculator to determine the zeros to the nearest hundredth.

   c) Use the quadratic formula to determine the exact values of the zeros in simplest radical form.

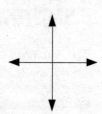

5. Sketch the graph of the functions whose equations are given below and state the domain and range using interval notation.

   a) $y = |x| + 4$ **b)** $y = |x + 3|$ **c)** $y = -|x + 2|$ **d)** $y = -|x| - 3$

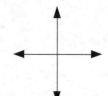   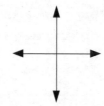   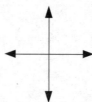   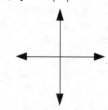

   domain

   range

6. Which of the graphs in Question #5 open up? Open down? What determines the direction of opening?

7. Sketch the graph of the functions whose equations are given and state the domain and range using interval notation. What shape is each graph?

   a) $y = \sqrt{16 - x^2}$ **b)** $y = -\sqrt{16 - x^2}$

                    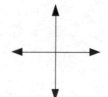

   domain

   range

8. Combining the equations from Questions #7a and #7b results in $y = \pm\sqrt{16 - x^2}$.

a) Square both sides of the equation to rewrite in the form $x^2 + y^2 = k$.

b) What geometrical shape is formed by combining the graphs from question #7a and #7b?

c) How does the value of k relate to the radius of the circle?

d) Without using a graphing calculator, sketch the graph of $x^2 + y^2 = 49$.

9. If $f(x) = x^3 - 5$, find the following in simplest form:

a) $f(-1)$

b) $4f(x)$

c) $f(4x)$

d) $f(x) + 5$

e) $f(x + 5)$

f) $f(-x)$

10. If $f(x) = \sqrt{x}$, write the following in terms of the function f.

a) $\sqrt{x} - 1$

b) $\sqrt{x + 3}$

c) $\sqrt{2x - 1}$

d) $-3\sqrt{x}$

11. If $f(x) = x^2$, write the following in terms of the function f.

a) $x^2 + 3$

b) $(x + 3)^2$

c) $3x^2$

d) $(3x)^2$

e) $4x^2 - 7$

f) $4(x^2 - 7)$

g) $-2x^2 - 1$

h) $(-x + 4)^2$

i) $-3(-x - 2)^2$

12. The function f is defined by $f(x) = 2x^2 + 3$. Which of the following represents $f(2x)$?

A. $2x^2 + 3$ **B.** $4x^2 + 3$

C. $8x^2 + 3$ **D.** $4x^2 + 6$

13. The function g is defined by $g(x) = x^4$.

Which of the following functions is represented by $\frac{1}{2}x^4$?

A. $g(\frac{1}{2}x)$ **B.** $g\left(\frac{1}{2} + x\right)$ **C.** $2g(x)$ **D.** none of the above

14. To the nearest hundredth, the largest zero of the function $P(x) = -2x^3 + 16x + 2$ is ____.

(Record your answer in the numerical response box from left to right.)

Answer Key

1. a) zeros: 2
Domain: $\{x \mid x \in R\}$
Range: $\{y \mid y \in R\}$

b) zeros: 2
Domain: $\{x \mid x \in R\}$
Range: $\{y \mid y \in R\}$

c) zeros: $-3, 5$
Domain: $\{x \mid x \in R\}$
Range: $\{y \mid y \geq -16, y \in R\}$

d) zeros: none
Domain: $\{x \mid x \in R\}$
Range: $\left\{y \mid y \leq -\frac{7}{4}, y \in R\right\}$

e) zeros: $-1, -2, 5$
Domain: $\{x \mid x \in R\}$
Range: $\{y \mid y \in R\}$

2. a) a **b)** b **c)** rises from left to right **d)** falls from left to right

3. If $a > 0$, the graph opens up. If $a < 0$, the graph opens down.

4. b) $-0.89, 3.39$ **c)** $x = \dfrac{5 \pm \sqrt{73}}{4}$

5. a) Domain: $(-\infty, \infty)$
Range: $[4, \infty)$

b) Domain: $(-\infty, \infty)$
Range: $[0, \infty)$

c) Domain: $(-\infty, \infty)$
Range: $(-\infty, 0]$

d) Domain: $(-\infty, \infty)$
Range: $(-\infty, -3]$

6. • Graphs a and b open up and graphs c and d open down.
• If there is a negative sign outside the absolute value symbol, the graph opens down.
If there is no negative sign outside the absolute value symbol, the graph opens up.

7. a) Domain: $[-4, 4]$
Range: $[0, 4]$
Each graph is a semi-circle.

b) Domain: $[-4, 4]$
Range: $[-4, 0]$

8. a) $x^2 + y^2 = 16$ **b)** circle **c)** $k = r^2$ **d)** circle centre $(0, 0)$ with radius 7

9. a) -6 **b)** $4x^3 - 20$ **c)** $64x^3 - 5$ **d)** x^3 **e)** $x^3 + 15x^2 + 75x + 120$ **f)** $-x^3 - 5$

10. a) $f(x) - 1$ **b)** $f(x + 3)$ **c)** $f(2x - 1)$ **d)** $-3f(x)$

11. a) $f(x) + 3$ **b)** $f(x + 3)$ **c)** $3f(x)$ **d)** $f(3x)$ **e)** $4f(x) - 7$
f) $4(f(x) - 7)$ **g)** $-2f(x) - 1$ **h)** $f(-x + 4)$ **i)** $-3f(-x - 2)$

12. C **13.** D **14.**

2	.	8	9

Functions and Relations Lesson #2:
Operations with Functions - Part One

Operations with Functions

The following properties apply to functions f and g, provided x is in the domain of f and g.

The <u>sum</u> of f and g	$\rightarrow$	$(f + g)(x) = f(x) + g(x)$
The <u>difference</u> of f and g	$\rightarrow$	$(f - g)(x) = f(x) - g(x)$
The <u>product</u> of f and g	$\rightarrow$	$(fg)(x) = f(x)g(x)$
The <u>quotient</u> of f and g	$\rightarrow$	$\left(\dfrac{f}{g}\right)(x) = \dfrac{f(x)}{g(x)}$, $g(x) \neq 0$

In this lesson, we will consider the sum and difference of two functions, and in the next two lessons we will consider the product and quotient of two functions.

Investigating the Sum & Difference of Two Functions

Part 1:

Two functions $f(x)$ and $g(x)$ are defined for all real numbers. The table of values below shows the values of f and g for certain values of x.

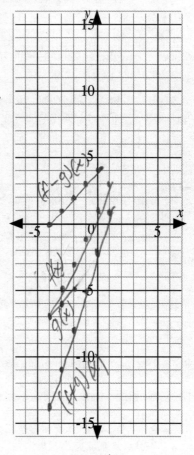

x	$f(x)$	$g(x)$	$(f + g)(x)$	$(f - g)(x)$
–4	–7	–7	–14	0
–3	–5	–6	–11	1
–2	–3	–5	–8	2
–1	–1	–4	–5	3
0	1	–3	–2	4
1	3	–2	1	5
2	5	–1	4	6
3	7	0	7	7
4	9	1	10	8

a) Plot the points $(x, f(x))$ on the grid and sketch the graph of $y = f(x)$ for $x \in R$.

b) Plot the points $(x, g(x))$ on the grid and sketch the graph of $y = g(x)$ for $x \in R$.

c) Complete the tables above for $(f + g)(x)$ and $(f - g)(x)$ and sketch the graphs of $y = (f + g)(x)$ and $y = (f - g)(x)$ for $x \in R$.

d) The functions *f* and *g* on the previous page are $f(x) = 2x + 1$ and $g(x) = x - 3$. Write expressions for the functions $(f + g)(x)$ and $(f - g)(x)$.

e) Use a graphing calculator to graph the functions $y = (f + g)(x)$ and $y = (f - g)(x)$ from part d) and compare these graphs with the graphs from part c).

f) State the domains and ranges of the functions $(f + g)(x)$ and $(f - g)(x)$.

g) Determine the values of $(f + g)(10)$ and $y = (f - g)(-10)$.

h) In this example, the sum and difference of two functions of degree 1 are also functions of degree 1. Can you find two functions of degree 1 whose sum or difference is not a function of degree 1?

Part 2:

The graphs of two quadratic functions, $y = f(x)$ and $y = g(x)$, $x \in R$, are shown on the grid. The points marked with dots have integer coordinates.

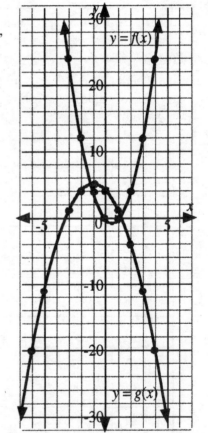

a) Use these graphs to sketch the graphs of $y = (f + g)(x)$ and $y = (f - g)(x)$ for $x \in R$.

b) The functions *f* and *g* above are $f(x) = 2x^2 - 2x$ and $g(x) = -x^2 - 2x + 4$. Write expressions for the functions $(f + g)(x)$ and $(f - g)(x)$.

c) Use a graphing calculator to graph the functions $y = (f + g)(x)$ and $y = (f - g)(x)$ from part b) and compare these graphs with the graphs from part a).

d) State the domains of the functions $(f + g)(x)$ and $(f - g)(x)$.

e) In this example, the sum and difference of two quadratic functions are quadratic functions. Can you find two quadratic functions whose sum or difference is not a quadratic function?

Class Ex. #1   Consider the functions $f(x) = x^3 - 2x^2 + 6$ and $g(x) = x^3 - 2x + 6, x \in R$.

a) Determine expressions for

   i) $f(x) + g(x)$ ii) $f(x) - g(x)$

b) Complete the following statements

   i) $f(x) + g(x)$ is a _____ of two functions f and g,
      and can be rewritten as $(f + g)(x) =$ _____ .

   ii) $f(x) - g(x)$ is a _____ of two functions f and g,
      and can be rewritten as _____ = _____ .

c) Evaluate

   i) $(f + g)(-2)$ ii) $(f - g)(\sqrt{6})$

Class Ex. #2   A multi-media production company produces DVDs which cost $3.00 per unit. The fixed costs, including the graphics, are $10 000 irrespective of the number of DVDs produced. Each DVD retails for $15.00.

If x is the number of units produced, answer the following in terms of x.

a) Write the total cost, $C(x)$, as a function of the number of units produced.

b) Write the revenue, $R(x)$, as a function of the number of units produced.

c) Write the company's profit, $P(x)$, as a function of the number of units produced.

d) Determine the company's profit if 20 000 DVDs are produced

---

Complete Assignment Questions #1 - #9

Assignment

1. Consider the functions $f(x) = 3x + 7$ and $g(x) = 2x - 4$, defined for all real numbers.

   a) Determine the following functions in simplest form and state the domain and range of each function.

   i) $(f + g)(x)$ **ii)** $(f - g)(x)$ **iii)** $(g - f)(x)$

   b) Evaluate

   i) $(f + g)(5)$ **ii)** $(f - g)(-3)$ **iii)** $(g - f)(0)$

2. If $P(x) = x^2 - 7x + 3$ and $Q(x) = 2x + 9$, evaluate $(P - Q)(-3)$ in two different ways.

3. Two functions $f(x)$ and $g(x)$ are defined for all real numbers. The table of values below shows the values of f and g for certain values of x.

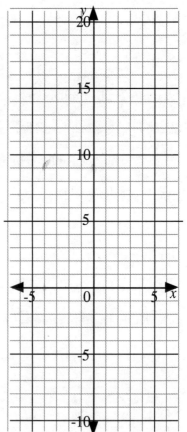

x	$f(x)$	$g(x)$	$(f + g)(x)$	$(f - g)(x)$
-4	9	-8		
-3	4	-7		
-2	1	-6		
-1	0	-5		
0	1	-4		
1	4	-3		
2	9	-2		
3	16	-1		
4	25	0		

   a) Plot the points $(x, f(x))$ on the grid and sketch the graph of $y = f(x)$ for $x \in R$.

   b) Plot the points $(x, g(x))$ on the grid and sketch the graph of $y = g(x)$ for $x \in R$.

   c) Complete the tables above for $(f + g)(x)$ and $(f - g)(x)$ and sketch the graphs of $y = (f + g)(x)$ and $y = (f - g)(x)$ for $x \in R$.

d) The functions f and g on the previous page are $f(x) = x^2 + 2x + 1$ and $g(x) = x - 4$. Write expressions for the functions $(f + g)(x)$ and $(f - g)(x)$.

e) Use a graphing calculator to graph the functions $y = (f + g)(x)$ and $y = (f - g)(x)$ from part d) and compare these graphs with the graphs from part c).

f) State the domains of the functions $(f + g)(x)$ and $(f - g)(x)$.

g) Determine the values of $(f + g)(8)$ and $y = (f - g)(-12)$.

h) In this example, the sum and difference of a linear function and a quadratic function are quadratic functions. Can you find a linear function and a quadratic function whose sum or difference is not a quadratic function?

4. The graphs of two quadratic functions, $y = f(x)$ and $y = g(x)$, $x \in R$, are shown on the grid.

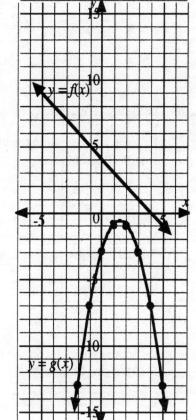

a) Use these graphs to sketch the graphs of $y = (f + g)(x)$ and $y = (f - g)(x)$ for $x \in R$.

b) The functions f and g above are $f(x) = 4 - x$ and $g(x) = -x^2 + 3x - 3$. Write expressions for the functions $(f + g)(x)$ and $(f - g)(x)$.

c) Use a graphing calculator to graph the functions $y = (f + g)(x)$ and $y = (f - g)(x)$ from part b) and compare these graphs with the graphs from part a).

d) State the domains of the functions $(f + g)(x)$ and $(f - g)(x)$.

e) Evaluate. **i)** $(f + g)(-10)$ **ii)** $(f - g)\left(\sqrt{3}\right)$

5. The graphs of two quadratic functions, $y = f(x)$ and $y = g(x)$, $x \in R$, are shown on the grid.

   a) Use these graphs to sketch the graphs of $y = (f - g)(x)$ and $y = (g - f)(x)$ for $x \in R$.

   b) How do the graphs of $y = (f - g)(x)$ and $y = (g - f)(x)$ relate to each other?

   c) The functions f and g above are $f(x) = 2x^2 - x - 8$ and $g(x) = -x^2 - 2x + 2$. Write expressions for the functions $(f - g)(x)$ and $(g - f)(x)$.

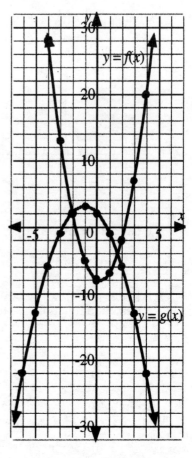

   d) Use a graphing calculator to graph the functions $y = (f - g)(x)$ and $y = (g - f)(x)$ from part c) and compare these graphs with the graphs from part a).

   e) Evaluate. **i)** $(f - g)\left(\dfrac{1}{2}\right)$ **ii)** $(g - f)\left(2\sqrt{2}\right)$

6. The figure shown has an area $A(x) = 2x^2 + 8x - 3 \text{ cm}^2$.

   a) Write an expression for the area, $B(x)$, of the bottom rectangular part of the figure.

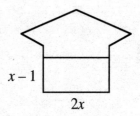

$x - 1$

$2x$

   b) Find an expression in simplest form for the area, $T(x)$, of the top part of the figure.

   c) If the area of the top is 9 cm^2, determine the value of x.

7. Partial graphs of functions f and g are shown on the grids.
In each case, sketch the graph of the indicated function.

a) $(f + g)(x)$

b) $(g - f)(x)$

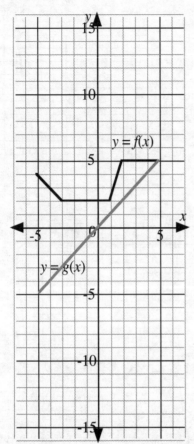

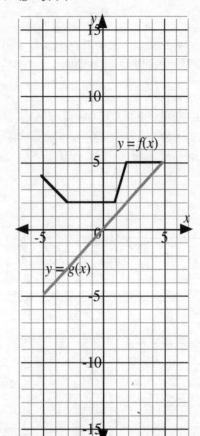

8. The graph of $y = f(x)$ includes the points $(2, 5), (4, 15), (7, 30)$.
The graph of $y = g(x)$ includes the points $(2, 6), (3, 16), (4, 30)$.

If f and g are defined for all real values of x, then which of the following points **must** lie on the graph of $y = (f - g)(x)$?

A. $(0, -1)$ **B.** $(0, 1)$

C. $(2, -1)$ **D.** $(3, 30)$

9. If $f(x) = \sqrt{3x} - 2$ and $g(x) = 5\sqrt{3x}$, then $2(g - f)(3)$, to the nearest tenth, is _____ .

(Record your answer in the numerical response box from left to right.)

Answer Key

1. a) (i) $5x + 3$ (ii) $x + 11$ (iii) $-x - 11$ all domains $x \in R$, all ranges $y \in R$
   b) (i) 28 (ii) 8 (iii) –11

2. $(P - Q)(-3) = P(-3) - Q(-3) = 33 - 3 = 30$ or $(P - Q)(x) = x^2 - 9x - 6$ so $(P - Q)(-3) = 30$

3. a), b), and **c)** See graph and table at the bottom of this page.
   d) $(f + g)(x) = x^2 + 3x - 3$, $(f - g)(x) = x^2 + x + 5$ **f)** $x \in R$ **g)** 85, 137 **h)** no

4. a) See graph at the bottom of the page. **b)** $(f + g)(x) = -x^2 + 2x + 1$, $(f - g)(x) = x^2 - 4x + 7$
   d) $x \in R$ **e)** (i) –119 (ii) $10 - 4\sqrt{3}$

5. a) See graph at the bottom of the page. **b)** reflection in the x-axis

   c) $(f - g)(x) = 3x^2 + x - 10$, $(g - f)(x) = -3x^2 - x + 10$ **e)** (i) $-\dfrac{35}{4}$ (ii) $-14 - 2\sqrt{2}$

6. a) $2x^2 - 2x$ cm^2 **b)** $10x - 3$ cm^2 **c)** $\dfrac{6}{5}$ **7. a), b)** See graphs at the bottom of the page.

8. C **9.** | 2 | 8 | . | 0 |

3. **4.** **5.**

x	$f(x)$	$g(x)$	$(f+g)(x)$	$(f-g)(x)$
–4	9	–8	1	17
–3	4	–7	–3	11
–2	1	–6	–5	7
–1	0	–5	–5	5
0	1	–4	–3	5
1	4	–3	1	7
2	9	–2	7	11
3	16	–1	15	17
4	25	0	25	25

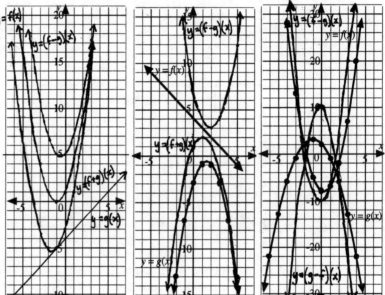

7. a) **b)**

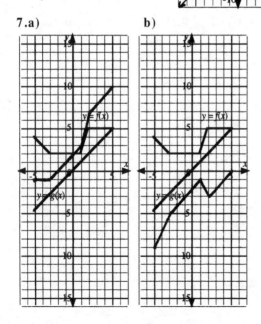

Functions and Relations Lesson #3:
Operations with Functions - Part Two

Investigating the Product of Two Functions

In this investigation we will use the same functions, f and g, as in the investigation in lesson 2.

x	$f(x)$	$g(x)$	$(fg)(x)$
−4	−7	−7	
−3	−5	−6	
−2	−3	−5	
−1	−1	−4	
0	1	−3	
1	3	−2	
2	5	−1	
3	7	0	
4	9	1	

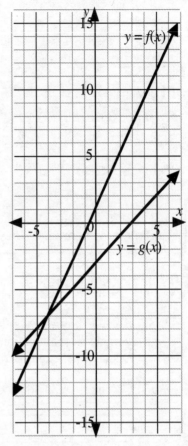

a) Complete the table above for $(fg)(x)$.

b) Plot the points from the table which will fit on the grid and complete the sketch of $y = (fg)(x)$ for $x \in R$.

c) The functions f and g above are $f(x) = 2x + 1$ and $g(x) = x - 3$. Write a simplified expression for the function $(fg)(x)$.

d) Use a graphing calculator to graph the function $y = (fg)(x)$ from part c) and compare this graph with the graph from part b).

e) Determine the domain and range of the function $(fg)(x)$.

f) Calculate the value of $(fg)(8)$ in two different ways.

g) Complete the statement.
" In this investigation, the product of two functions whose graphs are straight lines is
a _____ function."

Can you find two functions whose graphs are straight lines where this is not the case?

Class Ex. #1 Consider the functions $f(x) = 3\sqrt{x} - 2$ and $g(x) = \sqrt{x} - 5$.

a) Write an expression in simplest form for each of the following functions.

  i) $(f - g)(x)$ **ii)** $(fg)(x)$

b) Evaluate

  i) $(f - g)(16)$ **ii)** $(fg)(49)$

Complete Assignment Questions #1 - #6

Assignment

1. Consider functions f and g defined for all real numbers.
Partial graphs of the functions are shown on the grid.
Both functions have integer values when x is an integer.

  a) Complete the table above for $(fg)(x)$.

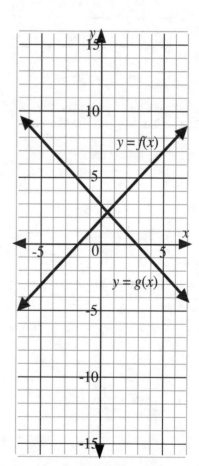

x	$f(x)$	$g(x)$	$(fg)(x)$
−4			
−3			
−2			
−1			
0			
1			
2			
3			
4			
5			

  b) Plot the points from the table which will fit on the grid
and complete the sketch of $y = (fg)(x)$ for $x \in R$.

c) The functions f and g above are $f(x) = 2 + x$ and $g(x) = 3 - x$.
Write a simplified expression for the function $(fg)(x)$.

d) Use a graphing calculator to graph the function $y = (fg)(x)$ from part c) and compare
this graph with the graph from part b).

e) Determine the domain and range of the function $(fg)(x)$.

f) Calculate the value of $(fg)\left(-\dfrac{1}{2}\right)$ in two different ways.

g) How does the graph of $(gf)(x)$ compare to the graph of $(fg)(x)$?

2. Partial graphs of functions f and g are shown on the grids. In each case, sketch the partial
graph of the function that is the product of these two functions.

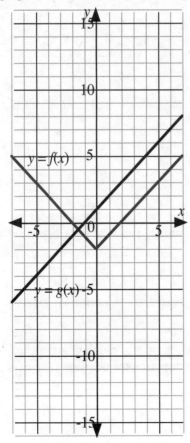
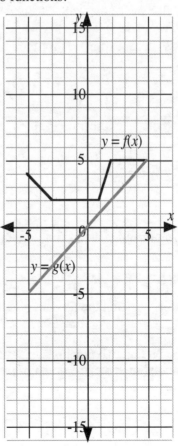

3. Consider functions *f* and *g* defined for all real numbers.
Partial graphs of the functions are shown on the grid.

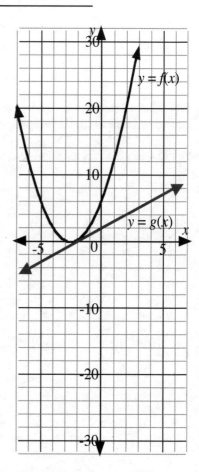

a) Complete the table using the values from the grid.

x	$f(x)$	$g(x)$	$(f + g)(x)$	$(fg)(x)$
−6				
−5				
−4				
−3				
−2				
−1				
0				
1				
2				

b) Plot the points from the table which will fit on the grid
and sketch the graphs of $y = (f + g)(x)$ and $y = (fg)(x)$.

c) The functions *f* and *g* above are $f(x) = (x + 3)(x + 2)$
and $g(x) = x + 2$.

   i) Write an expression for the function $(f + g)(x)$ in expanded form.

   ii) Write an expression for the function $(fg)(x)$ in expanded form.

d) Use a graphing calculator to graph the functions from part c) and verify the sketches from
part b).

e) Complete the statement.

   "In this question the product of a linear function and a quadratic function is
   a _____ function."

f) Can you find two functions, one whose graph is a straight line, and one whose graph is a
parabola, such that the graph of the product of the two functions is not the graph of a
cubic function?

4. Consider the functions $f(x) = 2\sqrt{x} - 5$ and $g(x) = \sqrt{x} - 5$.

   a) Determine the following functions in simplest form and state the domain of each function.

     i) $(f + g)(x)$ **ii)** $(g - f)(x)$ **iii)** $(gf)(x)$

   b) Evaluate.

     i) $(g + f)(4)$ **ii)** $(f - g)(49)$ **iii)** $(fg)(0.25)$

5. The points $(4, 1), (7, 4), (9, 6)$ lie on the graph of $y = P(x), x \in R$.
The points $(4, 3), (7, 6), (9, 8)$ lie on the graph of $y = Q(x), x \in R$.
Which of the following points **must** lie on the graph of $y = (PQ)(x)$?

   A. $(4, 3)$
   B. $(16, 3)$
   C. $(49, 24)$
   D. $(63, 6)$

6. Consider the functions $f(x) = 6 - 3x$ and $g(x) = 5 - 2x$. If the function $(fg)(x)$ is written in the form $ax^2 + bx + c$, then the value of $a - b + c$ is _____ .

(Record your answer in the numerical response box from left to right.)

Answer Key

1. a), b) See graph and table at the bottom of the page.

c) $(fg)(x) = 6 + x - x^2$ **e)** domain $x \in R$, range $\{y \mid y \le 6.25, y \in R\}$

f) $(fg)\left(-\dfrac{1}{2}\right) = f\left(-\dfrac{1}{2}\right) g\left(-\dfrac{1}{2}\right) = \left(\dfrac{3}{2}\right)\left(\dfrac{7}{2}\right) = \dfrac{21}{4}$ or $(fg)\left(-\dfrac{1}{2}\right) = 6 + \left(-\dfrac{1}{2}\right) - \left(-\dfrac{1}{2}\right)^2 = \dfrac{21}{4}$

g) It is identical.

2. See graphs below.

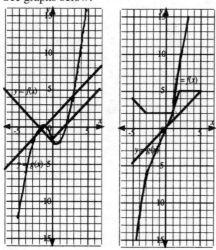

3. a), b) See graph and table at the bottom of the page.

c) (i) $x^2 + 6x + 8$ (ii) $x^3 + 7x^2 + 16x + 12$ **e)** cubic   **f)** $f(x) = 2$ $g(x) = x^2$

4. a) i) $3\sqrt{x} - 10, x \ge 0$ **ii)** $-\sqrt{x}, x \ge 0$ **iii)** $2x - 15\sqrt{x} + 25, x \ge 0$
b) i) -4 **ii)** 7 **iii)** 18

5. A   **6.**

6	3		

1.

x	$f(x)$	$g(x)$	$(fg)(x)$
-4	-2	7	-14
-3	-1	6	-6
-2	0	5	0
-1	1	4	4
0	2	3	6
1	3	2	6
2	4	1	4
3	5	0	0
4	6	-1	-6
5	7	-2	-14

3.

x	$f(x)$	$g(x)$	$(f+g)(x)$	$(fg)(x)$
-6	12	-4	8	-48
-5	6	-3	3	-18
-4	2	-2	0	-4
-3	0	-1	-1	0
-2	0	0	0	0
-1	2	1	3	2
0	6	2	8	12
1	12	3	15	36
2	20	4	24	80

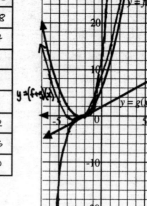

Functions and Relations Lesson #4:
Operations with Functions - Part Three

Two functions $f(x)$ and $g(x)$ are defined for all real numbers.
The graphs of the functions are shown on the grid.
The points marked with dots have integer coordinates.

a) Complete the table below.

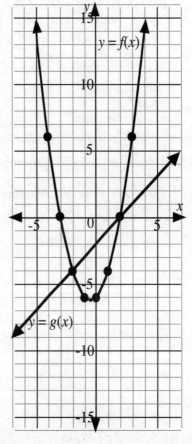

x	$f(x)$	$g(x)$	$\left(\dfrac{f}{g}\right)(x)$
4	14	2	14/2 = 7
3			
2			
1			
0			
−1			
−2			
−3			
−4			

b) Explain why the domain of the function $\left(\dfrac{f}{g}\right)(x)$ is not $x \in R$.

c) Sketch the graph of $y = \left(\dfrac{f}{g}\right)(x)$ showing the domain restriction by drawing an open circle on the graph.

d) The functions f and g above are $f(x) = x^2 + x - 6$ and $g(x) = x - 2$. Write and simplify an expression for the function $\left(\dfrac{f}{g}\right)(x)$, including the domain restriction.

e) Evaluate $\left(\dfrac{f}{g}\right)(-6)$.

Note

- In the Investigation, the graph of $\left(\dfrac{f}{g}\right)(x)$ cannot include the point $(2, 5)$ since there is a domain restriction $x \neq 2$. This results in a "hole" in the graph represented by an open circle. We refer to this hole as a **point of discontinuity** and this concept will be investigated in more detail in the unit on Rational Functions.

- In the Investigation, the quotient of a quadratic function and a linear function simplifies to a linear function with a domain restriction. This is not always the case. In many examples the quotient of two functions cannot be reduced to a simpler function.

Class Ex. #1

In each case, write and simplify (where possible) an expression for $\left(\dfrac{f}{g}\right)(x)$.

Include any domain restrictions.

a) $f(x) = 2x + 5, \ g(x) = x + 5$ **b)** $f(x) = x^2 - 2x - 35, \ g(x) = x - 7$

c) $f(x) = x - 2, \ g(x) = x^2 - 5x + 6$

Class Ex. #2

Consider the functions $f(x) = 2x^2 - 13x - 7$ and $g(x) = 2x + 1$.

a) State the domains of f and g.

b) Write an expression in simplest form for $\left(\dfrac{f}{g}\right)(x)$. State the domain.

c) **Explain** two different ways to evaluate $\left(\dfrac{f}{g}\right)(3)$. Calculate $\left(\dfrac{f}{g}\right)(3)$.

Complete Assignment Questions #1 - #7

Class Ex. #3

Consider the functions $f(x) = \dfrac{2x}{x-1}$ and $g(x) = \dfrac{x}{x-3}$.

a) State the domains of f and g.

b) Evaluate $3(fg)(2)$.

c) Write an expression in simplest form for $(f + g)(x)$. State any restrictions on x.

d) Write an expression in simplest form for $\left(\dfrac{f}{g}\right)(x)$. State any restrictions on x.

Complete Assignment Questions #8 - #11

Assignment

1. Two functions $f(x)$ and $g(x)$ are defined for all real numbers. The graphs of the functions are shown on the grid.

   a) Complete the table below.

x	$f(x)$	$g(x)$	$\left(\dfrac{f}{g}\right)(x)$
–4	–16	8	–16/8 = –2
–3			
–2			
–1			
0			
1			
2			
3			
4			
5			

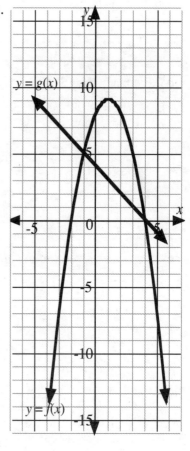

   b) Explain why the domain of the function $\left(\dfrac{f}{g}\right)(x)$ is not $x \in R$.

   c) Sketch the graph of $y = \left(\dfrac{f}{g}\right)(x)$ showing the domain restriction by drawing an open circle on the graph.

   d) The functions f and g above are $f(x) = 8 + 2x - x^2$ and $g(x) = 4 - x$. Write and simplify an expression for the function $\left(\dfrac{f}{g}\right)(x)$, including the domain restriction.

   e) Evaluate $\left(\dfrac{f}{g}\right)(12)$.

2. Two functions $f(x)$ and $g(x)$ are defined for all real numbers. The graphs of the functions are shown on the grid.

a) Complete the table below. Plot the points on the graph of $y = \left(\dfrac{f}{g}\right)(x)$, but do not connect the points at this time.

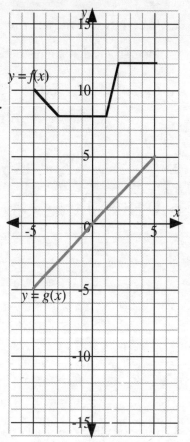

$y = f(x)$

$y = g(x)$

x	$f(x)$	$g(x)$	$\left(\dfrac{f}{g}\right)(x)$
–5			
–4			
–3			
–2			
–1			
0			
1			
2			
3			
4			
5			

b) State the domain of the function $\left(\dfrac{f}{g}\right)(x)$.

c) To investigate the behaviour of the function $\left(\dfrac{f}{g}\right)(x)$ near the domain restriction, complete the table to the right and plot the points on the grid.

d) Connect all the points on the grid and complete the graph of $y = \left(\dfrac{f}{g}\right)(x)$.

x	$f(x)$	$g(x)$	$\left(\dfrac{f}{g}\right)(x)$
–0.5			
–0.25			
0.25			
0.5			

Note   In this example, the y-axis is a vertical asymptote on the graph of $y = \left(\dfrac{f}{g}\right)(x)$.

This type of asymptotic behaviour on the graph of a function will be investigated further in the unit on Rational Functions.

3. In each case, write and simplify (where possible) an expression for $\left(\dfrac{f}{g}\right)(x)$. Include any domain restrictions.

   a) $f(x) = x + 6, \ g(x) = x + 3$

   b) $f(x) = x^2 - x - 20, \ g(x) = x - 5$

   c) $f(x) = x + 4, \ g(x) = x^2 + x - 12$

   d) $f(x) = 2x^2 - 7x - 15, \ g(x) = x - 5.$

4. Given $f(x) = 5x - 10$ and $g(x) = x - 2$, determine the following functions in simplest form and state any restrictions on x.

   a) $(f + g)(x)$

   b) $(f - g)(x)$

   c) $(fg)(x)$

   d) $\left(\dfrac{f}{g}\right)(x)$

5. Given $f(x) = x^2 - 9$ and $g(x) = x + 3$, determine the following functions in simplest form and state the restrictions on the variable.

   a) $(f + g)(x)$ **b)** $(f - g)(x)$

   c) $(fg)(x)$ **d)** $\left(\dfrac{f}{g}\right)(x)$

6. Consider the functions $f(x) = 6x^2 + 5x - 6$, and $g(x) = 6x^2 - 13x + 6$

   a) State the domains of f and g.

   b) Write an expression in simplest form for $\left(\dfrac{f}{g}\right)(x)$. State the domain.

   c) **Show** two different ways to evaluate $\left(\dfrac{f}{g}\right)(4)$.

7. In each case, find two functions f and g such that

   a) $(f + g)(x) = x^2 + 3x$

   b) $(f - g)(x) = x^2 + 3x$

   c) $(fg)(x) = x^2 + 3x$

   d) $\left(\dfrac{f}{g}\right)(x) = x^2 + 3x$

8. Given $f(x) = \dfrac{x}{x - 3}$ and $g(x) = \dfrac{2x}{x + 1}$, determine the following functions in simplest form and state any restrictions on x.

   a) $(f + g)(x)$

   b) $(f - g)(x)$

   c) $(fg)(x)$

   d) $\left(\dfrac{f}{g}\right)(x)$

9. Given $f(x) = x + 1$ and $g(x) = x^2 - 1$, determine the following functions in simplest form and state any restrictions on x.

a) $3(f - g)(x)$

b) $(ff)(x) - g(x)$

c) $\left(\dfrac{g}{f}\right)(x)$

Multiple Choice

10. Consider the functions $f(x) = \dfrac{x - 4}{x + 2}$ and $g(x) = \dfrac{x - 3}{x - 1}$. Which of the following are restrictions for $\left(\dfrac{f}{g}\right)(x)$?

    A. -2 and 1 only
    B. $-2, 1$, and 3 only
    C. $-2, 1$, and 4 only
    D. $-2, 1, 3$, and 4

Numerical Response

11. If $f(x) = 2x^2$ and $g(x) = \dfrac{x - 4}{2x}$, determine the values of:

    1. $(fg)(3)$ **2.** $(f - g)(4)$ **3.** $\left(\dfrac{f}{g}\right)(2)$ **4.** $(f + g)(1)$

Rearrange the four answers in increasing order. Write the question number corresponding to the smallest answer in the first box, the question number corresponding to the second smallest answer in the second box, etc.

(Record your answer in the numerical response box from left to right.)

Answer Key

1.a) See table below. **1 c)** See graph below. **2.a)** See table below. **2 d)** See graph below.

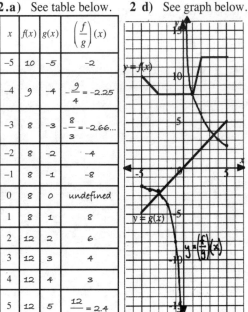

x	$f(x)$	$g(x)$	$\left(\dfrac{f}{g}\right)(x)$
-4	-16	8	-16/8 = -2
-3	-7	7	-1
-2	0	6	0
-1	5	5	1
0	8	4	2
1	9	3	3
2	8	2	4
3	5	1	5
4	0	0	Not defined (Indeterminant)
5	-7	-1	7

x	$f(x)$	$g(x)$	$\left(\dfrac{f}{g}\right)(x)$
-5	10	-5	-2
-4	9	-4	$-\dfrac{9}{4} = -2.25$
-3	8	-3	$-\dfrac{8}{3} = -2.66...$
-2	8	-2	-4
-1	8	-1	-8
0	8	0	undefined
1	8	1	8
2	12	2	6
3	12	3	4
4	12	4	3
5	12	5	$\dfrac{12}{5} = 2.4$

1.b) $\left(\dfrac{f}{g}\right)(x)$ is not defined when $g(x) = 0$ because division by zero is not defined. The domain is $\{x \mid x \neq 4, x \in R\}$.

1.d) $\left(\dfrac{f}{g}\right)(x) = \dfrac{8 + 2x - x^2}{4 - x} = 2 + x, x \neq 4$.

1.e) 14

2.b) The domain is $\{x \mid x \neq 0, x \in R\}$.

2.c)

x	$f(x)$	$g(x)$	$\left(\dfrac{f}{g}\right)(x)$
-0.5	8	-0.5	-16
-0.25	8	-0.25	-32
0.25	8	0.25	32
0.5	8	0.5	16

3. a) $\dfrac{x+6}{x+3}, x \neq -3$ **b)** $x + 4, x \neq 5$ **c)** $\dfrac{1}{x-3}, x \neq -4, 3$ **d)** $2x + 3, x \neq 5$

4. a) $6x - 12$ or $6(x-2)$ **b)** $4x - 8$ or $4(x-2)$
c) $5x^2 - 20x + 20$ or $5(x-2)^2$ **d)** 5 with restriction $x \neq 2$

5. a) $x^2 + x - 6$ or $(x+3)(x-2)$ **b)** $x^2 - x - 12$ or $(x+3)(x-4)$
c) $x^3 + 3x^2 - 9x - 27$ or $(x-3)(x+3)^2$ **d)** $x - 3$ with restriction $x \neq -3$

6. a) $x \in R$ **b)** $\dfrac{2x+3}{2x-3}, x \neq \dfrac{2}{3}, \dfrac{3}{2}$ **c)** $\left(\dfrac{f}{g}\right)(4) = \dfrac{f(4)}{g(4)} = \dfrac{11}{5}$ or $\left(\dfrac{f}{g}\right)(4) = \dfrac{2(4)+3}{2(4)-3} = \dfrac{11}{5}$

7. Answers may vary **a)** $f(x) = x^2, g(x) = 3x$ **b)** $f(x) = x^2, g(x) = -3x$
c) $f(x) = x + 3, g(x) = x$ **d)** $f(x) = x^3 + 3x^2, g(x) = x$

8. a) $\dfrac{3x^2 - 5x}{(x-3)(x+1)}$ or $\dfrac{x(3x-5)}{(x-3)(x+1)}, x \neq -1, 3$ **b)** $\dfrac{-x^2 + 7x}{(x-3)(x+1)}$ or $\dfrac{x(7-x)}{(x-3)(x+1)}, x \neq -1, 3$
c) $\dfrac{2x^2}{(x-3)(x+1)}, x \neq -1, 3$ **d)** $\dfrac{x+1}{2(x-3)}, x \neq -1, 0, 3$

9. a) $6 + 3x - 3x^2$ or $3(2-x)(1+x)$ **b)** $2x + 2$ or $2(x+1)$ **c)** $x - 1$ with restriction $x \neq -1$

10. B   **11.** | 3 | 1 | 4 | 2 |

Functions and Relations Lesson #5:
Composition of Functions

Combining Two Functions

A

When a pebble is dropped in a pool of water, ripples in the shape of circles form on the surface of the water. The radius of the outer ripple is given by the formula $r = 0.3t$, where r is the radius in metres and t is the time in seconds after the pebble hits the water.

If the area of the circle is $A = \pi r^2$, combine this formula with the radius formula for the outer ripple to write a formula for the area of the circular ripple after t seconds.

B

The 3.5L V6 2012 Toyota Camry has a fuel efficiency of approximately 8.2 litres per 100 km. The cost of gasoline is $1.25 per litre.

a) The volume, l litres, of fuel used can be written as a function of the distance, d km, travelled. Complete the following for l in terms of d.

$l = f(d) = $ _____

b) The cost, C dollars, of gasoline used can be written as a function of l. Complete the following for C in terms of l.

$C = g(l) = $ _____

c) We can find the cost of gasoline in terms of the distance travelled by combining these two functions. If we substitute the formula for the first function into the formula for the second function, we can write C as a function of d. Complete the following:

$C = h(d) = $

When two functions are combined in this manner, we say that the new function is a **composition** of the other two functions.

Investigating the Composition of Two Functions

Consider the function given by $h(x) = 2x + 3$. This function can be thought of as being composed of two functions - the "multiply by 2" function denoted by f, and the "add 3" function denoted by g.

The composite function, h, says first multiply by 2 and then add 3. An arrow diagram can be used to help explain this.

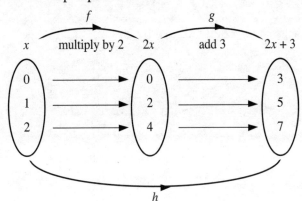

The function f applied to x maps to $2x$ so $f(x) = 2x$.

The function g applied to $2x$ maps to $2x + 3$ so

$g(2x) = 2x + 3$.

Replacing A for $2x$, we can write $g(A) = A + 3$ so $g(x) = $ ____

The function $h(x) = 2x + 3$ is a composition of two functions $f(x) = 2x$ and $g(x) = x + 3$.

The **composite function** $h(x)$ can be written in the form:

$$h(x) = g(f(x)) \qquad \text{read as} \qquad \text{"}g \text{ of } f \text{ of } x\text{"}$$

or

$$h(x) = (g \circ f)(x).$$

- When $h(x)$ is written as $g(f(x))$, note that function f is applied first and the function g is applied second.
- h is often referred to as a function of a function.
- The techniques used in Class Ex. #1 and Warm-Up #4 will benefit students who plan to study calculus (the Chain Rule) in future years.

Class Ex. #1

Consider the composite function $h(x) = x^2 - 2$.

a) Describe in words, two operations, in order, which can be applied to x to end up with $x^2 - 2$.

b) Complete the diagram and write $h(x)$ as a composition of two functions, f and g, where $h(x) = g(f(x))$.

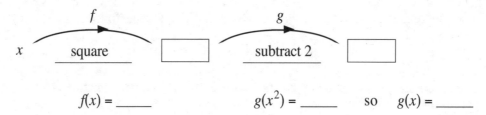

$$f(x) = \underline{\hspace{1cm}} \qquad\qquad g(x^2) = \underline{\hspace{1cm}} \qquad \text{so} \quad g(x) = \underline{\hspace{1cm}}$$

Class Ex. #2

Consider the composite function $h(x) = (x + 4)^3$.

a) Describe in words, two operations, in order, which can be applied to x to end up with $(x + 4)^3$

b) Complete the diagram and write $h(x)$ as a composition of two functions, f and g, where $h(x) = g(f(x))$.

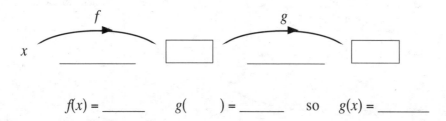

$$f(x) = \underline{\hspace{1cm}} \qquad g(\quad) = \underline{\hspace{1cm}} \qquad \text{so} \quad g(x) = \underline{\hspace{1cm}}$$

Developing a Method for the Composition of Two Functions

Consider two functions $f(x) = 3x$ and $g(x) = x - 5$.

a) Complete the diagram to determine a formula for the composite function $h(x) = g(f(x))$.

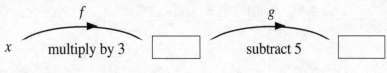

$$x \quad \text{multiply by 3} \quad \boxed{} \quad \text{subtract 5} \quad \boxed{}$$

$$h(x) = g(f(x)) = g(\underline{\hspace{1cm}}) = \underline{\hspace{2cm}}$$

b) Use a similar technique to determine a formula for the composite function $k(x) = f(g(x))$.

Complete Assignment Questions #1 - #6

Composition of Functions

Consider the composite function $\quad g(f(x)) = (g \circ f)(x) \quad$ where $f(x)$ and $g(x)$ are given.
Use the following procedure to determine $g(f(x))$.

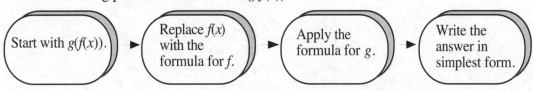

Start with $g(f(x))$. ▶ Replace $f(x)$ with the formula for f. ▶ Apply the formula for g. ▶ Write the answer in simplest form.

Class Ex. #3

Given $f(x) = 10x + 1$ and $g(x) = 2x - 5$, complete the work below to determine $(g \circ f)(x)$.

STEPS   WORK

Step 1: Start with $g(f(x))$ Step 1: $g(f(x))$

Step 2: Replace $f(x)$ with the formula for f.   Step 2:

Step 3: Apply the formula for g.   Step 3:

Step 4: Write the answer in simplest form.   Step 4:

Class Ex. #4

If $f(x) = 2x^2 - 1$ and $g(x) = 3x - 4$, find

a) $(g \circ f)(x)$ **b)** $(g \circ g)(x)$

Domain and Range of a Composite Function

Consider the functions $f(x) = x^2 - 3$ and $g(x) = \sqrt{x - 1}$.

a) Without finding a formula for $(f \circ g)(x)$ or $(g \circ f)(x)$, evaluate:

    i) $(f \circ g)(2)$ ii) $(f \circ g)(0)$ iii) $(g \circ f)(2)$ iv) $(g \circ f)(0)$

b) State the domains of f and g.   c) State the ranges of f and g.

d) In order to determine the domain and range of $f \circ g$ and $g \circ f$, Aaron found expressions for $(f \circ g)(x)$ and $(g \circ f)(x)$ and used his graphing calculator to sketch the graphs of the composite functions. He obtained the following graphs.

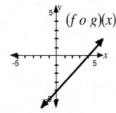

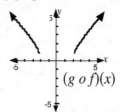

He concluded that

    domain of $f \circ g = \{x \mid x \in R\}$ domain of $g \circ f = \{x \mid x \le -2 \text{ or } x \ge 2, x \in R\}$

    range of $f \circ g = \{y \mid y \in R\}$ range of $g \circ f = \{y \mid y \ge 1, y \in R\}$

There are errors in Aaron's thinking.

    i) Find expressions for $(f \circ g)(x)$ and $(g \circ f)(x)$.

    ii) Use the expressions in d) i) and the results from a), b), and c) to complete the following:

        graph of $(f \circ g)(x)$ graph of $(g \circ f)(x)$

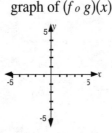

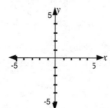

        domain of $f \circ g$ =   domain of $g \circ f$ =

        range of $f \circ g$ =   range of $g \circ f$ =

- When we calculate an expression for a composite function, there may be restrictions on domain and range.

- In most cases the domain and range of a composite function will be different from the domain and range of the original functions.

- The domain of a composite function $f \circ g$ cannot be more than the domain of g. The range of a composite function $f \circ g$ cannot be more than the range of f.

Complete Assignment Questions #7 - #18

Assignment

1. The 305 HP V6 2012 Ford Mustang Sports Car has a highway fuel efficiency of approximately 3.2 gallons per 100 miles. The cost of gasoline is $3.60 per gallon.

   a) The volume, v gallons, of fuel used can be written as a function of the distance, d miles, travelled. Complete the following for v in terms of d.

   $v = f(d) =$ _____

   b) The cost, C dollars, of gasoline used can be written as a function of v.
   Complete the following for C in terms of v.

   $C = g(v) =$ _____

   c) We can find the cost of gasoline in terms of the distance travelled by combining these two functions. If we substitute the formula for the first function into the formula for the second function, we can write C as a function of d. Complete the following:

   $C = h(d) =$

2. The function $p(d) = 0.62d$ converts Canadian dollars into British pounds.
   The function $e(p) = 1.15p$ converts British pounds into euros.

   a) Determine the function $e(d)$ that converts Canadian dollars into euros.

   b) Use these functions to convert C$2000 into euros.

   c) Determine the function $d(e)$ that converts euros into Canadian dollars and convert 2000 euros into Canadian dollars (to the nearest cent).

3. A composite function $h(x)$ is given. Use the methods of Class Ex. #1 to complete the diagram, and write $h(x)$ as a composition of two functions, f and g, where $h(x) = g(f(x))$.

a) $h(x) = (x - 5)^2$

x $\xrightarrow{f}$ ▭ $\xrightarrow{g}$ ▭

$f(x) =$ _____ $g(\_\_) =$ _____ $g(x) =$ _____

b) $h(x) = x^3 + 6$

x $\xrightarrow{f}$ ▭ $\xrightarrow{g}$ ▭

$f(x) =$ _____ $g(\_\_) =$ _____ $g(x) =$ _____

c) $h(x) = \sqrt{(x - 4)}$

x $\xrightarrow{f}$ ▭ $\xrightarrow{g}$ ▭

$f(x) =$ _____ $g(\_\_) =$ _____ $g(x) =$ _____

4. A composite function $h(x)$ is given. In each case, complete the diagram and write $h(x)$ as a composition of two functions, f and g, where $h(x) = f(g(x))$.

a) $h(x) = \sqrt{x} - 4$

x $\xrightarrow{g}$ ▭ $\xrightarrow{f}$ ▭

$g(x) =$ _____ $f(\_\_) =$ _____ $f(x) =$ _____

b) $h(x) = \dfrac{1}{x + 3}$

x $\xrightarrow{g}$ ▭ $\xrightarrow{f}$ ▭

$g(x) =$ _____ $f(\_\_) =$ _____ $f(x) =$ _____

5. Consider two functions $f(x) = x + 2$ and $g(x) = x^2$.

   a) Complete the diagram to determine a formula for the composite function $h(x) = g(f(x))$.

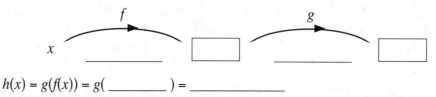

$h(x) = g(f(x)) = g(\,$ _____ $) =$ _____

   b) Use a similar technique to determine a formula for the composite function $k(x) = f(g(x))$.

6. Consider two functions $f(x) = \sqrt{x}$ and $g(x) = 4x$.

   a) Complete the diagram to determine a formula for the composite function $h(x) = g(f(x))$.

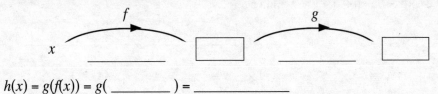

$$h(x) = g(f(x)) = g(\underline{\hspace{1.5cm}}) = \underline{\hspace{2.5cm}}$$

   b) Use a similar technique to determine a formula for the composite function $k(x) = f(g(x))$.

7. For each pair of functions, write a formula for $(f \circ g)(x)$.

   a) $f(x) = 2x + 1$, $g(x) = 5x$ **b)** $f(x) = 5x - 2$, $g(x) = x^3$ **c)** $f(x) = 2^x$, $g(x) = x + 4$

8. For each pair of functions, write a formula for $(g \circ f)(x)$.

   a) $f(x) = 2 - x$, $g(x) = |x + 2|$ **b)** $f(x) = 2x + 1$, $g(x) = x^4$ **c)** $f(x) = 3^x$, $g(x) = x - 1$

9. If $f(x) = x + 4$ and $g(x) = x - 1$, determine the value(s) of x for which

   a) $f(g(x)) = 50$ **b)** $(fg)(x) = 50$

10. Consider the functions $f(x) = \sqrt{x-3}$ and $g(x) = x^2 + 2$.

a) Find expressions for $(f \circ g)(x)$ and $(g \circ f)(x)$.

b) Determine the domains of
$f,\ g,\ f \circ g,$ and $g \circ f$.

c) Determine the ranges of
$f,\ g,\ f \circ g,$ and $g \circ f$.

d) In each case, sketch the graph of the function indicated.

i) $y = f(x)$ **ii)** $y = g(x)$ **iii)** $y = (f \circ g)(x)$ **iv)** $y = (g \circ f)(x)$

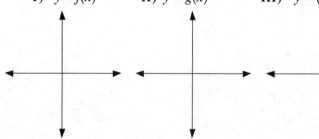

11. If $f(x) = 2x + 3$ and $g(x) = 5 - 2x$, determine the value of:

a) $f(g(5))$ **b)** $g(f(-3))$ **c)** $(f \circ g)(0)$ **d)** $-2(g \circ f)(0)$

12. If $f(x) = 2\sqrt{x}$ and $g(x) = 2 + 2x$, determine the value of:

a) $f(g(7))$ **b)** $g\left(f\left(\dfrac{1}{4}\right)\right)$ **c)** $(f \circ g)(5)$ **d)** $3(g \circ f)(5)$

13. Find $(f \circ g)(x), (g \circ f)(x)$, and $(f \circ f)(x)$ for the following. State any domain restrictions.

 a) $f(x) = -2x, \ g(x) = x^2 - 3$ **b)** $f(x) = \dfrac{1}{3 - x}, \ g(x) = x^2$ **c)** $f(x) = 3x, \ g(x) = \sqrt{x - 2}$

14. Given $f(x) = 4 - x$ and $g(x) = 3\sqrt{5x}$, then $(f \circ g)(5)$ is equal to

 A. -71

 B. -11

 C. -1

 D. 35

15. Given $f(x) = \dfrac{1}{x + 5}$ and $g(x) = 6x - 1$, then $(g \circ f)(-2)$ is equal to

 A. 1

 B. $\dfrac{16}{3}$

 C. $-\dfrac{1}{8}$

 D. -3

16. Given that $p(x) = 2x + 1$ and $q(x) = x^2 - 1$, then $p(q(x))$ equals

 A. $2x^2 + 1$ **B.** $2x^2 - 1$

 C. $4x^2$ **D.** $4x^2 + 4x$

17. The functions f, g, and h are given by $f(x) = x^2 - 1$, $g(x) = 3x + 2$, and $h(x) = |x + 2|$.

The value of $(f \circ g \circ h)(-8)$, to the nearest whole number, is _____ .

(Record your answer in the numerical response box from left to right.)

18. The functions f and g are given by $f(x) = \dfrac{1}{x}$, and $g(x) = \dfrac{1}{x + 1}$.

If $(f \circ f)(x) = (g \circ g)\left(\dfrac{1}{2}\right)$, then the value of x, to the nearest tenth, is _____ .

(Record your answer in the numerical response box from left to right.)

Answer Key

1. a) $v = 0.032d$ **b)** $C = 3.6v$ **c)** $C = 0.1152d$

2. a) $e(d) = 0.713d$ **b)** 1426 euros **c)** $d(e) = \dfrac{e}{0.713}$, \$2805.05

3. a) $f(x) = x - 5$, $g(x) = x^2$ **b)** $f(x) = x^3$, $g(x) = x + 6$ **c)** $f(x) = x - 4$, $g(x) = \sqrt{x}$

4. a) $f(x) = x - 4$, $g(x) = \sqrt{x}$ **b)** $f(x) = \dfrac{1}{x}$, $g(x) = x + 3$

5. a) $h(x) = (x + 2)^2$ **b)** $k(x) = x^2 + 2$

6. a) $h(x) = 4\sqrt{x}$ **b)** $k(x) = 2\sqrt{x}$

7. a) $(f \circ g)(x) = 10x + 1$ **b)** $(f \circ g)(x) = 5x^3 - 2$ **c)** $(f \circ g)(x) = 2^{x+4}$

8. a) $(g \circ f)(x) = |4 - x|$ **b)** $(g \circ f)(x) = (2x + 1)^4$ **c)** $(g \circ f)(x) = 3^x - 1$

9. a) $x = 47$ **b)** $x = -9, 6$

10. a) $(f \circ g)(x) = \sqrt{x^2 - 1}$, $x \leq -1$ or $x \geq 1$, $(g \circ f)(x) = x - 1$, $x \geq 3$

   b) Domain: f: $\{x \mid x \geq 3, x \in R\}$ $\qquad$ g: $\{x \mid x \in R\}$

   $f \circ g$: $\{x \mid x \leq -1$ or $x \geq 1, x \in R\}$ $\qquad$ $g \circ f$: $\{x \mid x \geq 3, x \in R\}$

   c) Range: f: $\{y \mid y \geq 0, y \in R\}$ $\qquad$ g: $\{y \mid y \geq 2, y \in R\}$

   $f \circ g$: $\{y \mid y \geq 0, y \in R\}$ $\qquad$ $g \circ f$: $\{y \mid y \geq 2, y \in R\}$

   d) i) $\qquad$ **ii)** $\qquad$ **iii)** $\qquad$ **iv)**

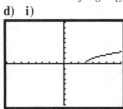 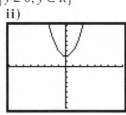 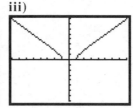 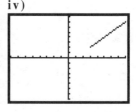

11. a) -7 **b)** 11 **c)** 13 **d)** 2

12. a) 8 **b)** 4 **c)** $4\sqrt{3}$ **d)** $6 + 12\sqrt{5}$

13. a) $(f \circ g)(x) = -2x^2 + 6$ $\qquad$ $(g \circ f)(x) = 4x^2 - 3$ $\qquad$ $(f \circ f)(x) = 4x$

   b) $(f \circ g)(x) = \dfrac{1}{3 - x^2}$, $x \neq \pm\sqrt{3}$ $\qquad$ $(g \circ f)(x) = \dfrac{1}{(3 - x)^2}$, $x \neq 3$ $\qquad$ $(f \circ f)(x) = \dfrac{3 - x}{8 - 3x}$, $x \neq \dfrac{8}{3}$, 3

   c) $(f \circ g)(x) = 3\sqrt{x - 2}$, $x \geq 2$ $\qquad$ $(g \circ f)(x) = \sqrt{3x - 2}$, $x \geq \dfrac{2}{3}$ $\qquad$ $(f \circ f)(x) = 9x$

14. B $\qquad$ **15.** A $\qquad$ **16.** B $\qquad$ **17.** | 3 | 9 | 9 | | $\qquad$ **18.** | 0 | . | 6 | |

Functions and Relations Lesson #6:
The Inverse of a Relation - Part One

In this lesson we will work with relations that are functions.

A **function** is a relation in which each element of a set A (the domain) is mapped to one and only one element of a set B (the range).

eg. **i)**
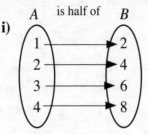
or
ii)
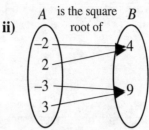

The **inverse of a function** is a relation which "undoes" what the function does. In other words, the elements in set B are mapped back to elements in set A.

i)
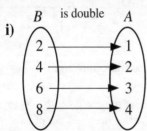
or
ii)
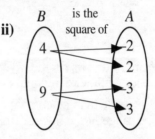

Referring to the cases above, complete the following by choosing the correct answer.

In case (i) the inverse (is / is not) a function.

In case (ii) the inverse (is / is not) a function.

- The **domain of the inverse** is the **range of the original** function.
- The **range of the inverse** is the **domain of the original** function.
- **The inverse of a function may or may not be a function**.

Class Ex. #1   Consider the "operation" of putting on your socks and then putting on your shoes. What would be the "inverse operation"?

Finding the Inverse of a Function Defined in Words

Class Ex. #2   Complete the table to describe the inverse of the function:

FUNCTION	INVERSE	Is the inverse a function?
multiply by 2	_____	_____
square	_____	_____
take the reciprocal	_____	_____
divide by 3, then add 1	_____	_____

Finding the Inverse of a Function Defined by Ordered Pairs

Consider the arrow diagram on the previous page.

The function which maps from *A* to *B* can be described
by the following set of ordered pairs:

{(1, 2), (

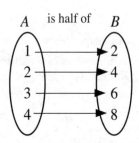

The inverse function which maps from *B* to *A* can be described
by the following set of ordered pairs:

{(2, 1),

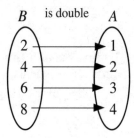

Notice that the ordered pairs for the inverse can be obtained by interchanging the first and
second coordinates of the ordered pairs of the original function.

This reinforces the rule that the domain of the inverse function is the range of the original
function, and the range of the inverse function is the domain of the original function.

Class Ex. #3

Consider the function defined by the following set of ordered pairs.

$$\{(-4,-2), (-2,-1), (-1,0), (0,1), (2,4), (3,8)\}$$

a) Describe the inverse of the function by a set of ordered pairs.

b) Graph the original function and the
inverse.

c) Draw a line which acts as a "mirror"
between the original function and its
inverse.

d) State the equation of the mirror line.

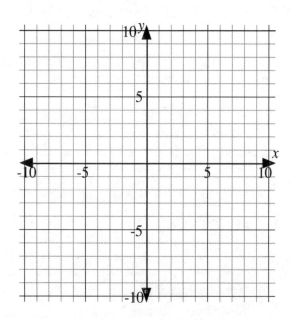

Finding the Inverse of a Function Defined by a Graph

To determine the inverse of a function defined by a graph, reflect the graph of the function in the line $y = x$.

Alternatively, select the coordinates of some key points, interchange the coordinates and plot the new points.

Class Ex. #4

Sketch the graph of the inverse of the functions defined by the following graphs. Is the inverse a function?

a)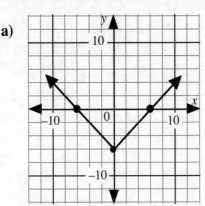

b)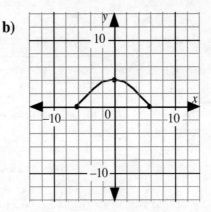

Finding the Inverse of a Function Defined by an Equation - Algebraically

When finding the inverse of a function defined by an equation,

interchange x and y in the equation and then solve for y.

Class Ex. #5

Consider the function defined by the equation $y = 3x + 2$.

a) Find an equation in the form "$y = mx + b$" for the inverse of the function.

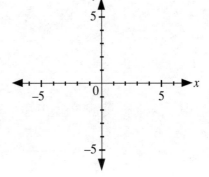

b) Graph the original and its inverse on the grid.

c) Is the inverse of the function defined by the equation $y = 3x + 2$ also a function?

Graphing the Inverse of a Function Defined by an Equation - by Calculator

A graphing calculator may be used to graph the inverse of a function defined by an equation. The following instructions are an example of finding an inverse using a TI-83 or TI-84 series graphing calculator.

1. Input the equation into Y_1 found in the Y = key and press GRAPH .

2. Access the "draw inverse" command by pressing 2nd then PRGM . Scroll down to "DrawInv", and press Enter .

3. To draw the inverse of the function in Y_1 press VARS , scroll to "Y-Vars", then to "Function", and press Enter   Enter .

4. Press Enter again. The graph of the inverse of the function is shown along with the original function.

- To graph only the inverse of the function and not the original, clear the "Y="editor, use "DrawInv" followed by the equation of the function, and press Enter .

- To graph a series of inverses by this method, use the following sequence to clear the graph screen between each graph:

    press 2nd then PRGM to "ClrDraw", and press Enter   Enter .

Class Ex. #6   Use the procedure to confirm the graph of the inverse in Class Ex. #4a). The original graph has equation $y = \left| x \right| - 3$.

Complete Assignment Questions #1 - #11

Assignment

1. The arrow diagram shows a function from set *A* to set *B*.

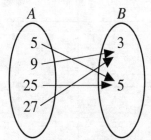  

   a) Draw an arrow diagram (above right) which represents the inverse of this function.

   b) Is the inverse of the function also a function?

2. Complete the table to describe the inverse of the function:

FUNCTION	INVERSE	Is the inverse a function?
divide by 3	_____	_____
cube	_____	_____
add 10, then multiply by 2	_____	_____
square, then subtract 5	_____	_____

3. Consider the function defined by the following set of ordered pairs.

$$\{(-2, 9),\ (-1, 7), (0, 5), (1, 3),\ (2, 1)\}$$

   a) Describe the inverse of the function by a set of ordered pairs.

   b) Is the inverse of the function also a function? Why?

4. Consider the function defined by the following set of ordered pairs.

$$\{(-2, 1),\ (-1, -2), (0, -3), (1, -2),\ (2, 1),\}$$

   a) Describe the inverse of the function by a set of ordered pairs.

   b) Is the inverse of the function also a function? Why?

5. Sketch the graph of the inverse of the function defined by the following graphs.
Is the inverse a function?

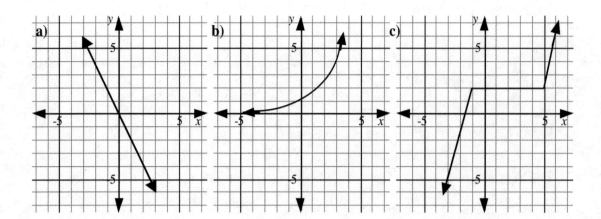

6. Find the inverse of the functions defined by the following equations.

a) $y = \dfrac{1}{3}x - 2$　　　　**b)** $y = 6 - 8x$　　　　**c)** $y = \dfrac{x - 2}{5}$

d) $3y = x - 7$　　　　**e)** $6x - \dfrac{1}{2}y + 4 = 0$　　　　**f)** $y = x^2$

7. Graph the inverse of the following functions using a graphing calculator.

a) $y = 4x - 8$ **b)** $y = |x + 2|$ **c)** $y = x^2 + 3$

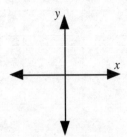   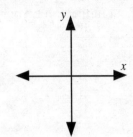   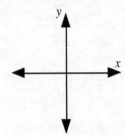

8. In each case graph the function defined by the equation and the inverse of the function on the grid provided.

a) $y = 9 - x^2$ **b)** $y = \sqrt{x - 4}$

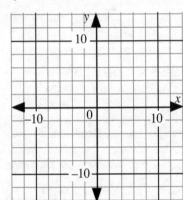   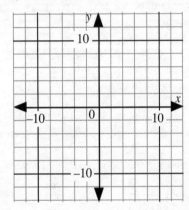

Multiple Choice 9. When a function and its inverse are graphed on the same grid, which of the following lines must be a line of symmetry for the graph?

   A. the x-axis   **B.** the y-axis   **C.** the line $y = x$ **D.** the line $y = -x$

10. A function is defined by the equation $y = 2x^2 - 3$. The inverse of the function has equation

   A. $y = \dfrac{x + 3}{2}$

   B. $y = 3 - 2x^2$

   C. $y = \pm\sqrt{\dfrac{x + 3}{2}}$

   D. $y = \pm\sqrt{\dfrac{2}{x + 3}}$

11.   The point $(a, 2)$ lies on the graph of a function and on the graph of the inverse of the function. The value of a is

A.   2   **B.**   0   **C.**   –2

D.   impossible to determine without further information.

Answer Key

1. a)   **b)** no

2.   **FUNCTION**   **INVERSE**   **Is the inverse a function?**

FUNCTION	INVERSE	Is the inverse a function?
divide by 3	multiply by 3	yes
cube	cube root	yes
add 10, then multiply by 2	divide by 2, then subtract 10	yes
square, then subtract 5	add 5, then square root	no

3. a) $\{(9, -2), (7, -1), (5, 0), (3, 1), (1, 2)\}$

  b)   yes because each element of the first set (x-coordinates) is mapped to one and only one element of the second set (y-coordinates).

4. a) $\{(1, -2), (-2, -1), (-3, 0), (-2, 1), (1, 2)\}$

  b)   no because the elements –2 and 1 in the first set both map to more than one element of the second set.

5. a)   The inverse is a function.   **b)**   The inverse is a function.   **c)**   The inverse is not a function.

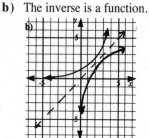
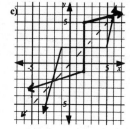

6. a) $y = 3x + 6$ **b)** $y = -\dfrac{1}{8}x + \dfrac{3}{4}$ **c)** $y = 5x + 2$

  d) $y = 3x + 7$ **e)** $y = \dfrac{1}{12}x - \dfrac{2}{3}$ **f)** $y = \pm\sqrt{x}$

7. a)   **b)**   **c)**

8. a)   **b)**

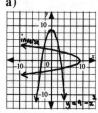
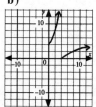

9. C   **10.** C   **11.** A

Functions and Relations Lesson #7:
The Inverse of a Relation - Part Two

- We have established three methods for determining the **inverse of a function**:
    1. Reverse the coordinates in a set of ordered pairs.
    2. Reflect the graph in the line $y = x$.
    3. Interchange x and y in the equation and solve for y.

- The **domain of the inverse** is the **range of the original** function.
- The **range of the inverse** is the **domain of the original** function.
- **The inverse of a function may or may not be a function**.

Inverse of a Relation

Some relations are functions and some are not. The inverse of a relation which is not a function can also be determined by the above methods (where appropriate).

Class Ex. #1

Consider the relation $(x - 3)^2 + y^2 = 9$ whose graph is a circle, centre $(3, 0)$, and radius 3.

a) Describe how to use the <u>graph</u> of the relation to draw the graph of the inverse of the relation.

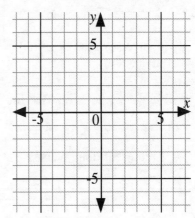

b) Sketch the graphs of the relation and its inverse on the grid.

c) Describe how to use the <u>equation</u> of the relation to determine the equation of the inverse of the relation.

d) Determine the equation of the inverse of the relation in the form $(x - h)^2 + (y - k)^2 = r^2$.

e) Write the equation of the inverse in d) by solving for y and verify the sketch in b) on a graphing calculator.

f) Using interval notation, state the domain and range of the relation and the domain and range of the inverse. Does this agree with the second and third bullets in the review at the top of the page?

Complete Assignment Questions #1 - #4

> ## *Using Function Notation to Write an Inverse*

If a function $f(x)$ has an inverse which is also a function, then the inverse is denoted by $f^{-1}(x)$ (*read as f inverse of x*).

If the inverse of $f(x)$ **is not a function**, then the notation $f^{-1}(x)$ should not be used. Instead, the inverse is written in the form $x = f(y)$.

Note that some textbooks do not make this distinction and use $f^{-1}(x)$ even when the inverse is not a function.

The steps are listed below.

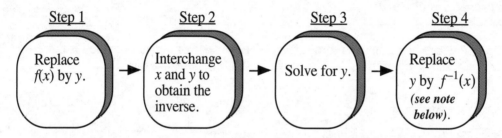

Step 1	Step 2	Step 3	Step 4
Replace $f(x)$ by y.	Interchange x and y to obtain the inverse.	Solve for y.	Replace y by $f^{-1}(x)$ (*see note below*).

- The inverse of the function $y = f(x)$ has the notation $y = f^{-1}(x)$, which is equivalent to $x = f(y)$.

- $f^{-1}(x)$ is the notation used for the inverse of $f(x)$ **when the inverse is a function**.
- Although $10^{-1} = \dfrac{1}{10}$, note that $f^{-1}(x) \neq \dfrac{1}{f(x)}$.

f^{-1} represents the inverse function, not the reciprocal function.

Class Ex. #2

Determine $f^{-1}(x)$ for the following.

a) $f(x) = 2x - 3$ **b)** $f(x) = x^3 + 4$

Class Ex. #3

Consider the function $f(x) = x^2 - 4$.

a) Graph $y = f(x)$ on the grid provided and state the domain and range.

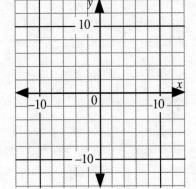

b) Determine $x = f(y)$, and solve for y.

c) Graph the inverse of $f(x)$ on the grid provided and state the domain and range.

d) Is the inverse of f a function? If not, how could the domain or range of f be restricted so that the inverse of f is also a function?

Class Ex. #4

Don incorrectly determined the inverse of the function defined by $y = \sqrt{x - 3}$ to be the equation $y = x^2 + 3$. He graphed the inverse of the function and obtained a parabola.

Explain why Don's equation of the inverse is not complete and why the graph of the correct inverse is not a parabola.

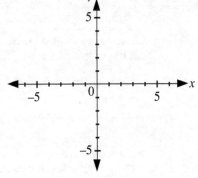

Note When determining the inverse of a function, domain restrictions, if any, must be included in the equation of the inverse. There may also be restrictions on the range of the inverse function.

> ## *Verifying that Functions are Inverses of Each Other*

Class Ex. #5

Determine $(f \circ f^{-1})(x)$ and $(f^{-1} \circ f)(x)$ for Class Ex. #2a), where $f(x) = 2x - 3$.
What do you notice?

> Two Functions f and g are Inverses of each other if $(f \circ g)(x) = x$ and $(g \circ f)(x) = x$

> **Complete Assignment Questions #5 - #14**

Assignment

1. Consider the relation $y^2 = x$ whose graph is a parabola.

    a) Write the relation in terms of y and sketch
    the graph of the relation on the grid.

    b) Determine the equation of the inverse of the relation and
    sketch the graph of the inverse on the grid.

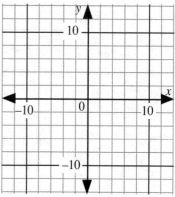

    c) State the domain and range of the relation and the domain and range of the inverse.
    Does this agree with the second and third bullets in the review at the beginning of the
    lesson?

2. A parabolic relation is shown in the diagram. The graph passes through the points $(1, -1)$, and $(-2, 1)$, and has a horizontal line of symmetry.

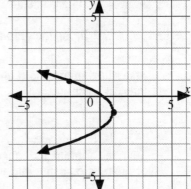

a) State the coordinates of one other point which lies on the parabola.

b) State the domain and range of the relation using interval notation.

c) State the domain and range of the inverse of the relation using interval notation.

d) Without using a calculator, sketch the inverse of the relation on the grid.

3. The diagram shows the relation with equation $\dfrac{(x-1)^2}{16} + \dfrac{(y+2)^2}{4} = 1$.

a) State the domain and range of the relation using interval notation.

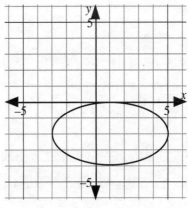

b) State the domain and range of the inverse of the relation using interval notation.

c) Without using a calculator, sketch the inverse of the relation on the grid.

d) Write the inverse of the relation in the form $\dfrac{(x-h)^2}{a^2} + \dfrac{(y-k)^2}{b^2} = 1$, and solve for y.

e) Use a graphing calculator to verify your sketch in c).

4. The diagram shows the relation with equation

$\dfrac{x^2}{4} - \dfrac{y^2}{9} = 1$. The points $(\pm 2, 0)$, $\left(\pm\sqrt{8}, \pm 3\right)$, and $\left(\pm 4, \pm\sqrt{27}\right)$ lie on the graph of the relation.

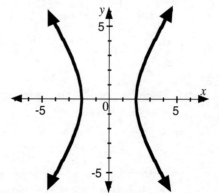

a) State the domain and range of the relation using interval notation.

b) State the domain and range of the inverse of the relation using interval notation.

c) Without using a calculator, sketch the inverse of the relation on the grid.

d) Write the inverse of the relation in terms of y.

e) Use a graphing calculator to verify your sketch in c).

5. Use function notation to write the inverse of the following functions.

a) $f(x) = 4x + 5$ **b)** $g(x) = \dfrac{3x - 1}{7}$ **c)** $h(x) = x^3 - 1$

6. a) Graph the function $f(x) = x^2 + 4$.

b) Graph the inverse of $f(x)$.

c) Find the equation of the inverse function in the form $x = f(y)$ and solve for y.

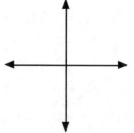

7. For each of the following functions
  - determine the inverse using the notation $f^{-1}(x)$, where appropriate
  - state the domain and range of the inverse

a) $f(x) = \sqrt{x + 2}$

b) $f(x) = (x - 2)^2$

c) $f(x) = x^2 - 25$

d) $f(x) = \sqrt{16 - x^2}$

8. In each of the following
  - **i)** sketch the graph of $y = f(x)$ on the grid provided
  - **ii)** determine $f^{-1}(x)$ for the function with restricted domain
  - **iii)** sketch the graph of $y = f^{-1}(x)$ on the grid provided

a) $f(x) = x^2, x \geq 0$

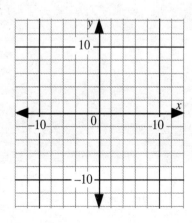

b) $f(x) = (x - 4)^2, \ x \geq 4$

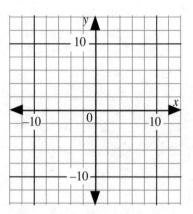

c) $f(x) = x^2 + 2, x \leq 0$

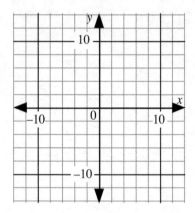

9. Kaleb incorrectly determined the inverse of $y = 4 - \sqrt{-x}$ to be $y = -(x - 4)^2$ and used the graphing calculator to obtain a parabola. Explain why the graph of the correct inverse is not a complete parabola.

10. Functions *f* and *g* are defined as $f(x) = 2x + 6$ and $g(x) = 3x$.

a) Determine $f^{-1}(x)$ and $g^{-1}(x)$.

b) Find expressions for

   i) $(f^{-1} \circ g^{-1})(x)$ **ii)** $(g^{-1} \circ f^{-1})(x)$

   iii) $(f \circ g)^{-1}(x)$ **iv)** $(g \circ f)^{-1}(x)$

c) Compare the answers in b). What do you notice?

11. Given that $f(x) = 1 - 2x, x \in R$, then $f^{-1}(x)$ is

    A. $\quad -\dfrac{x}{2} - 1$

    B. $\quad \dfrac{x}{2} - 1$

    C. $\quad \dfrac{1 - x}{2}$

    D. $\quad \dfrac{x - 1}{2}$

12. Given that $f(x) = (x - 2)^2, x \in R$, then the inverse of $f(x)$ is completely defined by

    A. $\quad \sqrt{x + 2}$

    B. $\quad \sqrt{x} + 2$

    C. $\quad -\sqrt{x} + 2$

    D. $\quad$ none of the above

13. Given that $f(x) = 2x$ and $g(x) = 3 - 5x$, then $(g \circ f)^{-1}(x)$ equals

    A. $\quad \dfrac{3}{11}$

    B. $\quad \dfrac{6}{11}$

    C. $\quad \dfrac{1}{10}(3 - x)$

    D. $\quad \dfrac{1}{10}(6 - x)$

14. The graph of $y = P(x)$ passes through the points $(14, 2)$, $(2, 15)$, and $\left(\dfrac{1}{2}, 10\right)$.

The value of $P^{-1}(2)$ is _____ .

(Record your answer in the numerical response box from left to right.)

Answer Key

1. a) $y = \pm\sqrt{x}$ **b)** $y = x^2$ **c)** Domain of relation $\{x \mid x \geq 0, x \in R\}$ Range of relation $y \in R$
Domain of inverse $x \in R$ Range of inverse $\{y \mid y \geq 0, x \in R\}$
Yes.

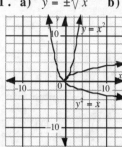

2. a) $(-2, -3)$ **2.d)**

    b) Domain of relation $(-\infty, 1]$
       Range of relation $(-\infty, \infty)$

    c) Domain of inverse $(-\infty, \infty)$
       Range of inverse $(-\infty, 1]$

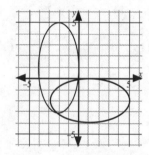

3. a) Domain of relation $[-3, 5]$ **3.c)**
       Range of relation $[-4, 0]$

    b) Domain of inverse $[-4, 0]$
       Range of inverse $[-3, 5]$

    d) $\dfrac{(x+2)^2}{4} + \dfrac{(y-1)^2}{16} = 1$, $y = 1 \pm \sqrt{16 - 4(x+2)^2}$

              or $y = 1 \pm 2\sqrt{4 - (x+2)^2}$

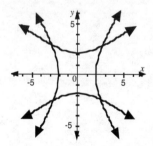

4. a) Domain of relation $(-\infty, -2]$ or $[2, \infty)$ **4.c)**
       Range of relation $(-\infty, \infty)$

    b) Domain of inverse $(-\infty, \infty)$
       Range of inverse $(-\infty, -2]$ or $[2, \infty)$

    d) $y = \pm\sqrt{\dfrac{36 + 4x^2}{9}}$ or $y = \pm\dfrac{2}{3}\sqrt{9 + x^2}$

5. a) $f^{-1}(x) = \dfrac{x-5}{4}$ or $f^{-1}(x) = \dfrac{1}{4}x - \dfrac{5}{4}$ **b)** $g^{-1}(x) = \dfrac{7x+1}{3}$ **c)** $h^{-1}(x) = \sqrt[3]{x+1}$

6. a) and b) See graph below.   **c)** $x = y^2 + 4$, $y = \pm\sqrt{x - 4}$

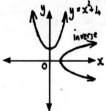

7. **a)** $f^{-1}(x) = x^2 - 2,\ x \geq 0$ Domain: $\{x \mid x \geq 0, x \in R\}$ Range: $\{y \mid y \geq -2, y \in R\}$

     b) $y = 2 \pm \sqrt{x}$ Domain: $\{x \mid x \geq 0, x \in R\}$ Range: $\{y \mid y \in R\}$

     c) $y = \pm\sqrt{x + 25}$ Domain: $\{x \mid x \geq -25, x \in R\}$ Range: $\{y \mid y \in R\}$

     d) $y = \pm\sqrt{16 - x^2},\ 0 \leq x \leq 4$ Domain: $\{x \mid 0 \leq x \leq 4, x \in R\}$ Range: $\{y \mid -4 \leq y \leq 4, y \in R\}$

8. **a)** $f^{-1}(x) = \sqrt{x}$ **b)** $f^{-1}(x) = \sqrt{x} + 4$ **c)** $f^{-1}(x) = -\sqrt{x - 2}$

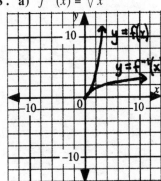 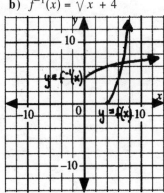 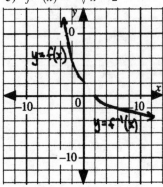

9. The correct inverse is $y = -(x - 4)^2,\ x \leq 4$, the graph of which is only half of a parabola.

10. **a)** $f^{-1}(x) = \frac{1}{2}x - 3,\ g^{-1}(x) = \frac{1}{3}x$ **b)** **i)** $\frac{1}{6}x - 3$ **ii)** $\frac{1}{6}x - 1$ **iii)** $\frac{1}{6}x - 1$ **iv)** $\frac{1}{6}x - 3$

     c) $(f \circ g)^{-1}(x) = (g^{-1} \circ f^{-1})(x)$ $(g \circ f)^{-1}(x) = (f^{-1} \circ g^{-1})(x)$

11. C   **12.** D   **13.** C   **14.**

1	4		

Functions and Relations Lesson #8:
Practice Test

1. If $f(x) = 3x^2 - 2$, then $f(3x)$ is

    A. $9x^2 - 2$ **B.** $9x^2 - 6$

    C. $27x^2 - 2$ **D.** $27x^2 - 6$

2. If a polynomial function is defined by $P(a) = a^3 + 1$, then $2a^3 + 1$ represents

    A. $2P(a)$

    B. $P(2a)$

    C. $2P(a) + 1$

    D. none of A, B, or C

Use the following information to answer the next question.

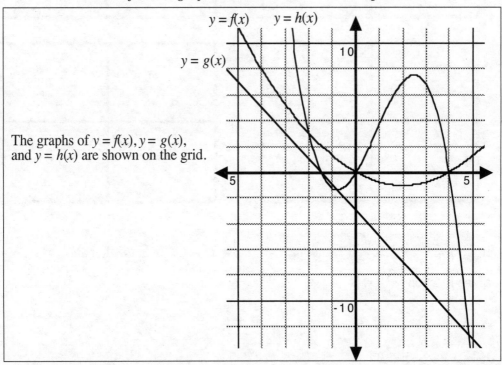

The graphs of $y = f(x)$, $y = g(x)$, and $y = h(x)$ are shown on the grid.

3. $h(x)$ is equivalent to

    A. $(f + g)(x)$ **B.** $(f - g)(x)$ **C.** $(g - f)(x)$ **D.** $(fg)(x)$

Use the following information to answer the next question.

The screen shot from a graphing calculator shows the graphs of $y = f(x)$ and $y = (f + g)(x)$.

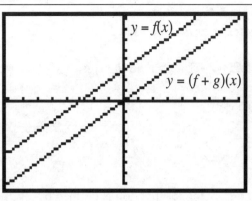

4. Which of the following screen shots shows the graph of $y = g(x)$?

A.

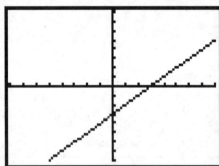

B.

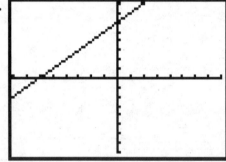

C.

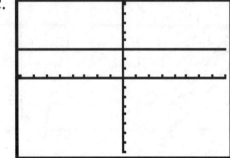

D.

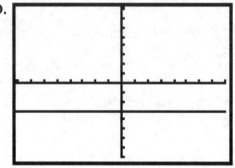

5. If $a(x) = 12x^2 - 25x + 12$ and $b(x) = 12x^2 + 7x - 12$, then the domain of the function $\left(\dfrac{a}{b}\right)(x)$ is

A. $x \neq \dfrac{3}{4}, -\dfrac{4}{3}, x \in R$

B. $x \neq -\dfrac{4}{3}, x \in R$

C. $x \neq \dfrac{3}{4}, \dfrac{4}{3}, x \in R$

D. $x \in R$

Use the following information to answer the next question.

Calculator representations of the graphs of two functions, *f*(x) and *g*(x), are shown.

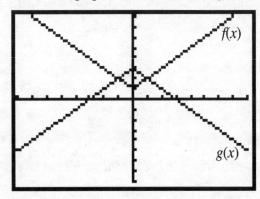

The calculator representations below show the graphs of operations on these functions.

Diagram 1

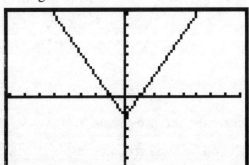

Diagram 2

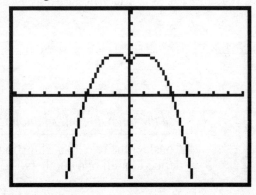

Diagram 3

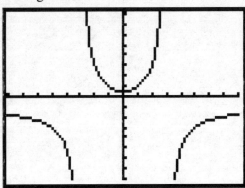

Diagram 4

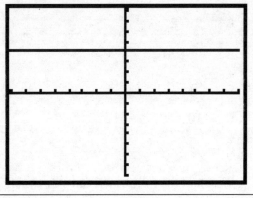

 1. Write the diagram number for the graph of $(f + g)(x)$ in the first box.

Write the diagram number for the graph of $(f - g)(x)$ in the second box.

Write the diagram number for the graph of $(fg)(x)$ in the third box.

Write the diagram number for the graph of $\left(\dfrac{f}{g}\right)(x)$ in the fourth box.

(Record your answer in the numerical response box from left to right.)

A graphing calculator may be used for the remainder of the test.

6.   If $f(x) = x^2 - 3x - 1$ and $g(x) = 2x - 5$, then the value of $(fg)(-1)$ is

    A. -7

    B. -21

    C. 7

    D. 21

 2. $P(x) = 8x^2 - 4x - 14$ and $Q(x) = 9 - 2x$. The function $(P + Q)(x)$ can be written in the form $(ax - b)(cx + d)$ where $a, b, c,$ and d are all positive integers.

    Write the value of a in the first box.   Write the value of b in the second box.
    Write the value of c in the third box.   Write the value of d in the fourth box.

    (Record your answer in the numerical response box from left to right.)

Use the following information to answer the next two questions.

> Consider the two linear functions $f(x) = 4x - 5$ and $g(x) = x - 3$, defined for all real numbers.

7.   Which of the following is an expression for $3(f + g)(x) - 2(f - g)(x)$?

    A. $9x - 8$

    B. $9x - 20$

    C. $9x - 28$

    D. $10x - 9$

8.   Which of the following is an expression for $(ff)(x)$?

    A. $8x - 10$

    B. $16x - 25$

    C. $16x^2 + 25$

    D. $16x^2 - 40x + 25$

3. If $f(x) = 3x^2 - 4x + 17$ and $g(x) = 5x^2 + 9x - 2$, then the value
of $(f - g)(-2) - (g - f)(2)$ is _____ .

(Record your answer in the numerical response box from left to right.)

Use the following information to answer the next two questions.

> Rational functions f and g are defined as $f(x) = \dfrac{x-1}{x+1}$ and $g(x) = \dfrac{2x-1}{2x+1}$.

9. $\left(\dfrac{f}{g}\right)(x)$ can be written in the form

  A. $\dfrac{2x^2 - 3x + 1}{2x^2 + 3x + 1}$

  B. $\dfrac{2x^2 - x - 1}{2x^2 + x - 1}$

  C. $\dfrac{2x^2 + x - 1}{2x^2 - x - 1}$

  D. $\dfrac{2x^2 + 3x + 1}{2x^2 - 3x + 1}$

10. The domain of the function $\left(\dfrac{f}{g}\right)(x)$ is

  A. $x \neq -1, \dfrac{1}{2}, x \in R$

  B. $x \neq -1, -\dfrac{1}{2}, \dfrac{1}{2}, x \in R$

  C. $x \neq -1, -\dfrac{1}{2}, 1, x \in R$

  D. $x \neq -1, -\dfrac{1}{2}, \dfrac{1}{2}, 1, x \in R$

11. If $f(x) = x^2 + 14x + 24$ and $g(x) = x + 2$, then the value of $\left(\dfrac{f}{g}\right)(-2)$ is

    A.   0

    B. -24

    C.   10

    D.   not defined

12. Given that $m(x) = 3x + 1$ and $n(x) = x^2 - 3$, then $m(n(x))$ equals

    A. $3x^2 - 2$

    B. $3x^2 - 8$

    C. $9x^2 + 6x - 2$

    D. $3x^3 + x^2 - 9x - 3$

Use the following information to answer the next two questions.

> Consider the functions $f(x) = x^2 + 4$ and $g(x) = \sqrt{4x}$.

13. The composite function $(g \circ f)(x)$ is

    A. $\sqrt{4x^2 + 16}$

    B. $\sqrt{4x^2 + 4}$

    C. $16x + 4$

    D. $4x + 4$

14. The domain and range of $y = (f \circ g)(x)$ are, respectively,

    A. $[0, \infty)$ and $[4, \infty)$

    B. $[0, \infty)$ and $[0, \infty)$

    C. $(-\infty, \infty)$ and $[0, \infty)$

    D. $(-\infty, \infty)$ and (∞, ∞)

4. The functions f, g, and h are given by $f(x) = |x + 15|$, $g(x) = 4x + 2$, and $h(x) = x^2 - 10$. The value of $(f \circ g \circ h)(-3)$, to the nearest whole number, is _____ .

(Record your answer in the numerical response box from left to right.)

15. Given $f(x) = \dfrac{1}{2x + 1}$ and $g(x) = 5x - 1$, then $(g \circ f)(x)$ can be written in the form

    A. $\dfrac{4 - 2x}{2x + 1}$

    B. $\dfrac{6 - 2x}{2x + 1}$

    C. $\dfrac{5}{2x}$

    D. $\dfrac{1}{10x - 1}$

5. $f(x) = 2^x$ and $g(x) = x - 2$. To the nearest tenth, the smallest positive solution of the equation $(f \circ g)(x) = (g \circ f)(x)$ is _____ .

(Record your answer in the numerical response box from left to right.)

16. If $g(x) = \dfrac{x^3 - 1}{2}$, $x \in R$, then $g^{-1}(x)$ is

    A. $\dfrac{2}{x^3 - 1}$

    B. $\sqrt[3]{2x + 1}$

    C. $2\sqrt[3]{x} + 1$

    D. 2

Use the following information to answer the next question.

The partial graph of the function $y = f(x)$ is shown.

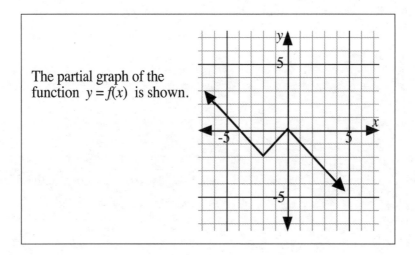

17.   Which of the following is the partial graph of $x = f(y)$?

A.

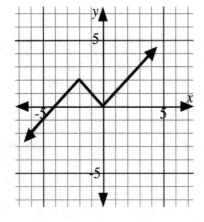

B.

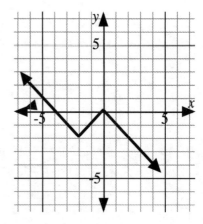

C.

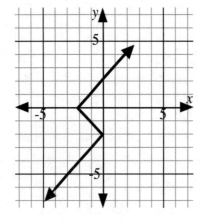

D.

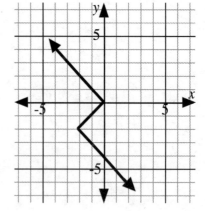

18. The graph of the function $y = f(x)$ is shown in the diagram below.

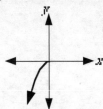

Which of the following represents $f^{-1}(x)$?

A. 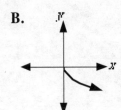   **B.** 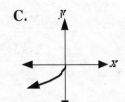   **C.** 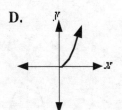   **D.**

Use the following information to answer the next two questions.

> The mapping diagram shows the composition of two functions f and g.
> $$x \xrightarrow{\ f\ } x^3 \xrightarrow{\ g\ } x^3 + 4$$

19. The expression which represents $g(x)$ is

   A. x^3

   B. $x^3 + 4$

   C. $x + 4$

   D. 4

20. The expression which represents $(g \circ f)^{-1}(x)$ is

   A. $\sqrt[3]{x} - 4$

   B. $\sqrt[3]{x - 4}$

   C. $4 - \sqrt[3]{x}$

   D. $\sqrt[3]{4 - x}$

Use the following graphs to answer the next question.

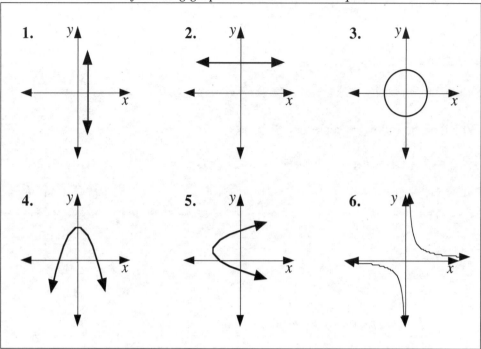

Numerical Response 6.   Consider the following questions:

a) Which graph represents a function whose inverse is also a function?

b) Which graph does not represent a function, but **could** be made to represent a function if the range were restricted to $y \geq 0$?

c) Which graph represents a function whose inverse is not a function, but **could** be made to represent a function whose inverse is also a function if the domain were restricted to $x \leq 0$?

d) Which graph represents a function whose inverse is not a function but could **not** be made to represent a function whose inverse is also a function if the domain were restricted to $x \leq 0$?

Write the graph number corresponding to answer a) in the first box, the graph number corresponding to answer b) in the second box, the graph number corresponding to answer c) in the third box, and the graph number corresponding to answer d) in the fourth box.

(Record your answer in the numerical response box from left to right.)

Written Response

Consider the functions $f(x) = x + 4$ and $g(x) = 2x - 3$ defined for all real numbers.

• Sketch the graphs of $y = f(x)$ and $y = g(x)$ on the grid.

• Explain how to use the graphs of f and g to sketch the graph of $f - g$.
Sketch the graph of $y = (f - g)(x)$ on the grid.

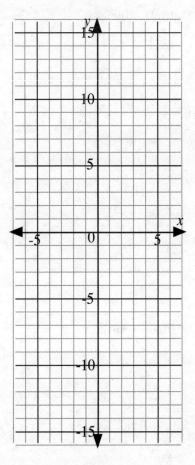

• Algebraically, determine to the nearest tenth the root(s) of the equation $(f \circ g)(x) = (fg)(x)$.

Answer Key

Multiple Choice

1. C **2.** D **3.** D **4.** D **5.** A **6.** B **7.** B **8.** D

9. B **10.** B **11.** D **12.** B **13.** A **14.** A **15.** A **16.** B

17. D **18.** C **19.** C **20.** B

Numerical Response

1.

4	1	2	3

2.

4	5	2	1

3.

2	2		

4.

1	3		

5.

1	.	4	

6.

6	3	4	2

Written Response

1. • See graph at the side.

• For integer values of x, subtract the corresponding y coordinate of $g(x)$ from the y-coordinate of $f(x)$ and plot the points (x, y). Join the points to form a straight line.

• –3.4, 1.9

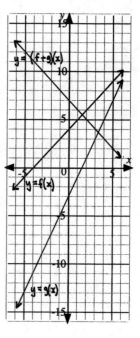

Transformations Lesson #1:
Horizontal and Vertical Translations - Part One

Overview

In this unit we will develop an understanding of the effects of **transformations** (operations which move (or map) a figure from an original position to a new position) on the graphs of functions and their related equations. The transformations we will consider are **translations**, **reflections**, **stretches**, and combinations of these.

In particular, we will consider replacements for x and/or y in the function $y = f(x)$ and investigate how the function $y - k = af[b(x - h)] + k$ is related to $y = f(x)$.

Translations

A **translation** is a transformation which slides each point of a figure the same distance in the same direction.

Comparing the Graphs of $y = f(x)$ and $y - k = f(x)$ [or $y = f(x) + k$]

Part 1

a) Complete the table of values. The first one has been completed.

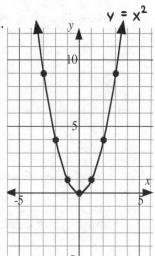

$y = x^2$		$y - 3 = x^2$		$y + 3 = x^2$	
x	y	x	y	x	y
-3	9	-3		-3	
-2	4	-2		-2	
-1	1	-1		-1	
0	0	0		0	
1	1	1		1	
2	4	2		2	
3	9	3		3	

b) Use the table of values in a) to graph and label each of the functions on the grid.

c) In the second table, y has been replaced by $y - 3$.

What is the effect of this replacement on the graph of $y = x^2$?

d) In the third table, y has been replaced by $y + 3$.

What is the effect of this replacement on the graph of $y = x^2$?

Part 2

a) Use a graphing calculator to graph the following functions:

    i) $y = |x|$ **ii)** $y = |x| + 2$ **iii)** $y = |x| - 3$

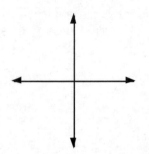 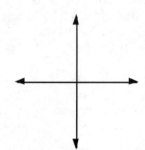 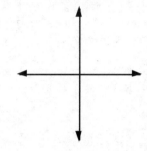

b) The equation $y = |x| + 2$ can be rewritten as $y - 2 = |x|$.
How does the replacement of y by $y - 2$ affect the graph of $y = |x|$?

c) The equation $y = |x| - 3$ can be rewritten as $y + 3 = |x|$.
How does the replacement of y by $y + 3$ affect the graph of $y = |x|$?

d) Using the results of Parts 1 and 2, answer the following questions
based on the graph of $y = f(x)$.

    i) What is the effect of the **parameter** k on the graph of the function $y = f(x) + k$?

    ii) What is the effect of the **parameter** k on the graph of the function $y - k = f(x)$?

e) Complete the following statements:

    • Compared to the graph of $y = f(x)$, the graph of $y - k = f(x)$ results in a _____
    translation of k units.

    • If $k > 0$, the graph moves _____. If $k < 0$, the graph moves _____.

 Note   The notation $y - k = f(x)$ is often used instead of $y = f(x) + k$ to emphasize that this is a
transformation on y. The concept of replacing y by $y - k$ will be very important in this course.

Comparing the Graphs of $y = f(x)$ and $y = f(x - h)$

Part 1

a) Complete the table of values.
The first one has been completed.

i) $y = x^2$

x	y
-4	16
-3	9
-2	4
-1	1
0	0
1	1
2	4
3	9
4	16

ii) $y = (x - 3)^2$

x	y
-1	
0	
1	
2	
3	
4	
5	
6	
7	

iii) $y = (x + 3)^2$

x	y
-7	
-6	
-5	
-4	
-3	
-2	
-1	
0	
1	

b) Use the table of values in a) to graph and label each of the functions on the same grid.

c) In the second table, x has been replaced by $x - 3$.
What is the effect of this replacement on the graph of $y = x^2$?

d) In the third table, x has been replaced by $x + 3$.
What is the effect of this replacement on the graph of $y = x^2$?

Part 2

a) Use a graphing calculator to graph the following functions, observing the effects of replacing x by $x - 4$, and x by $x + 2$.

i) $y = \sqrt{x}$ **ii)** $y = \sqrt{x - 4}$ **iii)** $y = \sqrt{x + 2}$

b) Based on the graph of $y = f(x)$, and using the results of Parts 1 and 2, describe the effect of the **parameter** h on the graph of the function $y = f(x - h)$.

c) Complete the following statements:

• Compared to the graph of $y = f(x)$, the graph of $y = f(x - h)$ results in a _____ translation of h units.

• If $h > 0$, the graph moves _____. If $h < 0$ the graph moves _____.

Replacements For Translations

Given the function $y = f(x)$:

- **replacing y with $y - k$,**   *(i.e. $y \rightarrow y - k$)*   **describes a vertical translation.**
  $y - k = f(x)$ **or** $y = f(x) + k$ **describes a vertical translation.**

- **replacing x with $x - h$,**   *(i.e. $x \rightarrow x - h$)*   **describes a horizontal translation.**
  $y = f(x - h)$ **describes a horizontal translation.**

In general, if
$$y - k = f(x - h)$$
or
$$y = f(x - h) + k \quad \text{then}$$

$k > 0$ the graph moves up ↑
$k < 0$ the graph moves down ↓
$h > 0$ the graph moves right →
$h < 0$ the graph moves left ←

Class Ex. #1   What happens to the graph of the function $y = f(x)$ if the following changes are made to its equation?

a) replace x with $x + 2$ **b)** replace y with $y - 8$

Class Ex. #2   Describe how the graphs of the following functions relate to the graph of $y = f(x)$.

a) $y = f(x - 3)$ **b)** $y = f(x) + 4$ **c)** $y - 1 = f(x + 10)$

Class Ex. #3   The point $(2, -3)$ lies on the graph of $y = f(x)$. State the coordinates of the image of this point under the following transformations.

a) $y + 8 = f(x)$ **b)** $y = f(x - 7) + 5$

Class Ex. #4   Write the equation of the image of $y = f(x)$ after each transformation.

a) A horizontal translation of 5 units left.   **b)** A translation of 3 units up.

c) A translation of m units right and p units down.

Class Ex. #5

Given the graph of the function $y = f(x)$, sketch the graph of the indicated function.

a) $y = f(x - 2)$

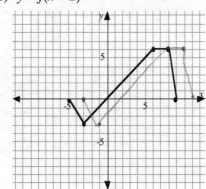

b) $y + 2 = f(x + 3)$

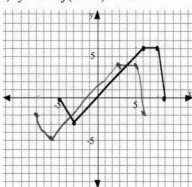

Replacment Notation and Mapping Notation

Do not confuse **mapping notation** with the notation we have used for replacements.

Consider the example where the graph of $y = f(x)$ is transformed to the graph of $y - 2 = f(x - 3)$.

In this example, the replacements for x and y may be written as $x \rightarrow x - 3$ and $y \rightarrow y - 2$.

Under this transformation, all points on the graph of $y = f(x)$ will move 3 units to the right and 2 units up. The point with coordinates $(4, 6)$ will be translated to the point $(7, 8)$. In general the point with coordinates (x, y) is translated to the point $(x + 3, y + 2)$.

The mapping notation for this translation may be written as $(x, y) \rightarrow (x + 3, y + 2)$, implying that the point with coordinates (x, y) is translated to the point $(x + 3, y + 2)$.

Notice that the mapping notation $(x, y) \rightarrow (x + 3, y + 2)$, is **NOT** the same as the replacement notation $x \rightarrow x + 3$ and $y \rightarrow y + 2$.

The mapping notation $(x, y) \rightarrow (x + 3, y + 2)$ **is equivalent to** the replacement notation $x \rightarrow x - 3$ and $y \rightarrow y - 2$.

Class Ex. #6

a) State the coordinates of the image of the point $(-3, 5)$ under the translation described by $(x, y) \rightarrow (x - 7, y + 4)$.

b) Write the equation of the image of $y = f(x)$ after the translation $(x, y) \rightarrow (x - 6, y + 1)$.

Complete Assignment Questions #1 - #10

Assignment

1. Describe how the graphs of the following functions relate to the graph of $y = f(x)$.

    a) $y = f(x + 9)$ **b)** $y = f(x) + 7$ **c)** $y = f(x - 4) + 4$

    d) $y - 6 = f(x)$ **e)** $y = 3 + f(x - 5)$ **f)** $y + 2 = f(x + 3) - 10$

2. Write the equation of the image of $y = f(x)$ after each transformation.
    a) a vertical translation of 10 units down

    b) a horizontal translation of 8 units right and a vertical translation of 9 units up

    c) a translation of t units up and s units left

3. The function $y = f(x)$ is transformed to $y = f(x - h) + k$. Find the values of h and k for the following translations.
    a) 7 units right   **b)** 4 units up and 2 units left   **c)** a units right and b units down.

4. The point $(-3, 5)$ lies on the graph of $y = f(x)$. State the coordinates of the image of this point under the following transformations.

    a) $y = f(x) + 3$ **b)** $y + 5 = f(x + 2)$ **c)** $(x, y) \rightarrow (x - 7, y - 1)$

5. What happens to the graph of the function $y = f(x)$ if you make these changes to its equation?
    a) replace x with $x - 8$ **b)** replace y with $y + 2$

    c) replace x with $x + 4$, and y with $y - 7$

6. Given the graph of the function $y = f(x)$, sketch the graph of the indicated function.

   a) $y = f(x - 4)$

   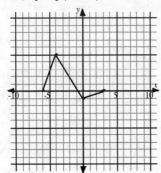

   b) $y - 3 = f(x)$

   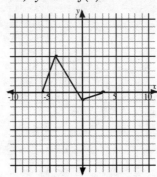

   c) $y = f(x + 2) - 3$

   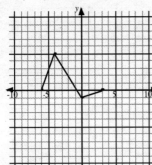

   d) $y + 2 = f(x - 5)$

   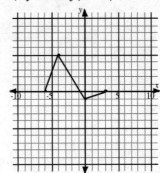

7. The function $y = f(x)$ is transformed to $y = f(x + 2) + 4$. If the point $(3, -1)$ lies on the graph of $y = f(x)$, which of the following points must lie on the graph of $y = f(x + 2) + 4$?

   A. $(5, 3)$ **B.** $(1, 3)$
   C. $(7, 1)$ **D.** $(7, -3)$

8. The function $y = f(x)$ is transformed to $y - 3 = f(x - 1)$. If the point $(-2, 4)$ lies on the graph of $y - 3 = f(x - 1)$, which of the following points must lie on the graph of $y = f(x)$?

   A. $(-1, 7)$
   B. $(-1, 1)$
   C. $(-3, 7)$
   D. $(-3, 1)$

9. The graph of $y = g(x)$ was transformed to the graph of $y = g(x - 7) + 2$. Which of the following statements describes the transformation?

   A. The graph of $y = g(x)$ has been translated 2 units to the right and 7 units upward.
   B. The graph of $y = g(x)$ has been translated 7 units to the left and 2 units downward.
   C. The point (x, y) on the graph $y = g(x)$ has been translated to point $(x + 7, y + 2)$.
   D. The point (x, y) on the graph $y = g(x)$ has been translated to point $(x - 7, y - 2)$.

Use the following information to answer the next question.

The graph of $y = f(x)$ is
shown on the grid to the right.

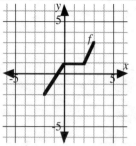

Transformations of the graph of $y = f(x)$ are shown below.

Graph 1

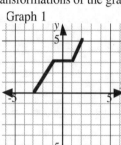

Graph 2

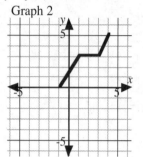

Graph 3

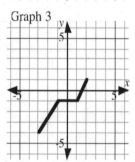

Graph 4

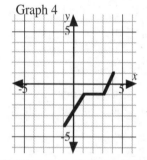

Numerical Response

10.   Write the graph number corresponding to $y - 2 = f(x - 1)$ in the first box.
Write the graph number corresponding to $y + 2 = f(x - 1)$ in the second box.
Write the graph number corresponding to $y - 2 = f(x + 1)$ in the third box.
Write the graph number corresponding to $y + 2 = f(x + 1)$ in the fourth box.

(Record your answer in the numerical response box from left to right.)

Answer Key

1. **a)** horizontal translation 9 units left   **b)** vertical translation 7 units up
    c) translation 4 units right and 4 units up   **d)** vertical translation 6 units up
    e) translation 5 units right and 3 units up   **f)** translation 3 units left and 12 units down
2. **a)** $y = f(x) - 10$ **b)** $y = f(x - 8) + 9$ **c)** $y = f(x + s) + t$
3. **a)** $h = 7, k = 0$ **b)** $h = -2, k = 4$ **c)** $h = a, k = -b$
4. **a)** $(-3, 8)$ **b)** $(-5, 0)$ **c)** $(-10, 4)$
5. **a)** horizontal translation 8 units right   **b)** vertical translation 2 units down
    c) translation 4 units left and 7 units up
6. **a)** the graph is translated 4 units right   **b)** the graph is translated 3 units up
    c) the graph is translated 2 units left and 3 units down
    d) the graph is translated 5 units right and 2 units down

7. B   8. D   9. C   10. | 2 | 4 | 1 | 3 |

Transformations Lesson #2:
Horizontal and Vertical Translations - Part Two

Review

Given the function $y = f(x)$:

- replacing y with $y - k$, (i.e. $y \rightarrow y - k$) describes a vertical translation.
  $y - k = f(x)$ or $y = f(x) + k$ describes a vertical translation.

- replacing x with $x - h$, (i.e. $x \rightarrow x - h$) describes a horizontal translation.
  $y = f(x - h)$ describes a horizontal translation.

In general, if $y - k = f(x - h)$ or $y = f(x - h) + k$, then

> $k > 0$ the graph moves up ↑
>
> $k < 0$ the graph moves down ↓
>
> $h > 0$ the graph moves right →
> $h < 0$ the graph moves left ←

Class Ex. #1 Write the replacements for x and/or y, and describe how the graph of the second function compares to the graph of the first function.

a) $y = x^4$, $y = x^4 + 3$

b) $y = 6x - 3$, $y = 6(x - 1) - 3$

c) $y = |x|$, $y = |x - 6| + 2$

d) $y = \dfrac{1}{\sqrt{x}}$, $y = \dfrac{1}{\sqrt{x + 1}}$

Class Ex. #2 Write the replacements for x and/or y, and hence the equation of the image of

a) $y = x^2$ after a horizontal translation of 3 units to the right.

b) $y = 10^x$ after a vertical translation of 2 units up.

c) $y = \sqrt{x}$ after a horizontal translation of 4 units to the left and a vertical translation of 3 units down.

Class Ex. #3

The function represented by the thick line is a transformation of the function represented by the thin line. Write an equation for each function represented by the thick line.

a)

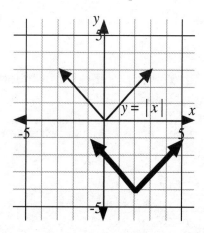

$y = |x|$

b)

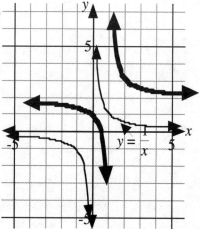

$y = \dfrac{1}{x}$

c)

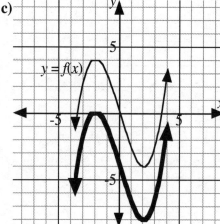

$y = f(x)$

d)

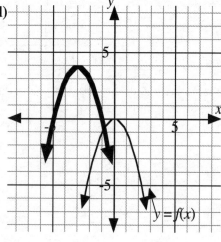

$y = f(x)$

Class Ex. #4

$y = \sqrt{x}$ is a radical function.

a) What vertical translation would be applied to $y = \sqrt{x}$ so that the translation image passes through $(16, 7)$?

b) What horizontal translation would be applied to $y = \sqrt{x}$ so that the translation image passes through $(17, 8)$?

Complete Assignment Questions #1 - #10

Assignment

1. Describe how the graph of the second function compares to the graph of the first function.

a) $y = x^3$

$y = x^3 - 1$

b) $y = 7x - 1$

$y = 7(x - 3) - 1$

c) $y = \cos x°$

$y = \cos (x + 45)°$

d) $y = |x|$

$y + 3 = |x + 6|$

e) $y = \dfrac{1}{x^2 + 1}$

$y - 2 = \dfrac{1}{(x - 3)^2 + 1}$

f) $y = a^x$

$y = a^{x + 1} + 1$

2. Write the equation of the image of:

a) $y = x^4$ after a horizontal translation of 2 units to the left.

b) $y = 2|x|$ after a translation of 3 units down and 1 unit left.

c) $y = \dfrac{1}{\sqrt{x}}$ after a horizontal translation of 3 units to the right and a vertical translation of 2 units up.

3. On a certain route, trains travel at an average speed of 90km/h. The distance, d kilometres, they travel can be described as a function of time, t hours, and represented by the equation $d = f(t) = 90t$.

A train leaves the station at 12:00 p.m. ($t = 0$). A second train travels with the same average speed, but leaves 3 hours later.

a) Sketch a distance time graph for each train on the grid.

b) Explain why the equation that describes the distance travelled by the second train is $d = 90(t - 3), t \geq 3$.

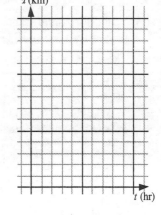

4. The function represented by the thick line is a transformation of the function represented by the thin line. Write an equation for each function represented by the thick line.

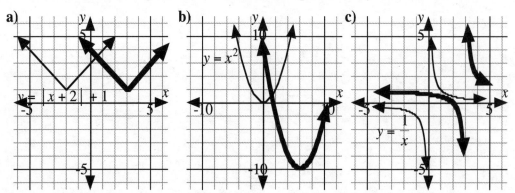

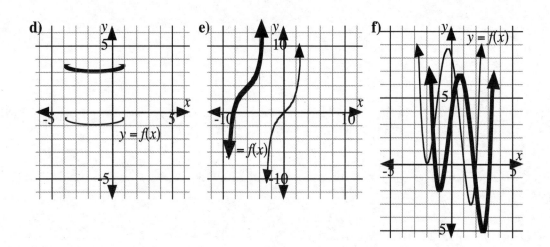

5. a) What vertical translation would be applied to $y = x^2$ so that the translation image passes through $(3, 5)$?

b) What horizontal translation would be applied to $y = x^3 + 1$ so that the translation image passes through $(5, 28)$?

c) What horizontal translation would be applied to $y = \dfrac{1}{x - 3}$ so that the translation image passes through $\left(1, \dfrac{1}{2}\right)$?

6. On a certain route into town, shuttle buses depart every 15 minutes from 06:30 until 07:30. The distance, d kilometres, they travel can be described as a function of time, t hours, and represented by the equation $d = f(t) = 60t$.

If $t = 0$ at 06:30, write an equation which represents the distance travelled by

a) the second bus   **b)** the third bus   **c)** the last bus

7. The graph of the function $y = f(x)$ passes through the point $(4, 7)$. Under a transformation, the point $(4, 7)$ is transformed to $(6, 6)$. A possible equation for the transformed function is

A. $y - 1 = f(x + 2)$
B. $y - 2 = f(x + 1)$
C. $y + 1 = f(x - 2)$
D. $y + 2 = f(x - 1)$

8. If $f(x) = 4 - x^2$, then the transformation represented by $f(x + 6) - 3$ will change

A.   the domain but not the range of $f(x)$
B.   the range but not the domain of $f(x)$
C.   neither the domain nor the range of $f(x)$
D.   both the domain and the range of $f(x)$

9. The function $f(x) = \sqrt{x} + 5$ is transformed by a translation of 2 units down and 4 units to the left. The transformed function passes through the point $(20, y)$.
To the nearest tenth, the value of y is _____ .

(Record your answer in the numerical response box from left to right.)

10.   The function $R(x) = \dfrac{1}{x+3}$ is transformed by a translation of 3 units up and 5 units to the right. The transformed function passes through the point $(x, 7)$.

The value of x to the nearest hundredth is _____ .

(Record your answer in the numerical response box from left to right.)

Answer Key

1. a)   vertical translation 1 unit down   **b)**   horizontal translation 3 units right
   c)   horizontal translation 45° left   **d)**   translation 6 units left and 3 units down
   e)   translation 3 units right and 2 units up   **f)**   translation 1 unit left and 1 unit up

2. a) $y = (x+2)^4$ **b)** $y = 2|x+1| - 3$ **c)** $y = \dfrac{1}{\sqrt{x-3}} + 2$

3. a) See graph below   **b)**   Compared to the graph of the first train, the graph for the second train is
a horizontal translation three units to the right. t is replaced by $t - 3$, to
give the equation $d = 90(t - 3)$. The domain restriction $t \geq 3$ is given
because the second train does not leave until 3:00 pm when $t = 3$.

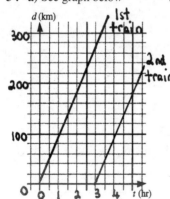

4. a) $y = |x - 3| + 1$ **b)** $y = (x - 6)^2 - 10$ **c)** $y = \dfrac{1}{x-3} + 1$

   d) $y = f(x) + 4$ **e)** $y = f(x + 6) + 4$ **f)** $y = f(x - 1) - 2$

5. a)   vertical translation 4 units down   **b)**   horizontal translation 2 units right
   c)   horizontal translation 4 units left

6. a) $d = 60\left(t - \dfrac{1}{4}\right)$ **b)** $d = 60\left(t - \dfrac{1}{2}\right)$ **c)** $d = 60(t - 1)$

7. C   **8.** B   **9.** | 7 | . | 9 | | **10.** | 2 | . | 2 | 5 |

Transformations Lesson #3:
Reflections - Part One

Invariant Points

Invariant points are points on a graph which do not move after a transformation.

Comparing the Graphs of $y = f(x)$ and $y = -f(x)$

Part 1

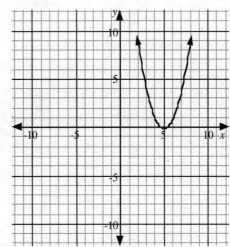

a) The graph of $y = f(x) = x^2 - 10x + 25$ is shown.
Write an equation which represents $y = -f(x)$.

b) Use a graphing calculator to sketch $y = -f(x)$ and
show the graph on the grid.

c) State the coordinates of the invariant point(s).

Part 2

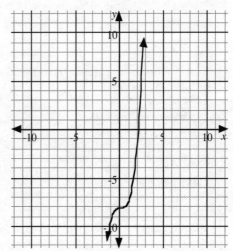

a) The graph of $y = f(x) = x^3 - 8$ is shown.
Write an equation which represents $y = -f(x)$.

b) Use a graphing calculator to sketch $y = -f(x)$ and
show the graph on the grid.

c) State the coordinates of the invariant point(s).

d) How does the graph of $y = -f(x)$ compare with
the graph of $y = f(x)$?

Part 3

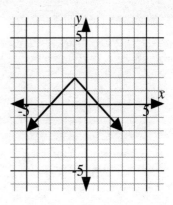

The graph of $y = f(x)$ is shown.
Sketch the graph of $y = -f(x)$.

 If we replace y with $-y$, then $y = f(x)$ becomes $-y = f(x)$,
which is equivalent to $y = -f(x)$.
So the replacement in this example is $y \to -y$.

Comparing the Graphs of y = f(x) and y = f(−x)

Part 1

a) The graph of $y = f(x) = x^2 - 10x + 25$ is shown. Write an equation which represents $y = f(-x)$.

b) Use a graphing calculator to sketch $y = f(-x)$ and show the graph on the grid.

c) State the coordinates of the invariant point(s).

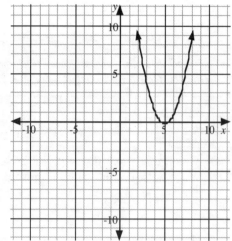

Part 2

a) The graph of $y = f(x) = x^3 - 8$ is shown. Write an equation which represents $y = f(-x)$.

b) Use a graphing calculator to sketch $y = f(-x)$ and show the graph on the grid.

c) State the coordinates of the invariant point(s).

d) How does the graph of $y = f(-x)$ compare with the graph of $y = f(x)$?

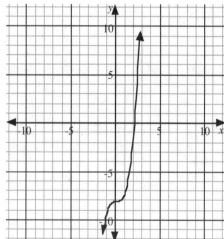

Part 3

The graph of $y = f(x)$ is shown.
Sketch the graph of $y = f(-x)$.

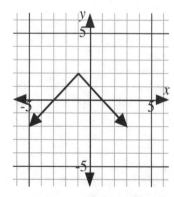

 If we replace x with $-x$, then $y = f(x)$ becomes $y = f(-x)$. So the replacement in this example is $x \rightarrow -x$.

Comparing the Graphs of y = f(x) and y = f⁻¹(x) or x = f(y)

Part 1

a) The graph of $y = f(x) = (x - 5)^2$ is shown.
   Write an equation which represents $x = f(y)$ and
   solve for y.

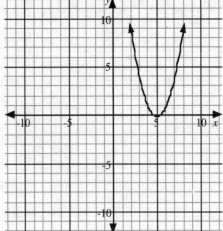

b) Use a graphing calculator to sketch $x = f(y)$ and
   show the graph on the grid.

c) Although there are four points of intersection of
   the graphs, explain why there are only two
   invariant points. Mark the invariant points on the grid.

Part 2

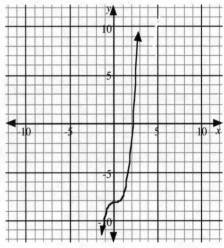

a) The graph of $y = f(x) = x^3 - 8$ is shown.
   Write an equation which represents $y = f^{-1}(x)$.

b) Use a graphing calculator to sketch $y = f^{-1}(x)$ and
   show the graph on the grid.

c) Mark the invariant point(s) on the grid.

d) How does the graph of $x = f(y)$ compare with the
   graph of $y = f(x)$?

Part 3

The graph of $y = f(x)$ is shown.
Sketch the graph of $x = f(y)$.

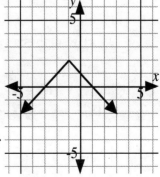

 If we replace x with y, and y with x, then $y = f(x)$ becomes $x = f(y)$.
So the replacements in this example are $x \rightarrow y$ and $y \rightarrow x$.

Reflections

A **reflection** is a transformation which reflects (or flips) a figure about a line.

Fill in the following blanks which summarize the previous investigations.

Reflection	Function	Graph
Reflection in the *x*-axis	If the graph of $y = f(x)$ is reflected in the _____ , then it is the graph of _____ .	$y = f(x)$ $y =$ _____
Reflection in the *y*-axis	If the graph of $y = f(x)$ is reflected in the _____ , then it is the graph of _____ .	$y = f(x)$ $y =$ _____
Reflection in the line $y = x$	If the graph of $y = f(x)$ is reflected in the line _____ , then it is the graph of _____ or _____ .	$y = f(x)$ $y = x$ $y =$ _____ or $x =$ _____

 Given the function $y = f(x)$:

- **replacing *x* with $-x$,   (*i.e.* $x \rightarrow -x$)   describes a reflection in the *y*-axis.**
  $y = f(-x)$ describes a reflection in the *y*-axis.

- **replacing *y* with $-y$,   (*i.e.* $y \rightarrow -y$)   describes a reflection in the *x*-axis.**
  $-y = f(x)$ or $y = -f(x)$ describes a reflection in the *x*-axis.

- **interchanging *x* and *y*, (*i.e.* $x \rightarrow y$, $y \rightarrow x$) describes a reflection in the line $y = x$.**
  $x = f(y)$ or $y = f^{-1}(x)$ describes a reflection in the line $y = x$.

Class Ex. #1   The graph of $y = f(x)$ is shown. Sketch:

a) $y = -f(x)$

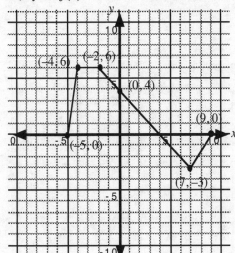

b) $y = f(-x)$

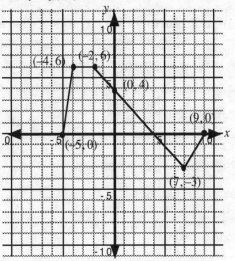

c) $x = f(y)$

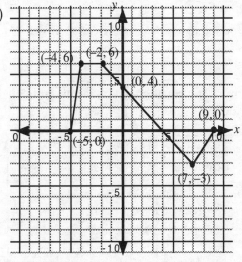

Class Ex. #2   The graph drawn in the thick line is a reflection of the graph drawn in the thin line. Write an equation for each graph drawn in the thick line.

a)

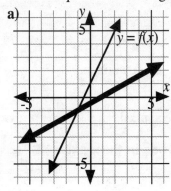

b)

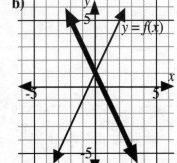

c)

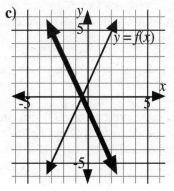

Complete Assignment Questions #1 - #6

Combining Reflections

Part 1 - Transforming $y = f(x)$ to $y = -f(-x)$

The table below shows how to "build" $y = -f(-x)$ from $y = f(x)$.

Transformation	Replacement for x or y	Current Equation
1. reflection in the x-axis	$y \to -y$	$-y = f(x)$ $y = -f(x)$
2. reflection in the y-axis	$x \to -x$	$y = -f(-x)$

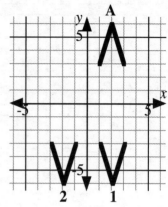

The transformations in the table are applied to shape **A** in the order shown.
The images are shown on the grid.

a) Complete the table below to determine the equation which results from changing the order in which the reflections are carried out.

Transformation	Replacement for x or y	Current Equation
1. reflection in the y-axis		
2. reflection in the x-axis		

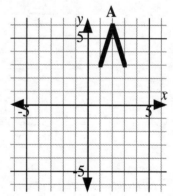

b) On the grid above, sketch the image of shape **A** under the combinations of transformations in a).

c) Does the order in which the reflections are carried out affect the final image?

d) Describe two sets of transformations, in order, which can be applied to the graph of $y = f(x)$ to produce the graph of $y = -f(-x)$.

Part 2 - Transforming $y = f(x)$ to $x = f(-y)$ and $x = -f(y)$

In each case, complete the table and sketch the combination of transformations on the grid.

Transformation	Replacement for *x* or *y*	Current Equation
1. reflection in the *y*-axis		
2. reflection in $y = x$		

Transformation	Replacement for *x* or *y*	Current Equation
1. reflection in $y = x$		
2. reflection in the *y*-axis		

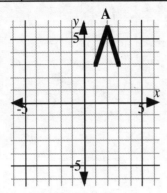

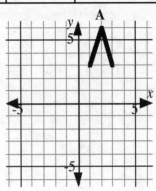

Transformation	Replacement for *x* or *y*	Current Equation
1. reflection in the *x*-axis		
2. reflection in $y = x$		

Transformation	Replacement for *x* or *y*	Current Equation
1. reflection in $y = x$		
2. reflection in the *x*-axis		

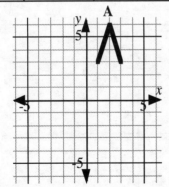

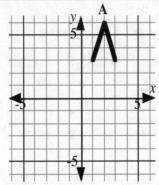

a) Describe two sets of transformations, in order, which can be applied to the graph of $y = f(x)$ to produce the graph of $x = f(-y)$.

b) Describe two sets of transformations, in order, which can be applied to the graph of $y = f(x)$ to produce the graph of $x = -f(y)$.

Complete Assignment Questions #7 - #14

Assignment

1. The graph of $y = f(x)$ is shown. Sketch the graph of $y = -f(x)$.

    a)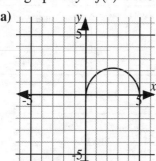

    b)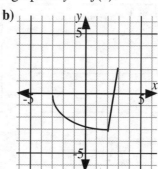

2. The graph of $y = f(x)$ is shown. Sketch the graph of $y = f(-x)$.

    a)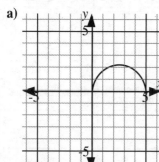

    b)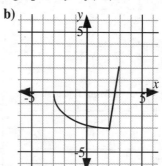

3. The graph of $y = f(x)$ is shown. Sketch the graph of $x = f(y)$.

    a)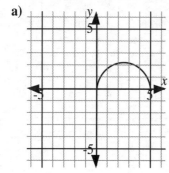

    b)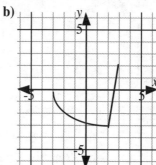

4. The function $y = f(x)$ is transformed to the function below. Given that there are invariant points, describe the location of these points.

    a) $y = -f(x)$ **b)** $y = f(-x)$ **c)** $x = f(y)$

5. The graph drawn in the thick line is a transformation of the graph drawn in the thin line. Write an equation for each graph drawn in the thick line and state whether this graph represents a function.

a)

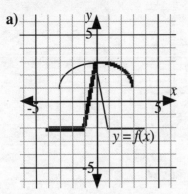

b)

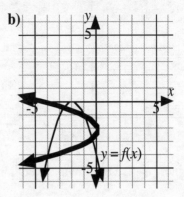

c)

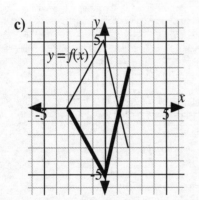

d)

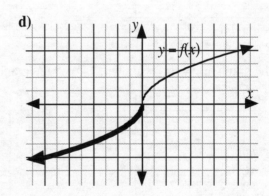

6. The point (x, y) lies on the graph of the function $y = f(x)$. State the coordinates of the image of (x, y) under the following transformations:

a) $y = -f(x)$ **b)** $y = f(-x)$ **c)** $x = f(y)$

7. The graph of $y = f(x)$ is shown. Sketch the graph of $y = -f(-x)$.

a)
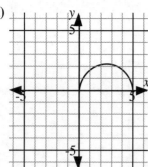

b)
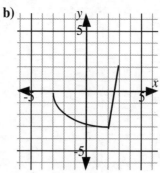

8. The graph of $y = f(x)$ is shown. Sketch the graph of $x = f(-y)$.

a)
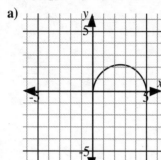

b)
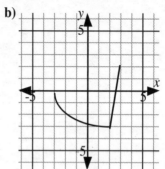

9. The graph of $y = f(x)$ is shown. Sketch the graph of $x = -f(y)$.

a)
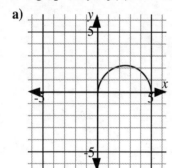

b)
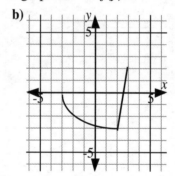

10. Consider the graph of a function of f and the graph of a function g, where $g(x) = f(-x)$. Any invariant points must lie on the

A. x-axis

B. y-axis

C. line $y = x$

D. line $y = -x$

Use the following information to answer the next four questions.

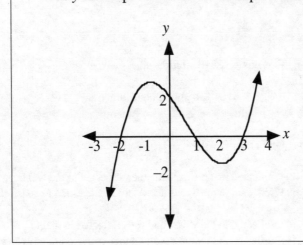

A partial graph of $y = f(x)$ is shown.
The y-intercept and all the x-intercepts are integers.

11. If $g(x) = -f(x)$, the largest x-intercept of the graph of g is

    A. –2   **B.** 1

    C. 2   **D.** 3

12. If $h(x) = f(-x)$, the smallest x-intercept of the graph of h is

    A. –3   **B.** –2

    C. 2   **D.** 3

13. On the graph of $x = -f(y)$, the y-intercept(s) is/are

    A. –2 only   **B.** 2 only

    C. –2, 1, and 3   **D.** –3, –1, and 2

Numerical Response **14.** If $P(x) = -f(-x)$, the largest x-intercept of the graph of P is _____ .

(Record your answer in the numerical response box from left to right.)

                                            | | | | |

Answer Key

1 . a) and **b)** graph is reflected in *x*-axis

2 . a) and **b)** graph is reflected in *y*-axis

3 . a) and **b)** graph is reflected in the line $y = x$

4 . a) on the *x*-axis   **b)** on the *y*-axis   **c)** on the line $y = x$

5 . a) $y = f(-x)$ is a function   **b)** $x = f(y)$ is a not a function
   c) $y = -f(x)$ is a function   **d)** $y = -f(-x)$ is a function

6 .   a) $(x, -y)$ **b)** $(-x, y)$ **c)** (y, x)

7 . a) and **b)** graph is either   **i)** reflected in the *x*-axis and then reflected in the *y*-axis
           or   **ii)** reflected in the *y*-axis and then reflected in the *x*-axis.

8 . a) and **b)** graph is either   **i)** reflected in the *y*-axis and then reflected in the line $y = x$
           or   **ii)** reflected in the line $y = x$ and then reflected in the *x*-axis.

9 . a) and **b)** graph is either   **i)** reflected in the *x*-axis and then reflected in the line $y = x$
           or   **ii)** reflected in the line $y = x$ and then reflected in the *y*-axis.

10. B   **11 .** D   **12 .** A   **13 .** C   **14.** | 2 | | | |

Transformations Lesson #4:
Reflections - Part Two

Review

Given the function $y = f(x)$:

- **replacing x with $-x$, (i.e. $x \rightarrow -x$) describes a reflection in the y-axis.**
  $y = f(-x)$ describes a reflection in the y-axis.

- **replacing y with $-y$, (i.e. $y \rightarrow -y$) describes a reflection in the x-axis.**
  $-y = f(x)$ or $y = -f(x)$ describes a reflection in the x-axis.

- **interchanging x and y, (i.e. $x \rightarrow y$, $y \rightarrow x$) describes a reflection in the line $y = x$.**
  $x = f(y)$ or $y = f^{-1}(x)$ describes a reflection in the line $y = x$.

Class Ex. #1

Write the equation of the image of:

a) $y = x^2$ after a reflection in the line $y = x$

b) $y = 10^x$ after a reflection in the y-axis

c) $y = \sqrt{x}$ after a reflection in the x-axis.

Class Ex. #2

Describe how the graph of the second function compares to the graph of the first function.

a) $y = x^3$ **b)** $y = 2^x$ **c)** $y = \sin x$
    $y = -x^3$ $x = 2^y$ $y = \sin(-x)$

Class Ex. #3

The graph drawn in the thick line is a transformation of the graph drawn in the thin line. Write an equation for each graph drawn in the thick line and state whether this graph represents a function.

a)

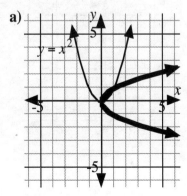

b)

Class Ex. #4

a) Sketch the graph of $f(x) = \dfrac{6}{x^2 + 3}$.

b) Write the equation for

i) $y = -f(x)$ **ii)** $y = f(-x)$ **iii)** $x = f(y)$

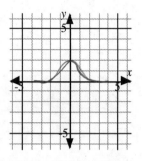

c) Sketch each graph in b) and state whether the graph represents a function.

i) $y = -f(x)$ **ii)** $y = f(-x)$ **iii)** $x = f(y)$

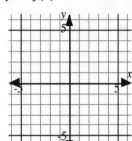   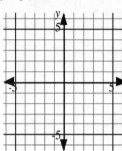   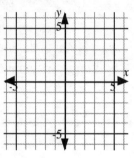

Class Ex. #5

a) Given $f(x) = 3x + 2$, determine:

i) $x = f(y)$ **ii)** $x = f(-y)$ **iii)** $x = -f(y)$

b) The graph of $y = 3x + 2$ is given. Sketch each graph in a).

i) $x = f(y)$ **ii)** $x = f(-y)$ **iii)** $x = -f(y)$

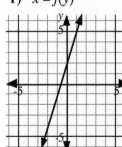   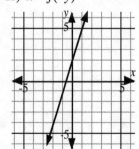   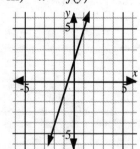

Complete Assignment Questions #1 - #9

Assignment

1. Write the equation of the image of

   a) $y = \dfrac{1}{x}$ after a reflection in the line $y = x$

   b) $y = x^3 + x$ after a reflection in the y-axis

   c) $y = |x|$ after a reflection in the x-axis

   d) $y = \sqrt{x - 2}$ after a reflection in the line $y = x$

   e) $y = x^2 + 1$ after a reflection in the y-axis

   f) $y = \cos x$ after a reflection in the x-axis

2. Describe how the graph of the second function compares to the graph of the first function.

   a) $y = 3x + 1$
      $y = -3x - 1$

   b) $y = 3x + 1$
      $y = -3x + 1$

   c) $y = 3x + 1$
      $x = 3y + 1$

   d) $y = 10^x$
      $y = 10^{-x}$

   e) $y = 10^x$
      $y = -10^x$

   f) $y = 4x^2$
      $y = \pm\dfrac{\sqrt{x}}{2}$

3. The graph drawn in the thick line is a transformation of the graph drawn in the thin line. Write an equation for each graph drawn in the thick line.

a)

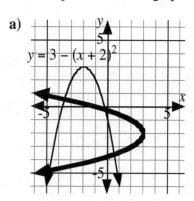

$y = 3 - (x + 2)^2$

b)

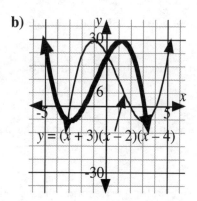

$y = (x + 3)(x - 2)(x - 4)$

c)

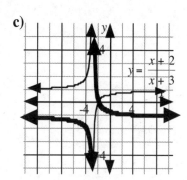

$y = \dfrac{x + 2}{x + 3}$

d)

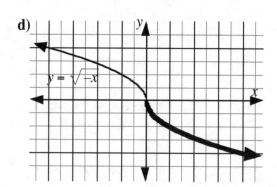

$y = \sqrt{-x}$

4.a) Sketch the graph of $f(x) = (x - 1)^2$.

b) Write the equation for:

   i) $y = -f(x)$ **ii)** $y = f(-x)$

   iii) $x = f(y)$

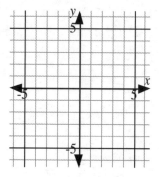

c) Sketch each graph in b) and state whether the graph represents a function.

  i) $y = -f(x)$ **ii)** $y = f(-x)$ **iii)** $x = f(y)$

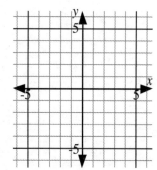
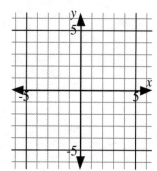
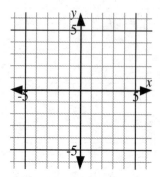

5.a) Sketch the graph of the semi-circle $f(x) = \sqrt{16 - x^2}$.

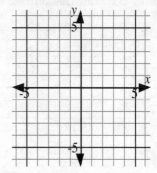

  b) Write the equation for:

    i) $y = -f(x)$ **ii)** $y = f(-x)$

    iii) $y = -f(-x)$ **iv)** $x = f(y)$

    v) $x = -f(y)$ **vi)** $x = f(-y)$

  c) Sketch each graph in b) and state whether the graph represents a function.

    i) $y = -f(x)$ **ii)** $y = f(-x)$ **iii)** $y = -f(-x)$

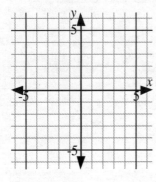 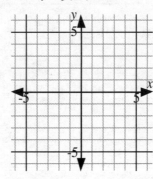 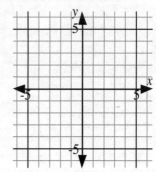

    iv) $x = f(y)$ **v)** $x = -f(y)$ **vi)** $x = -f(-y)$

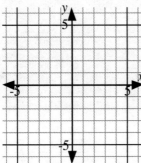 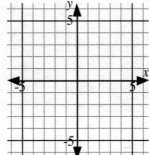 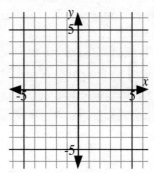

d) State the domain and range of each graph in c).

Question	Domain	Range
i) $y = -f(x)$		
ii) $y = f(-x)$		
iii) $y = -f(-x)$		
iv) $x = f(y)$		
v) $x = -f(y)$		
vi) $x = f(-y)$		

Use the following information to answer the next question.

> The graph of $y = 2x^5$ is transformed to the graph of $y = -2x^5$.
> Three statements are made about the transformed graph.
>
> **i)**   It is a reflection of the original graph in the x-axis.
> **ii)** It is a reflection of the original graph in the y-axis.
> **iii)** It is a reflection of the original graph in the line $y = x$.

6. How many of the above statements are **false**?

A. 0

B. 1

C. 2

D. 3

7. How could the graph of $y = 2x^3 + 1$ be used to graph $y = -2x^3 + 1$?

A. Translate the graph of $y = 2x^3 + 1$ vertically.
B. Reflect the graph of $y = 2x^3 + 1$ in the line $y = x$.
C. Reflect the graph of $y = 2x^3 + 1$ in the x-axis.
D. Reflect the graph of $y = 2x^3 + 1$ in the y-axis.

8. Consider the graph of the function $f(x) = x^2$.
Which of the following would result in an identical graph?

A. $-f(x)$

B. $f(-x)$

C. $-f(-x)$

D. $f(x + 1)$

Use the following information to answer the next question.

The graphs below represent transformations of the function $f(x) = x^2$.

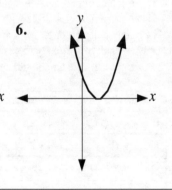

Numerical Response

9. Write the graph number corresponding to $f(-x)$ in the first box.
Write the graph number corresponding to $f(x + 2)$ in the second box.
Write the graph number corresponding to $f(x) - 2$ in the third box.
Write the graph number corresponding to $-f(x)$ in the fourth box.

(Record your answer in the numerical response box from left to right.)

Answer Key

1.a) $x = \dfrac{1}{y}$ or $y = \dfrac{1}{x}$ **b)** $y = -x^3 - x$ **c)** $y = -|x|$

d) $x = \sqrt{y - 2}$ or $y = x^2 + 2, x \geq 0$ **e)** $y = x^2 + 1$ **f)** $y = -\cos x$

2.a) reflection in the *x*-axis   **b)** reflection in the *y*-axis   **c)** reflection in the line $y = x$

d) reflection in the *y*-axis   **e)** reflection in the *x*-axis   **f)** reflection in the line $y = x$

3.a) $x = 3 - (y + 2)^2$ or $y = \pm\sqrt{3 - x} - 2$

b) $y = (-x + 3)(-x - 2)(-x - 4)$ or $y = -(x - 3)(x + 2)(x + 4)$

c) $y = -\dfrac{x + 2}{x + 3}$

d) $y = -\sqrt{x}$

4.a) parabola opening up with vertex $(1, 0)$

b) **i)** $y = -(x - 1)^2$ **ii)** $y = (-x - 1)^2$ or $y = (x + 1)^2$ **iii)** $x = (y - 1)^2$

c) **i)**   parabola opening down with vertex $(1, 0)$. Is a function.

ii) parabola opening up with vertex $(-1, 0)$. Is a function.

iii) parabola opening right with vertex $(0, 1)$. Is not a function.

5.a)   top half of a circle with centre at the origin and radius 4

b) **i)** $y = -\sqrt{16 - x^2}$ **ii)** $y = \sqrt{16 - x^2}$ **iii)** $y = -\sqrt{16 - x^2}$

iv) $x = \sqrt{16 - y^2}$ **v)** $x = -\sqrt{16 - y^2}$ **vi)** $x = \sqrt{16 - y^2}$

c) **i)**   bottom half of a circle with centre at the origin and radius 4. Is a function.

ii) top half of a circle with centre at the origin and radius 4. Is a function.

iii) bottom half of a circle with centre at the origin and radius 4. Is a function.

iv) right half of a circle with centre at the origin and radius 4. Is not a function.

v) left half of a circle with centre at the origin and radius 4. Is not a function.

vi) right half of a circle with centre at the origin and radius 4. Is not a function.

d)

Question	Domain	Range
i) $y = -f(x)$	$\{x \mid -4 \leq x \leq 4, x \in R\}$	$\{y \mid -4 \leq y \leq 0, y \in R\}$
ii) $y = f(-x)$	$\{x \mid -4 \leq x \leq 4, x \in R\}$	$\{y \mid 0 \leq y \leq 4, y \in R\}$
iii) $y = -f(-x)$	$\{x \mid -4 \leq x \leq 4, x \in R\}$	$\{y \mid -4 \leq y \leq 0, y \in R\}$
iv) $x = f(y)$	$\{x \mid 0 \leq x \leq 4, x \in R\}$	$\{y \mid -4 \leq y \leq 4, y \in R\}$
v) $x = -f(y)$	$\{x \mid -4 \leq x \leq 0, x \in R\}$	$\{y \mid -4 \leq y \leq 4, y \in R\}$
vi) $x = f(-y)$	$\{x \mid 0 \leq x \leq 4, x \in R\}$	$\{y \mid -4 \leq y \leq 4, y \in R\}$

6. B   **7.** D   **8.** B   **9.**

4	5	3	1

Transformations Lesson #5:
Stretches About the x- or y- axis - Part One

Comparing the Graphs of $y = f(x)$ and $y = af(x)$, where $a > 0$

Part 1

The graph of $y = f(x) = \sqrt{4 - x^2}$ is shown.

a) Write an equation which represents $y = 3f(x)$.

b) Use a graphing calculator to sketch $y = 3f(x)$ on the grid.

c) Describe how the number 3 in $y = 3f(x)$ affects:
- the general sketch of $y = f(x)$

- the x-intercepts of the graph of $y = f(x)$

- the y-intercept of the graph of $y = f(x)$.

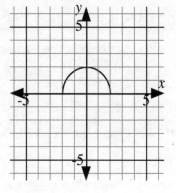

Part 2

a) Write an equation which represents $y = \dfrac{1}{2}f(x)$.

b) Use a graphing calculator to sketch $y = \dfrac{1}{2}f(x)$ on the grid.

c) Describe how the number $\dfrac{1}{2}$ in $y = \dfrac{1}{2}f(x)$ affects:
- the general sketch of $y = f(x)$

- the x-intercepts of the graph of $y = f(x)$

- the y-intercept of the graph of $y = f(x)$.

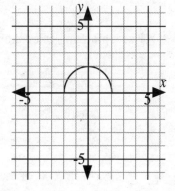

d) Complete the following statement using the results of Parts 1 and 2.

Compared to the graph of $y = f(x)$, the graph of $y = af(x)$
results in a _____ stretch about the ___-axis by a factor of _____ .

Note If we replace y with $\dfrac{1}{a}y$, then $y = f(x)$ becomes $\dfrac{1}{a}y = f(x)$, which is equivalent to $y = af(x)$.

So the replacement in this example is $y \rightarrow \dfrac{1}{a}y$.

> ## *Comparing the Graphs of y = f(x) and y = f(bx), where b > 0*

Part 1

The graph of $y = f(x) = \sqrt{4 - x^2}$ is shown.

a) Write an equation which represents $y = f(4x)$.

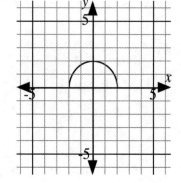

b) Use a graphing calculator to sketch $y = f(4x)$ on the grid.

c) Describe how the number 4 in $y = f(4x)$ affects:
   • the general sketch of $y = f(x)$

   • the x-intercepts of the graph of $y = f(x)$

   • the y-intercept of the graph of $y = f(x)$.

Part 2

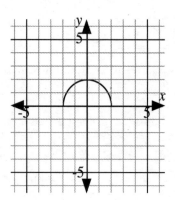

a) Write an equation which represents $y = f\left(\dfrac{1}{3}x\right)$.

b) Use a graphing calculator to sketch $y = f\left(\dfrac{1}{3}x\right)$ on the grid.

c) Describe how the number $\dfrac{1}{3}$ in $y = f\left(\dfrac{1}{3}x\right)$ affects:
   • the general sketch of $y = f(x)$

   • the x-intercepts of the graph of $y = f(x)$

   • the y-intercept of the graph of $y = f(x)$.

d) Complete the following statement using the results of Parts 1 and 2.

Compared to the graph of $y = f(x)$, the graph of $y = f(bx)$

results in a _____ stretch about the ___-axis by a factor of $\dfrac{1}{b}$.

Note If we replace x with bx, then $y = f(x)$ becomes $y = f(bx)$.
So the replacement in this example is $x \rightarrow bx$.

Comparing the Graphs of y = f(x) and y = af(x), where a < 0

The graph of $y = f(x) = x^3 - 2x^2 - 5x + 6$ is shown.

a) Write an equation which represents $y = -3f(x)$.

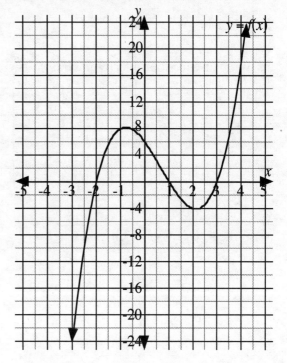

b) Use a graphing calculator to sketch $y = -3f(x)$.

c) Describe how the number –3 in $y = -3f(x)$ affects:

- the general sketch of $y = f(x)$

- the x-intercepts of the graph of $y = f(x)$

- the y-intercept of the graph of $y = f(x)$.

d) Complete the following statement.

Compared to the graph of $y = f(x)$, the graph of $y = af(x)$, where $a < 0$,

results in a __vertical__ stretch about the __y__-axis by a factor of $|a|$ together with

a reflection in the __x__ -axis.

Comparing the Graphs of $y = f(x)$ and $y = f(bx)$, where $b < 0$

The graph of $y = f(x) = x^3 - 2x^2 - 5x + 6$ is shown.

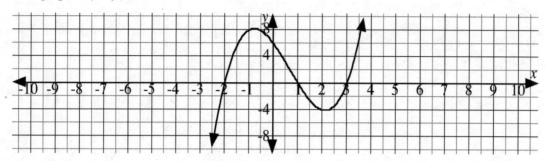

a) Write an equation which represents $y = f\left(-\frac{1}{3}x\right)$.

b) Use a graphing calculator to sketch $y = f\left(-\frac{1}{3}x\right)$.

c) Describe how the number $-\frac{1}{3}$ in $y = f\left(-\frac{1}{3}x\right)$ affects:

  • the general sketch of $y = f(x)$

  • the x-intercepts of the graph of $y = f(x)$

  • the y-intercept of the graph of $y = f(x)$.

d)   Complete the following statement.

   Compared to the graph of $y = f(x)$, the graph of $y = f(bx)$, where $b < 0$,

   results in a _____ stretch about the ____-axis by a factor of $\dfrac{1}{|b|}$ together with

   a reflection in the _____-axis.

Stretches

In mathematics we use the word **stretch** to represent both an expansion or a compression. In this course we only consider stretches about the *x*- and *y*-axis.

In the table below, the graph of $y = f(x)$ and the graph of $y = af(x)$ or $y = f(bx)$ is given. Fill in the blanks.

a or b	*Horizontal or Vertical Stretch*	*Graph*
$0 < a < 1$	The graph of $y = f(x)$ will be stretched _____ by a factor of ___ about the ___-axis.	
$a > 1$	The graph of $y = f(x)$ will be stretched _____ by a factor of ___ about the ___-axis.	
$a < 0$	The graph of $y = f(x)$ will be reflected in the _____ and stretched vertically about the ___-axis.	
$0 < b < 1$	The graph of $y = f(x)$ will be stretched _____ by a factor of ___ about the ___-axis.	
$b > 1$	The graph of $y = f(x)$ will be stretched _____ by a factor of ___ about the ___-axis.	
$b < 0$	The graph of $y = f(x)$ will be reflected in the _____ and stretched horizontally about the ___-axis.	

$y = af(x)$ can be written as $\dfrac{1}{a}y = f(x)$.

Given the function $y = f(x)$:

- **replacing x with bx,   ($i.e. x \rightarrow bx$)   describes a horizontal stretch about the y-axis.**
  i.e. $y = f(bx)$ describes a horizontal stretch.

- **replacing y with $\dfrac{1}{a}y$,   ($i.e.$ $y \rightarrow \dfrac{1}{a}y$)   describes a vertical stretch about the x-axis.**
  i.e. $\dfrac{1}{a}y = f(x)$ or $y = af(x)$ describes a vertical stretch.

In general, if $\dfrac{1}{a}y = f(bx)$ or $y = af(bx)$, then for

> $a > 0$ - vertical stretch about the x-axis by a factor of a
>
> $a < 0$ - vertical stretch about the x-axis by a factor of $|a|$
>   and a reflection in the x-axis
>
> $b > 0$ - horizontal stretch about the y-axis by a factor of $\dfrac{1}{b}$
>
> $b < 0$ - horizontal stretch about the y-axis a by a factor of $\dfrac{1}{|b|}$
>
>   and a reflection in the y-axis.

Class Ex. #1

Write the replacement for x or y and write the equation of the image of $y = f(x)$ after each transformation.

a)   a horizontal stretch by a factor of 6 about the y-axis

b)   a vertical stretch by a factor of $\dfrac{1}{5}$ about the x-axis

c)   a reflection in the x-axis and a vertical stretch about the x-axis by a factor of 3

d)   a horizontal stretch about the y-axis by a factor of $\dfrac{1}{2}$ and
       a vertical stretch about the x-axis by a factor of $\dfrac{1}{4}$

Class Ex. #2   How does the graph of $3y = f(x)$ compare with the graph of $y = f(x)$?

Class Ex. #3   What happens to the graph of the function $y = f(x)$ if you make these changes?

a) Replace x with $4x$.

b) Replace y with $\dfrac{1}{3}y$.

c) Replace y with $6y$ and x with $\dfrac{1}{3}x$.

Class Ex. #4   The graph of $y = f(x)$ is shown.

Sketch $y = f(-2x)$.

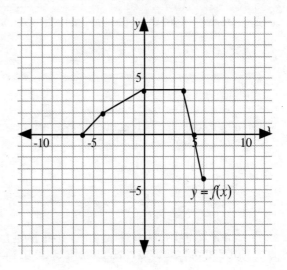

Complete Assignment Questions #1 - #7

Assignment

1. Write the replacement for x or y and write the equation of the image of $y = f(x)$ after each transformation.

   a) a horizontal stretch by a factor of 3 about the y-axis

   b) a vertical stretch by a factor of 6 about the x-axis

   c) a horizontal stretch about the y-axis by a factor of $\dfrac{5}{7}$

   d) a vertical stretch about the x-axis by a factor of $\dfrac{2}{3}$

   e) a reflection in the y-axis and a horizontal stretch by a factor of 3 about the y-axis

   f) a reflection in the x-axis and a vertical stretch by a factor of $\dfrac{3}{4}$ about the x-axis

   g) a reflection in the y-axis and a horizontal stretch about the y-axis by a factor of $\dfrac{3}{4}$

   h) a horizontal stretch about the y-axis by a factor of 4 and a vertical stretch about the x-axis by a factor of 4

   i) a horizontal stretch about the y-axis by a factor of 0.5, a vertical stretch by a factor of 2 about the x-axis and a reflection in the x-axis

2. The function $y = f(x)$ is transformed to $y = af(bx)$. Determine the values of a and b for:

a) a horizontal stretch by a factor of $\dfrac{2}{3}$ about the y-axis

b) a vertical stretch about the x-axis by a factor of 5

c) a horizontal stretch about the y-axis by a factor of $\dfrac{5}{2}$ and a reflection in the y-axis

d) a vertical stretch about the x-axis by a factor of $\dfrac{1}{3}$, a horizontal stretch about the y-axis by a factor of $\dfrac{1}{10}$ and a reflection in the y-axis

3. Consider the function $f(x) = x^2$

a) Determine the equation of the image of the function if it is stretched vertically by a factor of 4 about the x-axis.

b) Determine the equation of the image of the function if it is stretched horizontally by a factor of $\dfrac{1}{2}$ about the y-axis.

c) What do you notice?

d) Give an example of a function where the stretches in a) and b) would not result in the same image.

4. a) What information about the graph of $y = f(kx)$ does k provide?

b) What information about the graph of $ky = f(x)$ does k provide?

c) What information about the graph of $y - k = f(x)$ does k provide?

d) What information about the graph of $y = f(x - k)$ does k provide?

e) What information about the graph of $y = kf(x)$ does k provide?

5. The graph of $y = f(x)$ is shown. In each case:
   i)   sketch the graph of the transformed function
   ii) state the domain and range of the transformed function
   iii) state the coordinates of any invariant points.

a) $y = f(2x)$

b) $y = -2f(x)$

c) $y = \frac{1}{2}f\left(\frac{1}{2}x\right)$

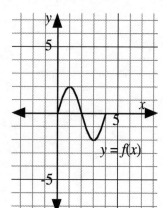
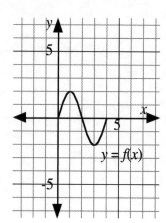
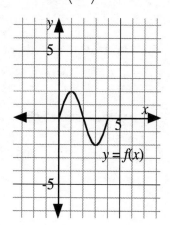

d) $y = f(2x)$

e) $y = -2f(x)$

f) $y = \frac{1}{2}f\left(\frac{1}{2}x\right)$

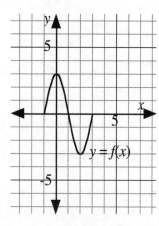
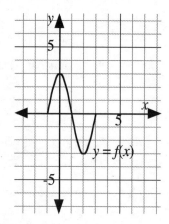
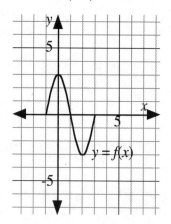

6. What happens to the graph of the function $y = f(x)$ if the following replacements are made?

a) Replace x with $\frac{1}{2}x$.

b) Replace y with $4y$.

c) Replace y with $-2y$ and x with $4x$.

d) Replace y with $y - 4$ and x with $-\frac{1}{4}x$.

7. The graph of $y = f(x)$ is stretched vertically by a factor of $\frac{1}{2}$ about the x-axis, stretched horizontally by a factor of $\frac{1}{4}$ about the y-axis, and reflected in the y-axis. If the equation of the image is written in the form $y = af(bx)$, the value of $a - b$, to the nearest tenth, is _____ .

(Record your answer in the numerical response box from left to right.)

Answer Key

1. **a)** $x \rightarrow \frac{1}{3}x,\ y = f\left(\frac{1}{3}x\right)$ **b)** $y \rightarrow \frac{1}{6}y,\ y = 6f(x)$ **c)** $x \rightarrow \frac{7}{5}x,\ y = f\left(\frac{7}{5}x\right)$

d) $y \rightarrow \frac{3}{2}y,\quad y = \frac{2}{3}f(x)$ **e)** $x \rightarrow -\frac{1}{3}x,\ y = f\left(-\frac{1}{3}x\right)$ **f)** $y \rightarrow -\frac{4}{3}y,\ y = -\frac{3}{4}f(x)$

g) $x \rightarrow -\frac{4}{3}x,\ y = f\left(-\frac{4}{3}x\right)$ **h)** $x \rightarrow \frac{1}{4}x$ and $y \rightarrow \frac{1}{4}y,\ y = 4f\left(\frac{1}{4}x\right)$

i) $x \rightarrow 2x$ and $y \rightarrow -\frac{1}{2}y,\quad y = -2f(2x)$

2. **a)** $a = 1 \quad b = \frac{3}{2}$ **b)** $a = 5 \quad b = 1$ **c)** $a = 1 \quad b = -\frac{2}{5}$ **d)** $a = \frac{1}{3} \quad b = -10$

3. **a)** $y = 4f(x) = 4x^2$ **b)** $y = (2x)^2 = 4x^2$ **c)** Both transformations result in the same image.
d) many possible answers including $f(x) = x, f(x) = x^3, f(x) = x^2 + 1$, etc.

4 . **a)**   horizontal stretch about the *y*-axis by a factor of $\frac{1}{k}$

    b)   vertical stretch about the *x*-axis by a factor of $\frac{1}{k}$

    c)   vertical translation of *k* units: up if $k > 0$, down if $k < 0$

    d)   horizontal translation of *k* units: right if $k > 0$, left if $k < 0$

    e)   vertical stretch about the *x*-axis by a factor of *k*

5 .

        a) 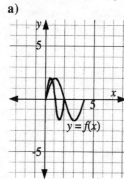   **b)** 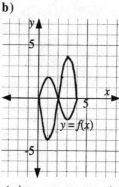   **c)**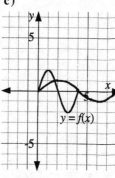

Domain: $\{x \mid 0 \le x \le 2, x \in R\}$ $\{x \mid 0 \le x \le 4, x \in R\}$ $\{x \mid 0 \le x \le 8, x \in R\}$

Range: $\{y \mid -2 \le y \le 2, y \in R\}$ $\{y \mid -4 \le y \le 4, y \in R\}$ $\{y \mid -1 \le y \le 1, y \in R\}$

Invariant Points: (0, 0)   (0, 0), (2, 0), (4, 0)   (0, 0)

        d) 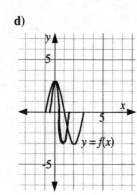   **e)** 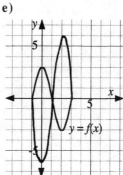   **f)**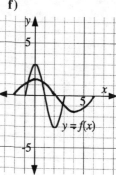

Domain: $\left\{x \mid -\frac{1}{2} \le x \le \frac{3}{2}, x \in R\right\}$ $\{x \mid -1 \le x \le 3, x \in R\}$ $\{x \mid -2 \le x \le 6, x \in R\}$

Range: $\{y \mid -3 \le y \le 3, y \in R\}$ $\{y \mid -6 \le y \le 6, y \in R\}$ $\left\{y \mid -\frac{3}{2} \le y \le \frac{3}{2}, y \in R\right\}$

Invariant Points: (0, 3)   (−1, 0), (1, 0), (3, 0)   none

6 . **a)**   horizontal stretch about the *y*-axis by a factor of 2

    b)   vertical stretch about the *x*-axis by a factor of $\frac{1}{4}$

    c)   horizontal stretch about the *y*-axis by a factor of $\frac{1}{4}$, vertical stretch about the *x*-axis

        by a factor of $\frac{1}{2}$, and a reflection in the *x*-axis.

    d)   horizontal stretch about the *y*-axis by a factor of 4, a reflection in the *y*-axis,
        followed by a vertical translation of 4 units up.

7 . | 4 | . | 5 | |

Transformations Lesson #6:
Stretches about the x- or y-axis - Part Two

Given the function $y = f(x)$:

- replacing x with bx, (*i.e.* $x \rightarrow bx$) describes a horizontal stretch about the y-axis.

    i.e. $y = f(bx)$ describes a horizontal stretch.

- replacing y with $\frac{1}{a}y$, (*i.e.* $y \rightarrow \frac{1}{a}y$) describes a vertical stretch about the x-axis.

    i.e. $\frac{1}{a}y = f(x)$ or $y = af(x)$ describes a vertical stretch.

In general, if $\frac{1}{a}y = f(bx)$ or $y = af(bx)$, then for:

> $a > 0$ - vertical stetch about the x-axis by a factor of a
>
> $a < 0$ - vertical stretch about the x-axis by a factor of $|a|$
>
> and a reflection in the x-axis
>
> $b > 0$ - horizontal stretch about the y-axis by a factor of $\frac{1}{b}$
>
> $b < 0$ - horizontal stretch about the y-axis a by a factor of $\frac{1}{|b|}$
>
> and a reflection in the y-axis.

Class Ex. #1

Write the equation of the image of

a) $y = x^2$ after a horizontal stretch about the y-axis by a factor of $\frac{3}{4}$

b) $y = \sqrt{x} - 3$ after a horizontal stretch by a factor of 4 about the y-axis and a vertical stretch by a factor of 2 about the x-axis

c) $y = 3x + 7$ after a vertical stretch about the x-axis by a factor of $\frac{1}{3}$ and a reflection in the x-axis.

Describe how the graph of the second function compares to the graph of the first function.

a) $y = f(x)$, $y = f\left(\dfrac{1}{2}x\right)$

b) $y = 2^x$, $y = 2^{3x}$

c) $y = |x|$, $y = -2|x|$

d) $y = x^3$, $3y = x^3$

e) $y = |x|$, $y = 2\left|\dfrac{1}{3}x\right|$

f) $y = |x|$, $y = |-2x|$

The function represented by the thick line is a stretch of the function represented by the thin line. Write an equation for each function represented by the thick line.

a)

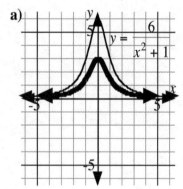

$y = \dfrac{6}{x^2 + 1}$

b)

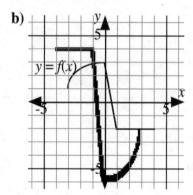

$y = f(x)$

c)

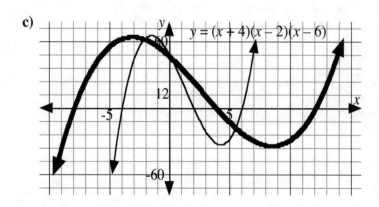

$y = (x + 4)(x - 2)(x - 6)$

Class Ex. #4

A polynomial function has the equation $P(x) = (x - 4)(x + 3)(x + 6)$.
Determine the zeros and the y-intercept if the following transformations are applied.

a) $y = -3P(x)$

b) $y = P\left(-\dfrac{1}{2}x\right)$

Complete Assignment Questions #1 - #6

Assignment

1. Write the equation of the image of

a) $y = |x + 1|$ after a vertical stretch about the x-axis by a factor of $\dfrac{7}{9}$

b) $y = 2^x$ after a horizontal stretch by a factor of 3 about the y-axis

c) $y = \sqrt{x - 2}$ after a vertical stretch about the x-axis by a factor of 4 and a reflection in the x-axis

d) $y = \sqrt{x - 2}$ after a horizontal stretch about the y-axis by a factor of 4 and a reflection in the y-axis

e) $y = \sin x°$ after a horizontal stretch about the y-axis by a factor of $\dfrac{3}{4}$ and

a vertical stretch about the x-axis by a factor of $\dfrac{1}{2}$

f) $y = 2x - 11$ after a horizontal stretch about the y-axis by a factor of $\dfrac{1}{3}$ and
a reflection in the y-axis

g) $y = \dfrac{1}{x + 3}$ after a horizontal stretch about the y-axis by a factor of 3, a vertical stretch
about the x-axis by a factor of 2, and a reflection in the y-axis

h) $y = \dfrac{1}{x} + 3$ after a vertical stretch about the x-axis by a factor of $\dfrac{1}{2}$, a horizontal stretch
about the y-axis by a factor of $\dfrac{1}{4}$, and a reflection in both the x-axis
and y-axis

2. Describe how the graph of the second function compares to the graph of the first function.

a) $y = \sqrt{x}$, $y = \sqrt{\dfrac{1}{3}x}$ **b)** $y = x^4$, $\dfrac{1}{4}y = x^4$ **c)** $y = 5x + 10$, $y = 5\left(-\dfrac{1}{4}x\right) + 10$

d) $y = \dfrac{1}{x + 1}$, $3y = \dfrac{1}{x + 1}$ **e)** $y = 5^x$, $y = 5^{0.5x}$ **f)** $y = \dfrac{1}{x + 1}$, $y = \dfrac{2}{x + 1}$

g) $y = \cos x°$, $y = 3\cos 2x°$

h) $y = \dfrac{1}{x+1}$, $y = -\dfrac{4}{2x+1}$

3. The function represented by the thick line is a stretch of the function represented by the thin line. Write an equation for each function represented by the thick line.

a)

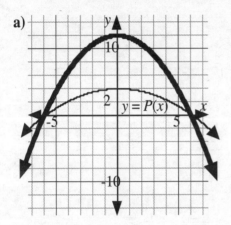

b)

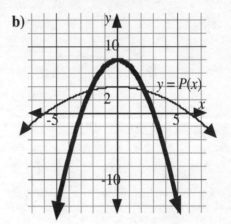

c)

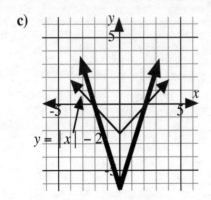

d)

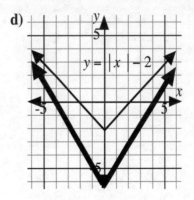

e)

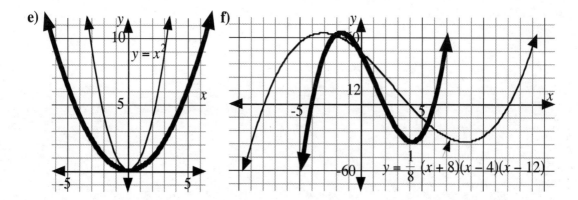

$y = x^2$

f)

$$y = \frac{1}{8}(x + 8)(x - 4)(x - 12)$$

g)

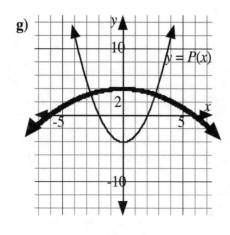

$y = P(x)$

h)

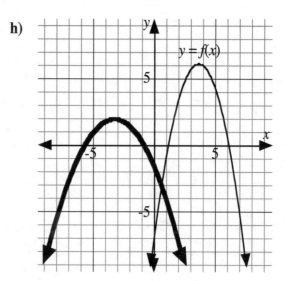

$y = f(x)$

4. A polynomial function has the equation $P(x) = (x - 5)(x - 2)(x + 1)$. Determine the zeros of the polynomial and the y-intercept of the graph of the polynomial if the following transformations are applied.

a) $y = 4P(x)$

b) $y = P(4x)$

c) $y = -\dfrac{1}{4}P(x)$

d) $y = P\left(-\dfrac{1}{4}x\right)$

5. A polynomial function has the equation $P(x) = x(x - a)^2$. Determine the zeros of the function and the y-intercept of the graph of the function under the following transformations.

a) $y = 7P(x)$

b) $y = P\left(\dfrac{4}{3}x\right)$

Multiple Choice

6. How is the graph of $\frac{1}{4}y = x^2$ related to the graph of $y = x^2$?

A. $y = x^2$ has been stretched horizontally about the y-axis by a factor of 4.

B. $y = x^2$ has been stretched horizontally about the y-axis by a factor of $\frac{1}{4}$.

C. $y = x^2$ has been stretched vertically about the x-axis by a factor of 4.

D. $y = x^2$ has been stretched vertically about the x-axis by a factor of $\frac{1}{4}$.

Answer Key

1. a) $y = \frac{7}{9}|x + 1|$ **b)** $y = 2^{\frac{1}{3}x}$ **c)** $y = -4\sqrt{x - 2}$ **d)** $y = \sqrt{-\frac{1}{4}x - 2}$

  e) $y = \frac{1}{2}\sin\frac{4}{3}x°$ **f)** $y = -6x - 11$ **g)** $y = \frac{2}{-\frac{1}{3}x + 3}$ or $y = -\frac{6}{x - 9}$ **h)** $y = \frac{1}{8x} - \frac{3}{2}$

2. a) horizontal stretch about the y-axis by a factor of 3
  b) vertical stretch about the x-axis by a factor of 4
  c) horizontal stretch about the y-axis by a factor of 4 and a reflection in the y-axis

  d) vertical stretch about the x-axis by a factor of $\frac{1}{3}$

  e) horizontal stretch about the y-axis by a factor of 2
  f) vertical stretch about the x-axis by a factor of 2

  g) vertical stretch about the x-axis by a factor of 3 and a horizontal stretch
    about the y-axis by a factor of $\frac{1}{2}$

  h) vertical stretch about the x-axis by a factor of 4, horizontal stretch
    about the y-axis by a factor of $\frac{1}{2}$, and a reflection in the x-axis

3. a) $y = 3P(x)$ **b)** $y = 2P(2x)$ **c)** $y = 3|x| - 6$ **d)** $y = 3\left|\frac{1}{2}x\right| - 6$

  e) $y = \frac{1}{4}x^2$ **f)** $y = (x + 4)(x - 2)(x - 6)$ **g)** $y = -P\left(\frac{1}{3}x\right)$ **h)** $y = \frac{1}{3}f(-x)$

4. a) zeros: $-1, 2, 5$ **b)** zeros: $-\frac{1}{4}, \frac{1}{2}, \frac{5}{4}$ **c)** zeros: $-1, 2, 5$ **d)** zeros: $4, -8, -20$

  y-intercept: 40 y-intercept: 10 y-intercept: $-\frac{5}{2}$ y-intercept: 10

5. a) zeros: $0, a$ y-intercept $= 0$ **b)** zeros: $0, \frac{3}{4}a$ y-intercept $= 0$

6. C

Transformations Lesson #7:
Combining Transformations - Part One

Combining Transformations

In the previous lessons, we have learned the following rules.

Given the equation of a function $y = f(x)$

- replacing x with $x - h$ or y with $y - k$ results in a horizontal or a vertical translation

- replacing x with $-x$ or y with $-y$ results in a reflection

- replacing x with bx or y with $\dfrac{1}{a}y$ results in a horizontal or a vertical stretch

In this lesson we are going to find out what happens when we combine different types of transformations.

Investigation #1 — *Combining a Horizontal Stretch and a Vertical Stretch*

The graph of $y = f(x)$ is shown.

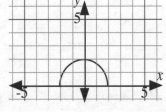

a) Sketch the image of the function after a horizontal stretch by a factor of 3 about the *y*-axis, followed by a vertical stretch by a factor of 2 about the *x*-axis.

b) Sketch the image of the function after a vertical stretch by a factor of 2 about the *x*-axis, followed by a horizontal stretch by a factor of 3 about the *y*-axis.

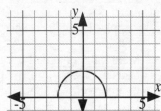

c) Does the order in which the two stretches are performed make a difference to the final graph?

Investigation #2 — *Combining a Vertical Translation and a Horizontal Stretch*

The graph of $y = f(x)$ is shown.

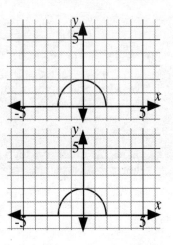

a) Sketch the image of the function after a vertical translation of 3 units up, followed by a horizontal stretch by a factor of 2 about the *y*-axis .

b) Sketch the image of the function after a horizontal stretch by a factor of 2 about the *y*-axis, followed by a vertical translation of 3 units up.

c) Does the order in which the vertical translation and the horizontal stretch are performed make a difference to the final graph?

Investigation #3   *Combining a Vertical Translation and a Vertical Stretch*

The graph of $y = f(x)$ is shown.

a) Sketch the image of the function after a vertical translation of 2 units down, followed by a vertical stretch by a factor of 3 about the x-axis.

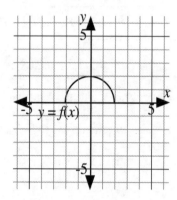

b) Sketch the image of the function after a vertical stretch by a factor of 3 about the x-axis, followed by a vertical translation of 2 units down.

c) Does the order in which the vertical translation and the vertical stretch are performed make a difference to the final graph?

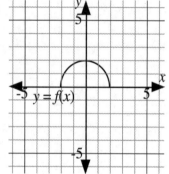

Investigation #4   *Combining a Horizontal Translation and a Horizontal Stretch*

The graph of $y = f(x)$ is shown.

a) Sketch the image of the function after a horizontal translation of 1 unit right, followed by a horizontal stretch by a factor of 2 about the y-axis.

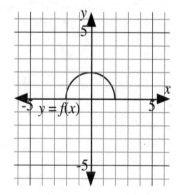

b) Sketch the image of the function after a horizontal stretch by a factor of 2 about the y-axis, followed by a horizontal translation of 1 unit right.

c) Does the order in which the horizontal translation and the horizontal stretch are performed make a difference to the final graph?

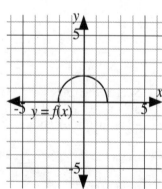

Order of Transformations

We have seen that when two transformations are applied to a graph, the order in which the transformations are performed may or may not make a difference to the final graph.

In general, the order **DOES NOT** matter when
- two translations are combined
- two stretches are combined
- a translation and a stretch at right angles to one another are combined
- reflections and stretches are combined

The order **DOES** matter when
- a translation and a stretch in the same direction are combined
- most reflections and translations are combined

Unless otherwise indicated, use the following order to describe how to transform from one graph to another.

      1. Stretches   **2.** Reflections   **3.** Translations.

Class Ex. #1

Describe a series of transformations required to transform graph A to graph B.

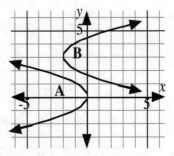

Class Ex. #2

Describe a series of transformations required to transform
a) graph A to graph B

b) graph A to graph C

c) graph B to graph C.

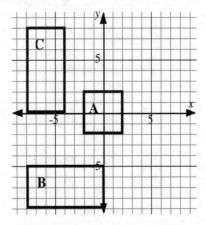

Complete Assignment Questions #1 - #2

Class Ex. #3   Describe which transformations are applied to a graph of a function when the following changes are made to its equation. Does the order in which the transformations are performed affect the final graph?

a) Replace x with $3x$ and y with $y + 4$.   **b)** Replace x with $\frac{2}{3}x$, y with $-3y$, and x with $x + 2$.

Class Ex. #4   A graph of the parabola $y = x^2 + 1$ is shown. The following transformations are applied to $y = x^2 + 1$ **in the order shown**.

- a horizontal translation 2 units left
- a reflection in the x-axis
- a vertical stretch about the x-axis by a factor of 0.5
- a vertical translation 3 units down

a) For each transformation

- graph the image on the grid
- write the replacement for x or y and the current equation in the table

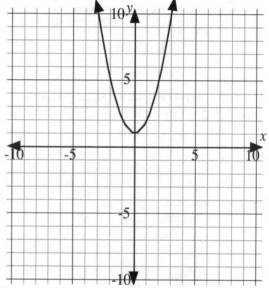

Transformation	Replacement	Current Equation
1. a horizontal translation 2 units left		
2. a reflection in the x-axis		
3. a vertical stretch about the x-axis by a factor of 0.5		
4. a vertical translation 3 units down		

b) Write the equation which represents the final position of the graph and verify using a graphing calculator.

Complete Assignment Questions #3 - #9

Assignment

1. Describe a series of transformations required to transform

 a) graph A to graph B

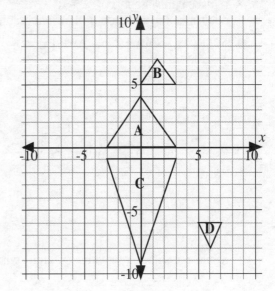

 b) graph A to graph C

 c) graph A to graph D

2. Describe a series of transformations required to transform

 a) graph A to graph B

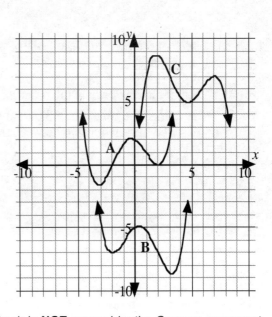

 b) graph A to graph C

3. In each of the following, transformations are applied to the graph of $y = f(x)$. In each case
- describe which transformations are applied to the graph when the indicated replacements are made
- determine the equation of the final graph if the replacements are made in the order given

a) Replace x with $x + 2$ and y with $-y$.

b) Replace x with $4x$ and y with $y - 7$.

c) Replace x with $\dfrac{1}{3}x$, y with $-2y$, and y with $y + 2$.

d) Replace x with $2x$, y with $\dfrac{1}{4}y$, x with $-x$, and y with $y + 10$.

4. a) In which of the parts of question 3 does the order in which the transformations are performed affect the final graph?

b) In each of the cases where the order matters in a)
- determine the equation of the final graph if the order is changed
- describe the relationship between the two graphs

5. A graph of the parabola $y = x^2 + 1$ is shown. The following transformations are applied to $y = x^2 + 1$ **in the order shown**:

• a vertical translation 3 units down

• a reflection in the x-axis

• a vertical stretch about the x-axis by a factor of 0.5

• a horizontal translation 2 units left

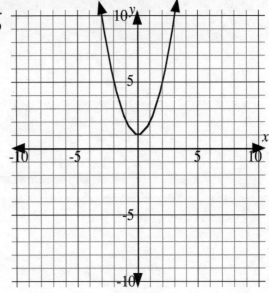

a) For each transformation
  • graph the image on the grid
  • write the replacement for x or y and the current equation in the table

Transformation	Replacement	Current Equation
1. a vertical translation 3 units down		
2. a reflection in the x-axis		
3. a vertical stretch about the x-axis by a factor of 0.5		
4. a horizontal translation 2 units left		

b) Write the equation which represents the final position of the graph.

c) Verify using a graphing calculator.

d) Explain why the equation in this example is different from the equation in Class Ex. #4.

6. The graph of $y = f(x)$ is reflected in the x-axis, then vertically stretched by a factor of 3 about the x-axis, and then translated 4 units to the right and 1 unit up.
Determine the equation of the final graph.

The following information refers to question #7.

Five students were asked to perform a combination of two transformations on the graph shown.

Student I: a reflection in the x-axis and a translation 3 units left

Student II: a reflection in the y-axis and a translation 3 units left

Student III: a horizontal stretch by a factor of 2 about the y-axis and a reflection in the x-axis

Student IV: a translation 2 units up and a vertical stretch by a factor of $\frac{1}{2}$ about the x-axis

Student V: a translation 2 units right and a vertical stretch by a factor of $\frac{1}{2}$ about the x-axis

---

Multiple Choice

7. For how many of the students does the order in which the transformations are performed affect the final graph?

    A.   One student

    B.   Two students

    C.   Three students

    D.   Four students

8. The graph of $y = f(x)$ is horizontally stretched by a factor of $\dfrac{1}{4}$ about the y-axis, and then translated 5 units to the left and 3 units up. The equation of the transformed graph is

A. $y = f\left(\dfrac{1}{4}(x + 5)\right) + 3$

B. $y = f\left(\dfrac{1}{4}x + 5\right) + 3$

C. $y = f(4x + 5) + 3$

D. $y = f[4(x + 5)] + 3$

9. Jack and Jill are working with the graph of the function $f(x) = x^2$.

Jack stretches the graph vertically by a factor of 4 about the x-axis, followed by a translation 2 units up.

Jill takes the graph of $f(x) = x^2$, and translates it 2 units up, followed by a vertical stretch by a factor of 4 about the x-axis. The images of the two graphs are identical except for a vertical separation of k units, $k > 0$.

The value of k, to the nearest tenth, is _____ .

(Record your answer in the numerical response box from left to right.)

Answer Key

1. a) vertical stretch by a factor of $\frac{1}{2}$ about the x-axis, horizontal stretch by a factor of $\frac{1}{2}$ about the y-axis, then a translation of 1.5 units right, and 5 units up

b) vertical stretch by a factor of 2 about the x-axis, a reflection in the x-axis, then a vertical translation 1 unit down

c) vertical stretch by a factor of $\frac{1}{2}$ about the x-axis, horizontal stretch by a factor of $\frac{1}{3}$ about the y-axis, a reflection in the x-axis, then a translation 6 units right and 6 units down

2. a) reflection in the y-axis, and a translation 7 units down

b) reflection in the x-axis, and then a translation 5 units right and 7 units up

3. a) horizontal translation 2 units left and a reflection in the x-axis; $y = -f(x + 2)$

b) horizontal stretch by a factor of $\frac{1}{4}$ about the y-axis, and a vertical translation 7 units up; $y = f(4x) + 7$

c) horizontal stretch by a factor of 3 about the y-axis, vertical stretch by a factor of $\frac{1}{2}$

about the x-axis, reflection in the x-axis and a vertical translation 2 units down; $y = -\frac{1}{2}f\left(\frac{1}{3}x\right) - 2$

d) horizontal stretch by a factor of $\frac{1}{2}$ about the y-axis, vertical stretch by a factor of 4 about the x-axis, a reflection in the y-axis and a vertical translation 10 units down; $y = 4f(-2x) - 10$

4. a) parts 3c) and 3d) only.

b) in 3c), $y = -\frac{1}{2}f\left(\frac{1}{3}x\right) + 1$, which is a vertical translation 3 units up from $y = -\frac{1}{2}f\left(\frac{1}{3}x\right) - 2$

in 3d), $y = 4f(-2x) - 40$, which is a vertical translation 30 units down from $y = 4f(-2x) - 10$

5. a)

Transformation	Replacement	Current Equation	
1. a vertical translation 3 units down	replace y with $y + 3$	$y + 3 = x^2 + 1$ $y = x^2 - 2$	
2. a reflection in the x-axis	replace y with $-y$	$-y = x^2 - 2$ $y = -x^2 + 2$	
3. a vertical stretch about the x-axis by a factor of 0.5	replace y with $2y$	$2y = -x^2 + 2$ $y = -\frac{1}{2}x^2 + 1$	
4. a horizontal translation 2 units left	replace x with $x + 2$	$y = -\frac{1}{2}(x + 2)^2 + 1$	

b) $y = -\frac{1}{2}(x + 2)^2 + 1$

d) The order of the transformations is different. In particular, changing the order of the vertical stretch and the vertical translation will result in a different equation.

6. $y = -3f(x - 4) + 1$

7. B   **8.** D   **9.** [6 | . | 0 |]

Transformations Lesson #8:
Combining Transformations - Part Two

Equations Combining Two or More Transformations

To apply a combination of transformations, consider the following:

$$y = a f\left[b(x - h)\right] + k \qquad \text{where}$$

$|a|$ is the <u>vertical stretch</u> factor. If a is negative, there is also a reflection in the x-axis

$\dfrac{1}{|b|}$ is the <u>horizontal stretch</u> factor. If b is negative, there is also a reflection in the y-axis.

h is the <u>horizontal translation</u> where
- if $h > 0$, the translation is to the right
- if $h < 0$, the translation is to the left.

k is the <u>vertical translation</u> where
- if $k > 0$, the translation is k units up
- if $k < 0$, the translation is k units down.

When graphing a combination of transformations <u>from an equation</u>, use the following order:

Step 1: Sketch the original function.

Step 2: Sketch any stretches.

Step 3: Sketch any reflections.

Step 4: Sketch any translations.

Class Ex. #1

The graph of $y = f(x)$ is shown.

Consider the function defined by the equation
$y = 2f\left(\dfrac{1}{2}(x + 5)\right) - 8.$

a) If the equation is written in the form
$y = af\left[b(x - h)\right] + k$, state the values of
$a, b, h,$ and k.

b) Write the transformations associated with
the parameters $a, b, h,$ and k.

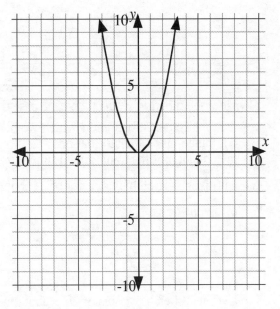

c) Put these transformations in an order which can be used to sketch the graph of the
function. Sketch the graph of the function.

d) The original graph has equation $y = x^2$.

Write the equation for the transformed function $y = 2f\left(\dfrac{1}{2}(x + 5)\right) - 8$.

e) Graph the equation in a) on a calculator and verify the sketch c).

Class Ex. #2

The graph of $y = f(x)$ is shown.

Sketch the graph of $y = -2f(x - 3) + 1$.

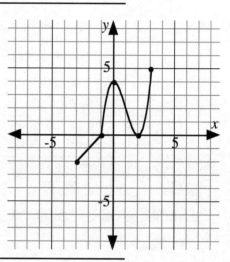

Class Ex. #3

Consider the function $y = f(x)$. In each case determine:
- the replacements for x and y which would result in the following combinations of transformations
- the equation of the transformed function in the form $y = af[b(x - h)] + k$

a) a horizontal stretch by a factor of $\dfrac{1}{4}$ about the y-axis and a vertical translation of 5 units down.

b) a vertical stretch by a factor of $\dfrac{3}{5}$ about the x-axis, a reflection in the y-axis, and a horizontal translation 2 units left.

Class Ex. #4   A function $G(x) = x^3$ is transformed into a new function $P(x)$. To form the new function $P(x)$, $G(x)$ is stretched vertically about the x-axis by a factor of 0.25, reflected in the y-axis, and translated 3 units to the right. Write the equation of the new function $P(x)$.

Class Ex. #5   Given the graph of $y = f(x)$, sketch the graph of the transformed function $y = f\left(\dfrac{1}{2}x + 3\right) - 8$.

Hint: Rewrite this function in the form $y = af[b(x - h) + k]$.

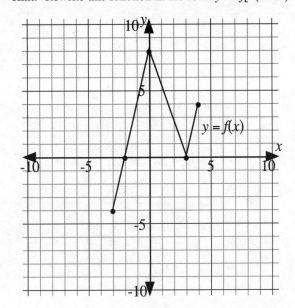

Class Ex. #6   The function $f(x) = \sqrt{x}$ has been transformed into the function $g(x) = -2\sqrt{3x - 12} + 5$. Complete the following statement.

" The function $f(x)$ has been transformed to the function $g(x)$ by stretching horizontally

about the y-axis by a factor of _____, stretching vertically about the x-axis by

a factor of _____, reflecting in the _____, translating _____units up

and _____ units horizontally to the _____ ."

Complete Assignment Questions #1 - #11

Assignment

1. Describe how the graph of $y = f(x)$ can be transformed to the graph of

    a) $y = f[2(x - 1)] + 5$

    b) $y = 2f(x + 4) - 5$

    c) $y = f\left(\dfrac{1}{2}x + 6\right) + 1$

2. Consider the function $y = f(x)$. In each case determine:
    - the replacements for x and y which would result in the following combinations of transformations
    - the equation of the transformed function in the form $y = af[b(x - h)] + k$

    a) a horizontal stretch by a factor of 3 about the y-axis and a vertical translation of 6 units up.

    b) a reflection in the y-axis, a horizontal translation of 3 units right, and a vertical translation of 5 units down.

    c) a horizontal stretch by a factor of $\dfrac{2}{3}$ about the y-axis, a vertical stretch by a factor of $\dfrac{2}{5}$ about the x-axis, a reflection in the x-axis, and a vertical translation of 1 unit up.

3. Describe how the graph of the second function compares to the graph of the first function.

 a) $y = x^4$, $-4y = (x - 2)^4$

 b) $y = |x|$, $y = \left| \frac{1}{3}(x + 2) \right|$

 c) $y = \sqrt{x}$, $y - 1 = 2\sqrt{4x - 8}$

4. In each case the transformations are applied in the order given to transform the graph of $y = f(x)$ to the graph of $y = af[b(x - h)] + k$. Determine the values of $a, b, h,$ and k.

 a) a horizontal stretch by a factor of $\frac{3}{5}$ about the y-axis and a reflection in the x-axis

 b) a vertical stretch by a factor of $\frac{1}{3}$ about the x-axis and a reflection in the y-axis

 c) a vertical stretch by a factor of 2 about the x-axis, then a translation 5 units to the left and 2 units up

 d) a horizontal stretch by a factor of 4 about the y-axis, a vertical stretch by a factor of 2 about the x-axis, a reflection in the y-axis and then a translation of 10 units down

 e) a translation of 6 units right, then a horizontal stretch by a factor of $\frac{1}{2}$ about the y-axis and a reflection in the x-axis

5. The function $f(x) = \sqrt{x}$ is transformed into the function $g(x)$ by stretching horizontally by a factor of 6 about the *y*-axis, stretching vertically by a factor of 3 about the *x*-axis, reflecting in the *x*-axis, and translating 1 unit up and $\frac{1}{2}$ unit to the right. Write the equation for $g(x)$.

6. The graph of $y = f(x)$ is shown. Sketch the graph of:

a) $y + 4 = -\frac{1}{2}f(x + 2)$

b) $y = -4f\left(\frac{1}{2}x + 1\right)$

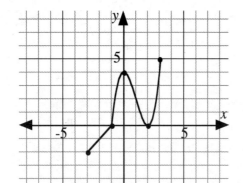
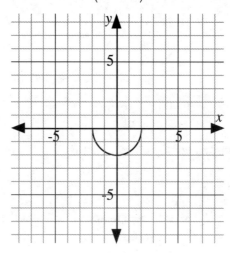

7. The function $f(x) = \sin x°$ is transformed into the function $g(x)$ by stretching horizontally by a factor of $\frac{1}{4}$ about the *y*-axis, stretching vertically by a factor of $\frac{2}{3}$ about the *x*-axis, reflecting in the *y*-axis, and translating 5 units down. Write the equation for $g(x)$.

8. The function $f(x) = \dfrac{1}{x}$ is transformed into the function $g(x)$ by stretching horizontally by a factor of 2 about the y-axis, stretching vertically by a factor of 5 about the x-axis, and translating 3 units to the left. Write the equation for $g(x)$.

9. The graph of $y = f(x)$ is the semi-circle centred at the origin. Which of the following shows the graph of $y = f(x)$ and $y = f(2x - 4)$?

A.

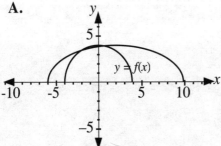

B.

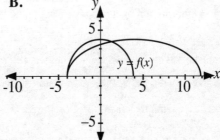

C.

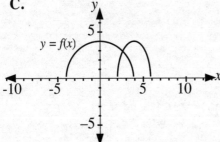

D.

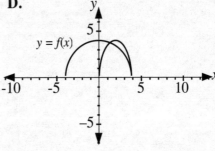

10. The graph of $y = \dfrac{1}{x}$ is transformed to the graph of $y = \dfrac{1}{5(x - 3)} + 4$ by a series of transformations. One of these transformations is a vertical stretch about the x-axis. The scale factor of the vertical stretch, to the nearest tenth, is _____ .

(Record your answer in the numerical response box from left to right.)

11.   The points $P(2, 4)$ and $Q(4, 2)$ are on the graph of $y = f(x)$. If the function f is transformed to function g, where $g(x) = 2f(2x) - 1$, then the points P and Q are transformed to $R(a, b)$ and $S(c, d)$, respectively.

Write the value of a in the first box.

Write the value of b in the second box.

Write the value of c in the third box.

Write the value of d in the fourth box.

(Record your answer in the numerical response box from left to right.)

Answer Key

1. a)   horizontal stretch by a factor of $\frac{1}{2}$ about the y-axis, then a translation 1 unit right and 5 units up

    b)   vertical stretch by a factor of 2 about the x-axis, then a translation 4 units left and 5 units down

    c)   horizontal stretch by a factor of 2 about the y-axis, then a translation 12 units left and 1 unit up

2. a)   replace x with $\frac{1}{3}x$ and y with $y - 6$ $y = f\left(\frac{1}{3}x\right) + 6$

    b)   replace x with $-x$, x with $x - 3$, and y with $y + 5$ $y = f(-(x - 3)) - 5$ or $y = f(-x + 3) - 5$

    c)   replace x with $\frac{3}{2}x$, y with $\frac{5}{2}y$, y with $-y$, and y with $y - 1$ $y = -\frac{2}{5}f\left(\frac{3}{2}x\right) + 1$

3. a)   vertical stretch by a factor of $\frac{1}{4}$ about the x-axis, reflection in the x-axis,

        and a horizontal translation 2 units right

    b)   horizontal stretch by a factor of 3 about the y-axis, then a horizontal translation 2 units left

    c)   vertical stretch by a factor of 2 about the x-axis, horizontal stretch by a factor of $\frac{1}{4}$

        about the y-axis, then a translation 2 units right and 1 unit up

4. a) $a = -1$ $b = \frac{5}{3}$ $h = 0$ $k = 0$ **b)** $a = \frac{1}{3}$ $b = -1$ $h = 0$ $k = 0$

    c) $a = 2$ $b = 1$ $h = -5$ $k = 2$ **d)** $a = 2$ $b = -\frac{1}{4}$ $h = 0$ $k = -10$

    e) $a = -1$ $b = 2$ $h = 3$ $k = 0$

5. $g(x) = -3\sqrt{\frac{1}{6}\left(x - \frac{1}{2}\right)} + 1$

6. a)

7. $g(x) = \frac{2}{3}\sin(-4x°) - 5$

8. $g(x) = \dfrac{10}{x + 3}$

9. D

10. | 0 | . | 2 | |
| --- | --- | --- | --- |

11. | 1 | 7 | 2 | 3 |
| --- | --- | --- | --- |

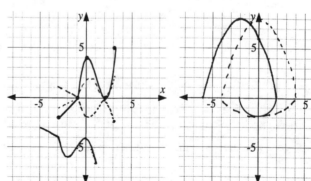

b)

Transformations Lesson #9:
Practice Test

No calculator may be used for this section of the test.

Use the following information to answer the next question.

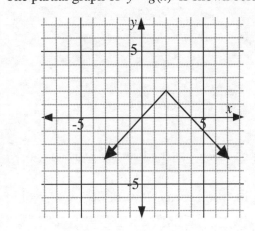

The partial graph of $y = g(x)$ is shown below.

1. Which of the following partial graphs represents the function $y = g(2x)$?

A.

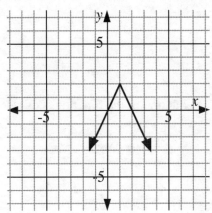

B.

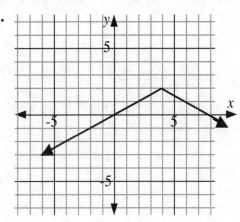

C.

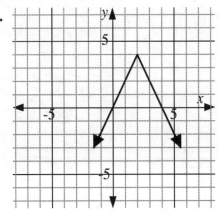

D.

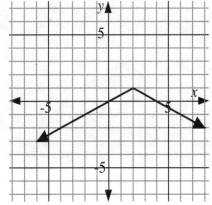

2.   The graph of $y = P(x)$ is translated 4 units up and 7 units right. The equation of the transformed graph is

   A. $y + 4 = P(x - 7)$

   B. $y - 4 = P(x + 7)$

   C. $y - 4 = P(x - 7)$

   D. $y + 4 = P(x + 7)$

3. How is the graph of $y = \left| \dfrac{x}{2} \right|$ related to the graph of $y = |x|$?

   A. The graph of $y = |x|$ has been stretched vertically by a factor of $\dfrac{1}{2}$ about the x-axis.

   B. The graph of $y = |x|$ has been stretched vertically by a factor of 2 about the x-axis.

   C. The graph of $y = |x|$ has been stretched horizontally by a factor of $\dfrac{1}{2}$ about the y-axis.

   D. The graph of $y = |x|$ has been stretched horizontally by a factor of 2 about the y-axis.

4.   The function $y = g(x)$ is shown in diagram 1. The equation of the function shown in diagram 2 could be

   A. $y = g(-x)$

   B. $y = -g(x)$

   C. $y = g^{-1}(x)$

   D. $y = -g(-x)$

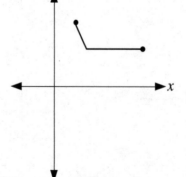
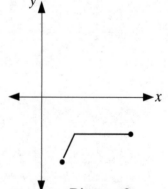

Diagram 1   Diagram 2

Numerical Response **1.** Consider the following equations of transformations of $y = P(x)$.

1. $y = P(x) + 9$ **2.** $y = P(x) - 9$

3. $y = P(x + 9)$ **4.** $y = P(x - 9)$

In the first box write the equation number for the translation 9 units left.

In the second box write the equation number for the translation 9 units right.

In the third box write the equation number for the translation 9 units up.

In the fourth box write the equation number for the translation 9 units down.

(Record your answer in the numerical response box from left to right.)

5. The graph of $y = f(x)$ is shown.

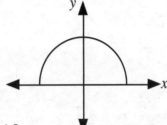

Which graph represents $x = -f(y)$?

A.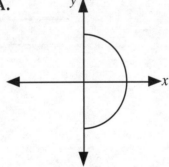

B.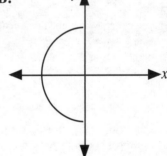

C.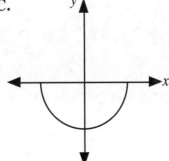

D.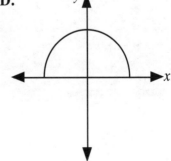

Section B   *A graphing calculator may be used for the remainder of the test.*

6.   The point $(2,-4)$ is on the graph of the function $y = f(x)$. The point which must be on the graph of $y = f^{-1}(x)$ is

   A. $(2, -\dfrac{1}{4})$ **B.** $(2, 4)$

   C. $(-2, -4)$ **D.** $(-4, 2)$

7.   The relation $x = \sqrt{4 - y^2}$ is stretched vertically by a factor of 3 about the x-axis and then translated 2 units to the left. The equation of the transformed relation is

   A. $x = 3\sqrt{4 - (y + 2)^2}$

   B. $x = \sqrt{4 - 9y^2} - 2$

   C. $x = \sqrt{4 - \dfrac{1}{9}y^2} + 2$

   D. $x = \sqrt{4 - \dfrac{1}{9}y^2} - 2$

 2.   The domain of the function $y = f(x)$ is $x \geq 4$. Function f is stretched horizontally by a factor of 5 about the y-axis to form a new function g. The domain of the function $g(x)$ can be written in the form $x \geq k$, where k is a whole number. The value of k is _____

   (Record your answer in the numerical response box from left to right.)

8.   The function, $f(x)$, whose graph has **two** x-intercepts is shown in the diagram .

   The function whose graph has only **one** x-intercept is

   A. $f(x - 2)$

   B. $f(x + 2)$

   C. $f(x) - 2$

   D. $f(x) + 2$

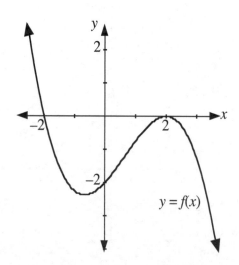

3. The function $f(x) = -\dfrac{28}{x+2}$ is reflected in the line $y = x$ to form function g.
The ordered pair $(k, -4)$, where $k \in W$, lies on the graph of $y = g(x)$.
The value of k is _____ .

(Record your answer in the numerical response box from left to right.)

9. The zeros of the function $y = P(x)$ are $-3, -1$ and 5.
The zeros of the transformed function $y = \dfrac{1}{2}P(x+1)$ are

A. $-4, -2, 4$ **B.** $-2, 0, 6$

C. $-2, -1, 2$ **D.** $-\dfrac{5}{2}, -\dfrac{3}{2}, \dfrac{3}{2}$

Use the following information to answer the next question.

The partial graph of $y = f(x)$ is shown.

$y = f(x)$

10. The number of solutions to the equation $f(x) - 1 = 0$ is

   A. 1   **B.** 2   **C.** 3   **D.** 4

11. The equation that would cause the graph of $y = g(x)$ to stretch vertically about the x-axis by a factor of $\dfrac{1}{6}$ and then reflect in the y-axis is

    A. $y = -6g(x)$

    B. $y = -\dfrac{1}{6}g(x)$

    C. $y = 6g(-x)$

    D. $y = \dfrac{1}{6}g(-x)$

Use the following information to answer the next question.

> The ordered pair (a,b) is on the graph of the function $y = f(x)$. Six ordered pairs, the images of (a,b) derived from transformations of $f(x)$, are shown below.
>
> **Ordered pair #1:** $(3a,b)$ **Ordered pair #2:** $(3a,3b)$ **Ordered pair #3:** $\left(\dfrac{a}{3}, \dfrac{b}{3}\right)$
>
> **Ordered pair #4:** $\left(a, \dfrac{b}{3}\right)$ **Ordered pair #5:** $\left(\dfrac{a}{3}, b\right)$ **Ordered pair #6:** $(a, 3b)$

 4. In box 1 write the ordered pair # for the function $3f(x)$.

In box 2 write the ordered pair # for the function $f\left(\dfrac{1}{3}x\right)$

In box 3 write the ordered pair # for the function $\dfrac{1}{3}f(x)$

In box 4 write the ordered pair # for the function $f(3x)$

(Record your answer in the numerical response box from left to right.)

12. The point $(-9, 3)$ is on the graph of the function $y = f(x)$. The point which must be on the graph of $y = \dfrac{1}{3}f(-x)$ is

    A. $(9, 1)$

    B. $(-3, -3)$

    C. $(-9, 1)$

    D. $(-9, -1)$

13. The function $y = g(x)$ is graphed to the left below.
The equation of the function shown to the right is

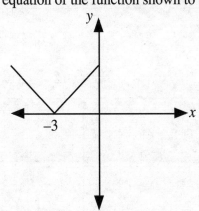

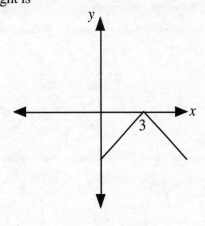

A. $y = g(-x + 6)$ **B.** $y = g(-x - 6)$

C. $y = g^{-1}(x)$ **D.** $y = -g(-x)$

14. The equation which represents the graph of $y = x^3$ after it is reflected in the line $y = x$ is

A. $x = y^3$

B. $y = -x^3$

C. $y = x^3$

D. $y = \dfrac{1}{x^3}$

15. A partial graph of a cubic function with equation $y = f(x)$ is shown.

A function g is defined by $g(x) = f(x + 2) + 4$.

The range of values for which $g(x) = k$ has three distinct real roots is

A. $2 < k < 6, \ k \in R$

B. $4 < k < 8, \ k \in R$

C. $-2 < k < 2, \ k \in R$

D. $-4 < k < 0, \ k \in R$

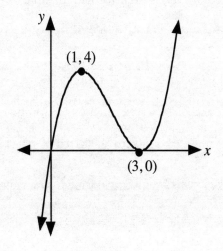

Use the following information to answer the next question.

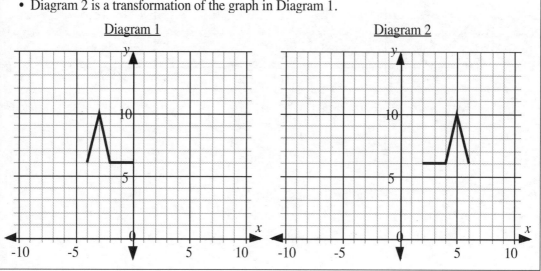

- The graph of $y = f(x)$ is shown in Diagram 1 .
- Diagram 2 is a transformation of the graph in Diagram 1.

Diagram 1   Diagram 2

16.   The equation of the graph shown in Diagram 2 is

A. $y = -f(x - 2)$

B. $y = -f(x + 2)$

C. $y = f[-(x - 2)]$

D. $y = f(-x - 2)$

17.   The ordered pair (p, q) is on the function $y = g(x)$. The function is transformed and the resulting function has the equation $y - 6 = g(x + 4)$. The ordered pair which **must** be on the transformed function is

A. $(p + 4, q + 6)$ B. $(p - 4, q + 6)$

C. $(p + 4, q - 6)$ D. $(p - 4, q - 6)$

18.   The transformation of $y = g(x)$ to $y = -10g(x)$ is

A.   a vertical stretch by a factor of 10 about the x-axis and a reflection in the x-axis

B.   a vertical stretch by a factor of $\dfrac{1}{10}$ about the x-axis and a reflection in the x-axis

C.   a vertical stretch by a factor of 10 about the x-axis and a reflection in the y-axis

D.   a vertical stretch by a factor of $\dfrac{1}{10}$ about the x-axis and a reflection in the y-axis

Numerical Response 5. The range of the function $y = f(x)$ is $y \le 16$. The range of the function $y = f(x + 6) - 3$ is $y \le c$ where c is a whole number. The value of c is _____

(Record your answer in the numerical response box from left to right.)

19. The point $(8, -4)$ is on the graph of the function $y = f(x)$. The point which must be on the graph of $4y = -f(-x)$ is

A. $(-2, 4)$

B. $(-32, 4)$

C. $(-8, 1)$

D. $(-8, 16)$

20. The function $f(x) = kx^2$, where $k < 0$, is transformed to $g(x) = k(x + 2)^2 - 6$. The range of the transformed function is

A. $y \ge -6$

B. $y \le -6$

C. $y \le 6$

D. none of the above

Numerical Response 6. The point $P(4, 12)$ is on the graph of $y = 2^x - 4$. As a result of the transformation of the graph $y = 2^x - 4$ into the graph of $y = 2^{\frac{1}{2}x - 8} - 4$, the point P is transformed to the point $Q(a, 12)$. The value of a is _____ .

(Record your answer in the numerical response box from left to right.)

Use the following information to answer this question.

A Tschirnhausen Cubic is a curve given by an equation such as $y^2 = x^3 + 3x^2$. A partial graph of $y^2 = x^3 + 3x^2$ is shown below.

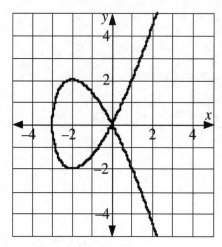

The graph passes through the points $(-3, 0), (-2, 2), (-2, -2)$ and $(0, 0)$.

The questions below are about various transformations applied to the Tschirnhausen Cubic with equation $y^2 = x^3 + 3x^2$.

- If the Tschirnhausen Cubic with equation $y^2 = x^3 + 3x^2$ is transformed 3 units to the right, state the domain and range of the transformed relation.

- Describe a single transformation applied to the Tschirnhausen Cubic with equation $y^2 = x^3 + 3x^2$ such that the graph of the image coincides with the original curve.

- Write the replacement for *x* or *y* associated with the transformation in the previous bullet and show that the equation of the image is identical to the original equation.

• The image of the Tschirnhausen Cubic with equation $y^2 = x^3 + 3x^2$ is given by the equation $(y + 2)^2 = (x - 1)^3 + 3(x - 1)^2$.

On the grid shown, sketch the transformed image, and mark on the grid the coordinates of the images of the four points given in the information above.

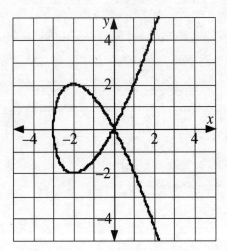

• The Tschirnhausen Cubic with equation $y^2 = x^3 + 3x^2$ is reflected in the line $y = x$.

Determine the equation of the image of the Tschirnhausen Cubic as a result of this reflection and sketch the transformed relation on the grid below.

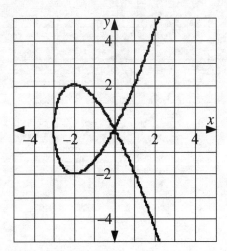

Answer Key

Multiple Choice

1. A	**2.** C	**3.** D	**4.** B	**5.** B	**6.** D	**7.** D	**8.** C
9. A	**10.** A	**11.** D	**12.** A	**13.** D	**14.** A	**15.** B	**16.** C
17. B	**18.** A	**19.** C	**20.** B				

Numerical Response

1.

3	4	1	2

2.

2	0		

3.

1	4		

4.

6	1	4	5

5.

1	3		

6.

2	4		

Written Response

- Domain $\{x \mid x \ge 0, x \in R\}$ Range $y \in R$

- a reflection in the *x*-axis

- $y \to -y$

- $(-2,-2), (1,-2), (-1,-4), (-1, 0)$

- $x^2 = y^3 + 3y^2$

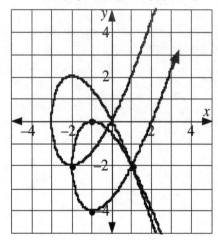

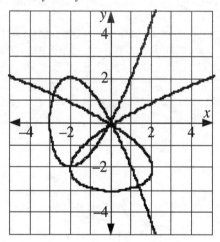

Exponential and Logarithmic Functions Lesson #1:
Review of Exponents

Overview

In this unit we will explain the relationship between logarithmic and exponential functions, and introduce the product, quotient, and power laws of logarithms.
We will graph and analyze exponential and logarithmic functions, and solve problems involving exponential and logarithmic equations.

Review of Exponent Laws

The exponent laws involve operations on powers.
The parts of a power are shown.

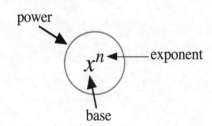

Complete the following exponent laws.

Product Law $x^m x^n =$

Quotient Law $x^m \div x^n =$

Power of a Power $(x^m)^n =$

Power of a Product $(xy)^m =$

Power of a Quotient $\left(\dfrac{x}{y}\right)^m =$ $, y \neq 0$

Integral Exponent Rule $x^{-m} =$ $,$ where $x \neq 0$

Rational Exponents $x^{\frac{m}{n}} =$ or $\left(\right)^m$

Class Ex. #1   Write each expression without brackets and with positive exponents.

a) $\dfrac{1}{2}y^{-6}$

b) $\dfrac{5x^{-3}}{y^{-2}}$

c) $(4x^3 y)(2x^{-4}y^2)$

d) $\dfrac{24m^5 p^{-3} q^4}{-4m^4 p^2 q^{-2}}$

e) $(3x^2 y^3)^3$

f) $\dfrac{12b^{-\frac{1}{2}}}{3b}$

Class Ex. #2

Simplify the following. Write the answers with positive exponents.

a) $(4xy^{-2})^{-3}$

b) $\left(\dfrac{3x^3}{4y^{-2}}\right)^{-2}$

Class Ex. #3

Without using a calculator, determine exact value of the following. Verify with a calculator.

a) 2^{-3}

b) $81^{\frac{3}{4}}$

c) 25^0

d) $16^{-\frac{1}{2}}$

Complete Assignment Questions #1 - #3

Changing Base

Class Ex. #4

Convert each of the following to the base indicated.

a) 9^{2x} to base 3

b) 125^{2-x} to base 5

c) $8 \cdot 16^x$ to base 2

d) $\dfrac{1}{512^{3x}}$ to base 2

e) $\left(\dfrac{16}{81}\right)^{x+5}$ to base $\dfrac{2}{3}$

Complete Assignment Questions #4 - #5

Solving Equations with Rational Exponents

We have already met this concept in earlier courses. Consider the following example:

The volume of a beach ball is 50 965 cm³. Determine the radius of the ball

to the nearest tenth of a cm. $\left(\text{Volume of sphere} = \dfrac{4}{3}\pi r^3\right)$

Sara and Lee are solving the problem and the first four steps in their solutions are identical as shown below.

$$V_{Sphere} = \frac{4}{3}\pi r^3 \;\Rightarrow\; 50965 = \frac{4}{3}\pi r^3 \;\Rightarrow\; 3(50965) = 4\pi r^3 \;\Rightarrow\; \frac{3(50965)}{4\pi} = r^3$$

a) Sara completed the solution by taking the cube root of each side of the equation.

Complete Sara's solution.

$$r^3 = \frac{3(50965)}{4\pi}$$

$$r =$$

b) Lee completed the solution by raising each side of the equation to a specific power.

i) Which power did he use?

ii) Complete Lee's method.

$$r^3 = \frac{3(50965)}{4\pi}$$

$$r =$$

Note Use the following procedure to solve an equation where the exponent is rational:
- Raise both sides to the reciprocal power of the exponent
- Simplify and solve for the variable.

Class Ex. #5   Solve for x in the following.

a) $x^{-\frac{4}{3}} = 81$

b) $(3x - 5)^{\frac{3}{2}} = 27$

Complete Assignment Questions #6 - #9

Assignment

1. Write each expression without brackets and with positive exponents.

    a) $4xy^{-3}$

    b) $\dfrac{15y^{-3}}{5y}$

    c) $(3x^3y)(5x^{-2}y^4)$

    d) $\dfrac{24p^{-8}}{16p^{-3}}$

    e) $\dfrac{2}{a^{-\frac{1}{3}}}$

    f) $(2x^{-2})^3$

2. Simplify the following. Write the answers with positive exponents.

    a) $\dfrac{x^5y^{-1}}{x^2y^{-4}}$

    b) $\left(\dfrac{5x^3}{2y^4}\right)^{-3}$

    c) $(4m^2n)^{-1} \times 2mn^5$

    d) $\dfrac{3x^2y^0z^{-4}}{(2xyz)^3}$

3. Without using a calculator, determine exact the value of the following. Verify with a calculator.

    a) 5^{-2} **b)** $27^{\frac{4}{3}}$ **c)** $\left(\dfrac{4}{9}\right)^{-\frac{3}{2}}$ **d)** $125^{\frac{1}{3}} - 10^0(64)^{\frac{2}{3}}$ **e)** $\left(\dfrac{1}{4}\right)^{-2}$

4. Convert each of the following to the base indicated.

a) 32^x to base 2

b) 81^{x-2} to base 3

c) $\dfrac{1}{64^{2x}}$ to base 4

d) $\left(\dfrac{1}{16}\right)^{x+1}$ to base 2

e) $\left(\dfrac{25}{49}\right)^{3x}$ to base $\dfrac{5}{7}$

f) $\left(\dfrac{27}{64}\right)^{x+2}$ to base $\dfrac{4}{3}$

5. Convert each of the following to the base indicated.

a) $2 \cdot 4^x$ to base 2

b) $9 \cdot 27^{x-1}$ to base 3

c) $\dfrac{1}{4} \cdot \left(\dfrac{1}{16}\right)^{4-x}$ to base 4

6. Solve for x.

a) $x^{\frac{1}{2}} = 5$

b) $x^{-\frac{1}{2}} = 5$

c) $x^{\frac{1}{3}} = -5$

d) $4x^{-\frac{2}{3}} = 16$

7. $(4x^{-3}y^5)^2$ is equal to

A. $\dfrac{16y^{10}}{x^6}$

B. $\dfrac{4y^{10}}{x^6}$

C. $\dfrac{16y^{10}}{x^3}$

D. $\dfrac{16x^6}{y^{10}}$

8. $(36x^{-4})^{-\frac{1}{2}}$ is equal to

A. $\dfrac{6}{x^2}$

B. $-18x^2$

C. $\dfrac{x^2}{6}$

D. $\dfrac{x^{-4.5}}{6}$

9. When $16(8)^{x-1}$ is converted to base 2, the exponent is

A. $3x + 1$

B. $3x + 3$

C. $7x - 7$

D. $12x - 12$

Answer Key

1. **a)** $\dfrac{4x}{y^3}$ **b)** $\dfrac{3}{y^4}$ **c)** $15xy^5$ **d)** $\dfrac{3}{2p^5}$ **e)** $2a^{\frac{1}{3}}$ **f)** $\dfrac{8}{x^6}$

2. **a)** x^3y^3 **b)** $\dfrac{8y^{12}}{125x^9}$ **c)** $\dfrac{n^4}{2m}$ **d)** $\dfrac{3}{8xy^3z^7}$

3. **a)** $\dfrac{1}{25}$ **b)** 81 **c)** $\dfrac{27}{8}$ **d)** -11 **e)** 16

4. **a)** 2^{5x} **b)** 3^{4x-8} **c)** 4^{-6x} **d)** 2^{-4x-4} **e)** $\left(\dfrac{5}{7}\right)^{6x}$ **f)** $\left(\dfrac{4}{3}\right)^{-3x-6}$

5. **a)** 2^{2x+1} **b)** 3^{3x-1} **c)** 4^{2x-9}

6. **a)** $x = 25$ **b)** $x = \dfrac{1}{25}$ **c)** $x = -125$ **d)** $x = \dfrac{1}{8}$

7. A   8. C   9. A

Exponential and Logarithmic Functions Lesson #2:
Solving Exponential Equations with a Common Base

Review

Simplify $(9^{2x+3} \div 27^{3x-1}) \times 81^{x-1}$ by converting each term to a common base.

Solving Exponential Equations with a Common Base

An **exponential equation** is an equation where the <u>variable</u> is in the exponent.

Use the following procedure to solve an equation where the variable is in the exponent.

- Write each side of the equation in the same base.

- If necessary, use exponent laws so that each side of the equation contains only one base.

- Equate the exponents on each side of the equation.

- Determine the value of the variable.

Class Ex. #1

Solve the following exponential equations.

a) $5^{2x+3} = 5^7$ **b)** $7^{x-2} = 343$ **c)** $3^{5x-1} = 81^{3x}$ **d)** $3^x = 27\sqrt{3}$

Class Ex. #2 A bacterium triples every six days. The number of bacteria n, present after x days, is given by the formula $n = 3^{\frac{x}{6}}$.   After how many days are there 243 bacteria?

Class Ex. #3 Solve the following exponential equations by converting each side to a common base.

a) $27^{x-2} = \dfrac{1}{81^{x+3}}$

b) $\left(\dfrac{125}{216}\right)^{\frac{-x}{4}} = \left(\dfrac{6}{5}\right)^{3x-3}$

Complete Assignment Questions #1 - #12

Assignment

1. Simplify.

    a) $49^{x-1} \times 7^{2x-3}$

    b) $216^x \div (1296^{5x-4} \times 36^{x+5})$

2. Solve the following exponential equations.

a) $2^{5x + 2} = 2^{17}$

b) $2^{2 - 3x} = 2^{7x - 8}$

c) $9^{c + 1} = 729$

d) $5^{4a + 2} = 25^a$

e) $2^{-t} = 64$

f) $10^{10x - 2} = 1000^{20x - 42}$

3. Solve for x.

a) $2^x = 16\sqrt{2}$

b) $8^{3x} = 4^{1 - x}$

c) $9^{3x + 1} = 27^{3x}$

4. A bacterium doubles every 12 hours. The number of bacteria, N, present after H hours is given by the formula $N = 2^{\frac{H}{12}}$.

a) After how many hours are there 256 bacteria?

b) Estimate how many hours it would take for the number of bacteria to reach 1000? (*An algebraic technique to determine the exact answer to this problem will be shown later in this unit.*)

5. A radioactive isotope has a mass of 512 grams, and has a half life of 45 minutes.

The number of grams, N, present after m minutes, is given by the formula $N = 512\left(\dfrac{1}{2}\right)^{\frac{m}{45}}$.

How long would it take for the mass to reduce to one gram?

6. Solve for x.

a) $\left(\dfrac{4}{7}\right)^{5x} = \left(\dfrac{64}{343}\right)^{2x-1}$

b) $49\left(\dfrac{7}{12}\right)^{2x} = 144$

c) $\left(\dfrac{125}{216}\right)^{-\frac{x}{2}} = \left(\dfrac{6}{5}\right)^{3x+2}$

d) $\left(\dfrac{9}{4}\right)^{x+3} = \left(\dfrac{8}{27}\right)^{-5}$

7. Solve for x.

a) $2^{x-1} = (128^x)(2^x)$

b) $\left(\dfrac{1}{4}\right)^{x-12} = (2)(32)^{2x+1}$

c) $\sqrt[3]{\dfrac{27^{2x-1}}{3^{x+1}}} = 9$

8. Solve the equation $2(6^{2x}) - 74(6^x) + 72 = 0$.

(Hint: Write as a quadratic equation with the variable as 6^x.)

Multiple
Choice **9.** If $4^{2x-7} = \dfrac{1}{64}$, then the value of $\sqrt{x}$ is

A. 2

B. $\sqrt{2}$

C. $\sqrt{5}$

D. $\dfrac{3}{2}$

Numerical
Response **10.** The solution to the equation $25^{x+1} = 5^{3(x-1)}$, to the nearest tenth, is $x = $ _____ .

(Record your answer in the numerical response box from left to right.)

11. The solution to the equation $\left(\dfrac{1}{8}\right)^{x-3} = (2)(16)^{2x+1}$,

to the nearest hundredth, is $x = $ _____ .

(Record your answer in the numerical response box from left to right.)

12. The solution to the equation $8^{2x-1} = 16$, to the nearest tenth, is $x = $ _____ .

(Record your answer in the numerical response box from left to right.)

Answer Key

1 . a) 7^{4x-5} **b)** 6^{-19x+6}

2 . a) 3   **b)** 1   **c)** 2   **d)** –1   **e)** –6   **f)** $\dfrac{62}{25}$ or 2.48

3 . a) $x = \dfrac{9}{2}$ **b)** $x = \dfrac{2}{11}$ **c)** $x = \dfrac{2}{3}$

4 . a) 96 hours   **b)** 120 hours

5 . 6 hours and 45 minutes

6 . a) $x = 3$ **b)** $x = -1$ **c)** $x = -\dfrac{4}{3}$ **d)** $x = \dfrac{9}{2}$

7 . a) $x = -\dfrac{1}{7}$ **b)** $x = \dfrac{3}{2}$ **c)** $x = 2$

8 . $x = 0, x = 2$

9 .   B

10 . | 5 | . | 0 | | **11 .** | 0 | . | 3 | 6 | **12 .** | 1 | . | 2 | |

Exponential and Logarithmic Functions Lesson #3:
Exponential Functions

Exploring Exponential Growth

Mallory, a medical research scientist, discovered a new bacteria culture which could help strengthen a person's immune system. To find the growth rate, she isolated 5 cells of the culture and observed the following growth pattern:

t	$N(t)$
0	5
1	10
2	20
3	40

- after one hour there were 10 cells
- after two hours there were 20 cells
- after three hours there were 40 cells

a) Let t represent the time in hours and $N(t)$ represent the number of cells after t hours.

   The formula for $N(t)$ as a function of t can be written in the form $N(t) = ab^t$, where a and b are constants and $a, b > 0$. Determine the values of a and b and write the function.

b) Use the formula to determine how many cells there were after 8 hours.

c) After 12 hours there are 20 480 cells. How many hours did it take to have half that amount?

d) Use a graphing calculator to graph the function.
   A graph of this type represents **exponential growth**.

Exploring Exponential Decay

Chernobyl is a city in the former Soviet Union. In April 1986, there was a nuclear accident and the atmosphere was contaminated with quantities of a type of radioactive iodine. At the time of the explosion the atmosphere was contaminated with 32 768 units of radioactive iodine. The following data was recorded for the dissipation of the radioactive iodine:

- after 1 week there were 16 384 units left in the atmosphere
- after 2 weeks there were 8192 units left in the atmosphere
- after 3 weeks there were 4096 units left in the atmosphere

a) Use t to represent the time in weeks and $N(t)$ to represent the number of units of radioactive iodine after t weeks. Complete the following equation of the function which represents the information provided.

   $N(t) = 32\ 768\ (\quad)^t$

b) Use the formula to determine how many units of radioactive iodine were left after 14 weeks.

```
Xmin=-1
Xmax=8
Xscl=1
Ymin=-30000
Ymax=64000
Yscl=10000
Xres=1
```

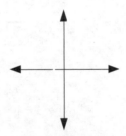

c) Use a graphing calculator to graph the function using the Window shown.
   A graph of this type represents **exponential decay**.

The explorations on the previous page are examples of **exponential functions.**
An **exponential function** is a function whose equation is of the form

$$y = ab^x$$ where $a \neq 0, b > 0, b \neq 1, x \in R$

Comparing the Graphs $y = 2^x$ and $y = \left(\dfrac{1}{2}\right)^x$

a) State the values of a and b for $y = 2^x$ and $y = \left(\dfrac{1}{2}\right)^x$.

b) Sketch the graph of the exponential function with equation $y = 2^x, x \in R$, using the table of values and grid.

x	-3	-2	-1	0	1	2	3	4
y								

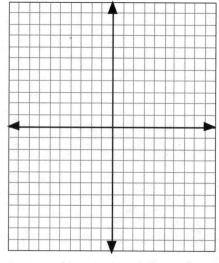

c) Sketch the graph of the exponential function with equation $y = \left(\dfrac{1}{2}\right)^x, x \in R$, using the table of values and grid.

x	-3	-2	-1	0	1	2	3	4
y								

d) An **asymptote** is a line whose distance from a given curve gets closer and closer to zero. In the above graphs, the x-axis is a horizontal asymptote. Complete the following chart.

Equation of Function	Domain of Function	Range of Function	x-intercept of Graph	y-intercept of Graph	Equation(s) of Asymptotes
$y = 2^x$					
$y = \left(\dfrac{1}{2}\right)^x$					

e) Complete the following statements using the words "growth" or "decay".

- $f(x) = 2^x$ is an example of a _____ function.

- $f(x) = \left(\dfrac{1}{2}\right)^x$ is an example of a _____ function.

> ### *Exploring the Value of b in y = ab^x, where a = 1*

a) By using a graphing calculator or other technology, sketch the exponential functions with equation:

(i) $y = 3^x$

(ii) $y = 10^x$

(iii) $y = \left(\dfrac{1}{3}\right)^x$

(iv) $y = \left(\dfrac{1}{10}\right)^x$

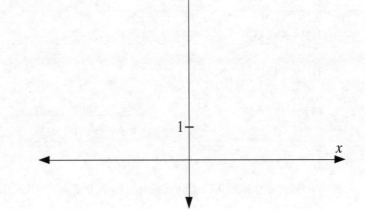

b) The value of b affects the steepness of the graph as x increases. Complete the following.
- When $b > 1$, the curve _____ more sharply as b increases.
- When $0 < b < 1$, the curve _____ more sharply as b decreases.

c) Without using a graphing calculator, make a sketch of the graphs of:

i) $y = 5^x$ ii) $y = (0.2)^x$

d) Verify the solution in c) using a graphing calculator.

e) State the *x*-intercept for each of the graphs of the form $y = b^x$.

f) State the *y*-intercept for each of the graphs of the form $y = b^x$.

g) State the domain for each of the graphs of the form $y = b^x$.

h) State the range for each of the graphs of the form $y = b^x$.

i) State the equation of the horizontal asymptote for each of the graphs of the form $y = b^x$.

Exploring the Value of a in y = ab^x

Consider the following functions with
equations of the form $y = ab^x$:

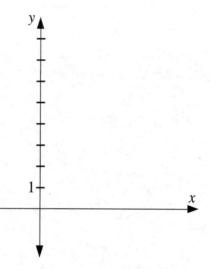

i) $y = 3^x$

ii) $y = (2)3^x$

iii) $y = (5)3^x$

iv) $y = (0.5)3^x$

a) Graph the functions using a graphing calculator. Sketch the graphs on the grid .

b) Complete the following table for these equations of the form $y = ab^x$.

	$y = 3^x$	$y = (2)3^x$	$y = (5)3^x$	$y = (0.5)3^x$
Value of a				
Value of b				
y-intercept of the graph				

c) What is the effect on the graph of changing the value of a?

d) If $f(x) = 3^x$, write the following in terms of the function f.
   i) $y = 3^x$ ii) $y = (2)3^x$ iii) $y = (5)3^x$ iv) $y = (0.5)3^x$

e) Which transformations are associated with d): ii), iii), iv).

f) What is the effect of the parameter a on the graph of $y = ab^x$

g) State the y-intercept for each of the graphs of the form $y = ab^x$.

Characteristics of the Graph of the Exponential Function $f(x) = ab^x$

The following summarizes the basic characteristics of the graph of the exponential function with equation $y = ab^x$.

Use the information from the previous explorations to complete the following.

- The y-intercept is _____ .   • There is _____ x-intercept.

- The x-axis is a _____ _____.

- The domain is _____.

- The range is _____.

- For $a > 0$,
    - When $b > 1$, the function represents a _____ function.
    - When _____, the function represents a decay function .

- The value of b affects the steepness of the graph as x increases.
    - When $b > 1$, the curve _____ sharply as b increases.
    - When $0 < b < 1$, the curve _____ sharply as b decreases.

- The value of a affects the vertical stretch of the graph. Choose the correct alternative.
    - When $a > 1$, the stretch is a(n) (expansion / compression).
    - When $0 < a < 1$, the stretch is a(n) (expansion / compression).
    - When $a < 0$, there is also a reflection in the (x-axis / y-axis).

Class Ex. #1

Describe how the graph of the second function compares to the graph of the first function.

a) $y = 4^x$, $y = 2(4)^{x-2}$ **b)** $y = 2^x$, $y + 4 = -2^{\frac{x}{5}}$

Class Ex. #2

Explain, using transformations, why the graph of $y = \left(\dfrac{1}{3}\right)^x$ is a reflection in the y-axis of the graph of $y = 3^x$.

Class Ex. #3

Consider the function $f(x) = 4^{x+2} - 6$. Without using a graphing calculator, determine

a) the domain and range of the function

b) the *y*-intercept of the graph of the function

c) the equation(s) of any asymptotes of the graph of the function

---

Complete Assignment Questions #1 - #11

Assignment

1. State the *x* and *y*-intercepts for the graphs of the following:

  a) $f(x) = 2^x$ **b)** $f(x) = (2)10^x$ **c)** $f(x) = 2^{10x}$ **d)** $y = \left(-\dfrac{1}{2}\right)\left(\dfrac{3}{5}\right)^x$

2. a) State the domain and range of the function $f(x) = ab^x, a, b > 0, x \in R$.

  b) Which of the following transformations applied to the graph of $y = ab^x, a, b > 0, x \in R$, would result in a change to the **domain** of the function?

  i) horizontal stretch about the *y*-axis   **ii)** vertical stretch about the *x*-axis

  iii) horizontal translation   **iv)** reflection in the *x*-axis

  v) reflection in the *y*-axis   **vi)** reflection in the line $y = x$

  c) Which of the above transformations applied to the graph of $y = ab^x, a, b > 0, x \in R$, would result in a change to the **range** of the function?

Use the following information to answer the next question.

The graph of the exponential function with equation $y = 4^x$ is shown.

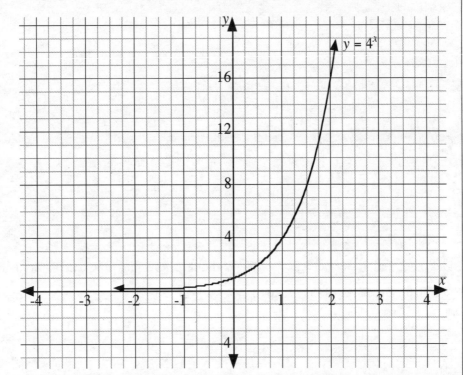

3. a) Use the graph to **estimate**, to one decimal place, the solution to the equation $4^x = 12$.

b) Use a graphing calculator to determine, to one decimal place, the solution to the equation $4^x = 12$.

c) Explain how to use the graph of $y = 4^x$ to graph the function with equation $y = \left(\dfrac{1}{4}\right)^x$. Sketch the graph on the grid.

d) Without using the grid or a graphing calculator, state the solution to the equation $\left(\dfrac{1}{4}\right)^x = 12$.

e) Use transformations to sketch the graph of the function with equation $y = \left(\dfrac{1}{4}\right)^{x-2} - 4$ and state the domain and the range of the function.

4. Describe how the graph of the second function compares to the graph of the first function.

a) $y = 10^x$, $y = 10^{-x} - 3$

b) $y = 2^x$, $y = 5\left(\dfrac{1}{2}\right)^x$

c) $y = 6^x$, $y = \left(\dfrac{1}{6}\right)^{-x}$

d) $y = a^x$, $y = -a^{\frac{x}{2}}$

5. Consider the function $y = f(x) = 5^{x+4} + 3$. Without using a graphing calculator, determine

a) the domain and range of the function

b) the x and y-intercepts of the graph of the function

c) the equation(s) of any asymptotes of the graph of the function

6. Consider the function $f(x) = b^{x-h} + k$. Determine

a) the domain and range of the function

b) the y-intercept of the graph of the function

c) the equation of the horizontal asymptote of the graph of the function

7. The graph of $f(x) = b^x$ is shown. Sketch $f^{-1}(x)$.

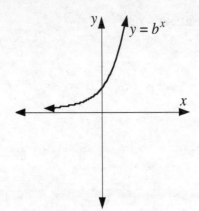

a) State the domain and range of $f(x)$.

b) State the domain and range of $f^{-1}(x)$.

c) State the asymptotes for $y = f(x)$ and $y = f^{-1}(x)$.

d) Write the equation for the inverse function in the form $x = f(y)$ and try to solve for y.
Explain what happens.

Multiple
Choice **8.** Which equation represents an exponential function?

A. $y = 2x^8$ **B.** $y = (-3)^x$ **C.** $y = \dfrac{3^{x-2}}{2}$ **D.** $y = \dfrac{1}{3x}$

Use the following information to answer the next three questions.

> A student is attempting to sketch the graph of the function
> $f(x) = 3^{x-2} - 1$ without using a graphing calculator.

9. Which of the following is an asymptote of the graph?

A. $x = -2$ **B.** $x = 2$

C. $y = 1$ **D.** $y = -1$

10. The range of f is

A. $f(x) \in R$ **B.** $\{f(x) \mid f(x) > -2, f(x) \in R\}$

C. $\{f(x) \mid f(x) \ge -1, f(x) \in R\}$ **D.** $\{f(x) \mid f(x) > -1, f(x) \in R\}$

11. The x-intercept of the graph is

A. 0   **B.** 2   **C.** 3   **D.** there is no x-intercept

Answer Key

1. **a)** *x*-intercept: none   **b)** *x*-intercept: none   **c)** *x*-intercept: none   **d)** *x*-intercept: none

   y-intercept: 1   *y*-intercept: 2   *y*-intercept: 1   *y*-intercept: $-\dfrac{1}{2}$

2. **a)** Domain: $x \in R$ Range: $\{y \mid y > 0, y \in R\}$ **b)** vi   **c)** iv, vi

3. **a)** 1.8   **b)** 1.8

   c) $\left(\dfrac{1}{4}\right)^x$ is equivalent to 4^{-x}, so the replacement is $x \to -x$, which is a reflection in the *y*-axis.

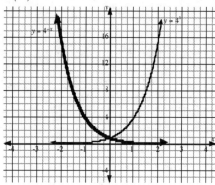

   d) −1.8

   e) Domain: $x \in R$ Range: $\{y \mid y > -4, y \in R\}$

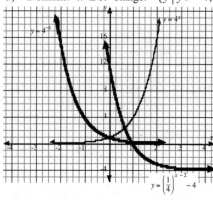

4. **a)** a reflection in the *y*-axis, and a vertical translation 3 units down
   b) a vertical stretch by a factor of 5 about the *x*-axis, and a reflection in the *y*-axis
   c) identical   **d)** a horizontal stretch by a factor of 2 about the *y*-axis, and a reflection in the *x*-axis

5. **a)** $x \in R$, $\{y \mid y > 3, y \in R\}$ **b)** no *x*-intercept, *y*-intercept is 628   **c)** $y = 3$

6. **a)** $x \in R$, $\{f(x) \mid f(x) > k, f(x) \in R\}$ **b)** *y*-intercept is $b^{-h} + k$ **c)** $y = k$

7. **a)** Domain: $x \in R$ Range: $\{y \mid y > 0, y \in R\}$ **b)** Domain: $\{x \mid x > 0, x \in R\}$ Range: $y \in R$
   c) for $y = f(x)$ the asymptote is $y = 0$ for $y = f^{-1}(x)$ the asymptote is $x = 0$
   d) $x = b^y$ don't know how to solve for *y* until the next lesson

8. C   **9.** D   **10.** D   **11.** B

Exponential and Logarithmic Functions Lesson #4:
Logarithmic Functions

Exploring the Inverse of an Exponential Function

In this example we will consider the exponential function $y = 2^x$.

Part 1   Exploring the Inverse of $y = 2^x$ Algebraically

To find the inverse of a function algebraically, we must switch x and y and then solve for y.

a) Attempt to determine the inverse of $y = 2^x$ algebraically.

b) What difficulty did you encounter?

At this stage we are unable to write the inverse of $y = 2^x$ in terms of y.

Part 2   Exploring the Inverse of $y = 2^x$ Graphically

To determine the inverse of $y = 2^x$ graphically, we switch the x and y-coordinates of each point on the graph to produce the graph of $x = 2^y$.

a) Complete the tables below and sketch the graphs of $y = 2^x$ and $x = 2^y$ on the grid.

Graph of $y = 2^x$

x	−3	−2	−1	0	1	2	3	4
y								

Graph of $x = 2^y$

x								
y	−3	−2	−1	0	1	2	3	4

b) State the equation of the line of symmetry of the completed graphs.

Note $y = 2^x$ is the exponential function with base 2. The inverse of this function, $x = 2^y$, is also a function, but we are unable to write its equation in terms of y.

To do this, we introduce a new function, called the **logarithmic function**.

Logarithmic Function

A **logarithmic function** is the inverse of an exponential function.

The inverse of the exponential function with base 2, i.e. $y = 2^x$, is the logarithmic function with base 2, written as $y = \log_2 x$.

Note that the graph of $y = \log_2 x$ is the same as the graph of $x = 2^y$.

$$x = 2^y \quad \Leftrightarrow \quad y = \log_2 x$$

In general, we write $y = \log_b x$ rather than $x = b^y$ to express the inverse of $y = b^x$.

The **logarithmic function** with base b has the equation

$$y = \log_b x, \quad x > 0, \ x \in R, \ b > 0 \text{ and } b \neq 1$$

Note
- The inside of the logarithm, in this case x, is called the **argument** of the logarithm.
- The argument can never be negative.

value $\longrightarrow$ $y = \log_b x$ $\longleftarrow$ argument
of the logarithm   of the logarithm

base
of the logarithm

Class Ex. #1

The graphs of $y = 2^x$ and $x = 2^y$ are shown.

a) Write the label "$y = \log_2 x$" beside the appropriate graph on the grid.

b) Complete the table below.

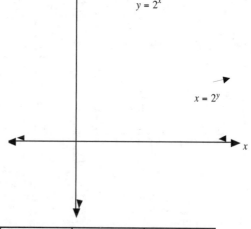

Function	Domain	Range	x-intercept	y-intercept	Asymptote
$y = 2^x$					
$y = \log_2 x$					

Class Ex. #2

The tables below show the coordinates of points on the graphs of $y = 2^x$ and $y = \log_2 x$.

Graph of $y = 2^x$

x	-3	-2	-1	0	1	2	3	4
y	$\frac{1}{8}$	$\frac{1}{4}$	$\frac{1}{2}$	1	2	4	8	16

Graph of $y = \log_2 x$

x	$\frac{1}{8}$	$\frac{1}{4}$	$\frac{1}{2}$	1	2	4	8	16
y	-3	-2	-1	0	1	2	3	4

Notice that

- the point $(3, 8)$ on the graph of $y = 2^x$ indicates that $8 = 2^3$

- the point $(8, 3)$ on the graph of $y = \log_2 x$ indicates that $3 = \log_2 8$

a) What statement can be made from the point $\left(-2, \frac{1}{4}\right)$ on the graph of $y = 2^x$?

b) What statement can be made from the point $(16, 4)$ on the graph of $y = \log_2 x$?

c) Complete the table below showing statements in exponential form and logarithmic form.

Logarithmic Form	Exponential Form	Logarithmic Form	Exponential Form
$\log_2 8 = 3$	$8 = 2^3$	$\log_2 \frac{1}{8} =$	$\frac{1}{8} = 2^{-3}$
$\log_2 4 =$			$\frac{1}{4} = 2^{-2}$
$\log_2 2 =$			$\frac{1}{2} = 2^{-1}$
$\log_2 1 =$			

Class Ex. #3

a) Use patterns developed from Class Ex. #2 to write the exponential statement $10^3 = 1000$ in logarithmic form.

b) Use patterns developed from Class Ex. #2 to write the logarithmic statement $\log_5 625 = 4$ in exponential form.

Characteristics of the Graph of the Logarithmic Function $y = \log_b x$

- The x intercept is 1.

- There is no y-intercept.

- The y-axis is a vertical asymptote with equation $x = 0$.

- Domain $= \{x \mid x > 0, x \in R\}$.

- Range $= \{y \mid y \in R\}$.

- $y = \log_b x$ is equivalent to $x = b^y$, where $x > 0$ and $b > 0, b \ne 1$.

- b is the base of both the logarithmic function and the exponential function.

- **Since the logarithmic function $y = \log_b x$ is only defined for positive values of x, the logarithm of a negative number cannot be determined.**

- **The logarithmic equation $y = \log_b x$ can be expressed in exponential form as $x = b^y$.**

- **The exponential equation $y = b^x$ can be expressed in logarithmic form as $\log_b y = x$.**

Class Ex. #4

State the inverse of the following functions. Answer in the form $y =$ _____ .

a) $y = \log_3 x$ **b)** $y = 8^x$

Class Ex. #5

Convert each of the following from logarithmic form to exponential form.

a) $\log_7 x = 4$ **b)** $\log_5 15 = y$ **c)** $m = \log_t B$ **d)** $5 = 4\log_b 6$

Class Ex. #6

Convert each of the following from exponential form to logarithmic form.

a) $4^3 = 64$ **b)** $2^{-3} = \dfrac{1}{8}$ **c)** $e^d = f$ **d)** $(2x + 4) = a^5$

Class Ex. #7   Calculate the value of t if $\log_2 x = 3$ and $\log_2 t = x$.

Complete Assignment Questions #1 - #7

The Logarithmic Form of $y = ab^x$

We have seen how to change forms between the exponential form $y = b^x$ and the logarithmic form $\log_b y = x$.

We now consider how to write the exponential form $y = ab^x$ in logarithmic form.

This can be done using the following procedure:

1. Write the exponential form $y = ab^x$ as $\dfrac{y}{a} = b^x$.

2. Change $\dfrac{y}{a} = b^x$ to logarithmic form.

The logarithmic form of $y = ab^x \left(\text{or } \dfrac{y}{a} = b^x \right)$ is _____ .

Class Ex. #8   Change each of the following from exponential form to logarithmic form.

a) $y = 2(3^x)$ **b)** $h = 7(4)^k$ **c)** $t = r(s)^p$ **d)** $y = \dfrac{3}{2}(10)^x$

Class Ex. #9   Change each of the following from logarithmic form to exponential form $y = ab^x$.

a) $\log_7\left(\dfrac{y}{3}\right) = x$ **b)** $\log_{10}\left(\dfrac{y}{4}\right) = x$ **c)** $\log_5(7y) = x$ **d)** $\log_e\left(\dfrac{y}{5}\right) = x$

Complete Assignment Questions #8 - #15

Assignment

1. Complete the following from the graphs of $y = b^x$ and $y = \log_b x, b > 0$.

Function	Domain	Range	x-intercept	y-intercept	Asymptote
$y = b^x$					
$y = \log_b x$					

2. Why does x have to be greater than zero in the domain of $y = \log_b x$, and not in $y = b^x, b > 0$?

3. Express each of the following in logarithmic form.

   a) $5^2 = 25$　　　　**b)** $3^0 = 1$　　　　**c)** $2^{-4} = \dfrac{1}{16}$

   d) $\left(\dfrac{1}{2}\right)^4 = \dfrac{1}{16}$　　　**e)** $b^d = e$

4. Express each of the following in exponential form.

   a) $\log_3 9 = 2$　　　　**b)** $\log_5 625 = 4$　　　　**c)** $\log_4 \dfrac{1}{4} = -1$

   d) $\log_a f = i$　　　　**e)** $\log_{10} 0.001 = -3$

5. Is $y = \log_3 x$ the logarithmic form of $y = 3^x$? Explain your answer.

6. Complete the following table:

Logarithmic Form	Exponential Form	Value of x
$\log_4 x = 2$		
	$7 = 49^x$	
$\log_x\left(\dfrac{1}{64}\right) = -3$		
	$x + 2 = 4^2$	
$\log_{32} x = \dfrac{1}{5}$		
	$\dfrac{1}{2} = 16^x$	

7. By converting to exponential form, solve the equation $\log_2(\log_2(x - 7)) = 3$.

8. Determine the inverse of the following functions. Answer in the form $y = \underline{\hspace{2cm}}$.

   a) $y = 3^x$ **b)** $y = \log_4 x$ **c)** $y = 3x^2 + 2$

   d) $y = \log_3 x$ **e)** $y = 20^x$ **f)** $x = 20^y$

9. Change each of the following from exponential form to logarithmic form.

   a) $y = 3(2)^x$ **b)** $y = 10(3)^x$ **c)** $y = \dfrac{5}{6}(10)^x$ **d)** $a = b(c)^d$

10. Change each of the following from logarithmic form to exponential form $y = ab^x$.

a) $\log_8\left(\dfrac{y}{9}\right) = x$ b) $\log_{20}(6y) = x$ c) $\log_e\left(\dfrac{y}{5}\right) = x$ d) $\log_{10}(0.5y) = x$

11. By converting to exponential form, solve the following equations for y.

a) $3 = \log_2\left(\dfrac{y}{4}\right)$ b) $\log_2\left(\dfrac{y}{5}\right) = -3$ c) $2 = \log_4 32y$

Multiple Choice

12. If $\log_4(4096x) = 64$, then the value of x is

A. $4^{\frac{32}{3}}$

B. 4^{58}

C. 4^6

D. 4^{32}

13. The graph of $\log_x y = 1$ is

A.
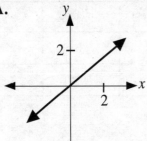

B.
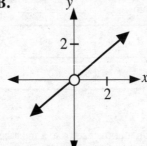

C.
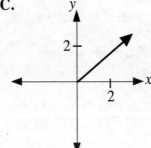

D.
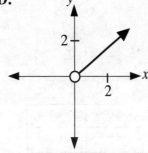

Numerical Response **14.** To the nearest tenth, the *y*-intercept of the graph of $\log_5(y + 2) = x + 1$ is _____ .

(Record your answer in the numerical response box from left to right.)

15. If $\log_b 81 = \dfrac{2}{3}$, then the value of *b* is to the nearest whole number is _____ .

(Record your answer in the numerical response box from left to right.)

Answer Key

	Function	Domain	Range	x-intercept	y-intercept	Asymptote
1	$y = b^x$	$x \in R$	$\{y \mid y > 0, y \in R\}$	none	1	$y = 0$
	$y = \log_b x$	$\{x \mid x > 0, x \in R\}$	$y \in R$	1	none	$x = 0$

2. $y = \log_b x \Rightarrow x = b^y$

Since $b > 0$, b^y must be greater than zero, so x must be greater than zero.

$y = b^x$ can be determined for all values of x: positive, negative, or zero.

3. **a)** $\log_5 25 = 2$ **b)** $\log_3 1 = 0$ **c)** $\log_2\left(\dfrac{1}{16}\right) = -4$ **d)** $\log_{\frac{1}{2}}\left(\dfrac{1}{16}\right) = 4$ **e)** $\log_b e = d$

4. **a)** $3^2 = 9$ **b)** $5^4 = 625$ **c)** $4^{-1} = \dfrac{1}{4}$ **d)** $a^i = f$ **e)** $10^{-3} = 0.001$

5. No, it is the inverse. The logarithmic form of $y = 3^x$ is $x = \log_3 y$.

6.

Logarithmic Form	Exponential Form	Value of x
$\log_4 x = 2$	$x = 4^2$	$x = 16$
$\log_{49} 7 = x$	$7 = 49^x$	$x = \dfrac{1}{2}$
$\log_x\left(\dfrac{1}{64}\right) = -3$	$\dfrac{1}{64} = x^{-3}$	$x = 4$
$\log_4(x + 2) = 2$	$x + 2 = 4^2$	$x = 14$
$\log_{32} x = \dfrac{1}{5}$	$x = 32^{\frac{1}{5}}$	$x = 2$
$\log_{16}\left(\dfrac{1}{2}\right) = x$	$\dfrac{1}{2} = 16^x$	$x = -\dfrac{1}{4}$

7. 263

8. **a)** $y = \log_3 x$ **b)** $y = 4^x$ **c)** $y = \pm\sqrt{\dfrac{x - 2}{3}}$

d) $y = 3^x$ **e)** $y = \log_{20} x$ **f)** $y = 20^x$

9. **a)** $\log_2\left(\dfrac{y}{3}\right) = x$ **b)** $\log_3\left(\dfrac{y}{10}\right) = x$ **c)** $\log_{10}\left(\dfrac{6y}{5}\right) = x$ **d)** $\log_c\left(\dfrac{a}{b}\right) = d$

10. **a)** $y = 9(8)^x$ **b)** $y = \dfrac{1}{6}(20)^x$ **c)** $y = 5(e)^x$ **d)** $y = 2(10)^x$

11. **a)** 32 **b)** $\dfrac{5}{8}$ **c)** $\dfrac{1}{2}$

12. B **13.** D **14.** | 3 | . | 0 | | **15.** | 7 | 2 | 9 | |

Exponential and Logarithmic Functions Lesson #5:
Evaluating Logarithms

In the last lesson we compared the graphs of $y = 2^x$ and $y = \log_2 x$.

We learned

- the point $(3, 8)$ on the graph of $y = 2^x$ indicates that $8 = 2^3$

- the point $(8, 3)$ on the graph of $y = \log_2 x$ indicates that $3 = \log_2 8$

- the exponential form $8 = 2^3$ and the logarithmic form $3 = \log_2 8$ are equivalent

In this lesson, we will learn how to evaluate logarithms like $\log_3 8$ without reference to a graph or table.

Evaluating Logarithms by Converting to Exponential Form

Kelcie was asked to evaluate $\log_2 8$. Her work is shown below.
Study her work and describe each step on the lines provided.

$\log_2 8 = v$ <u>Represent $\log_2 8$ with the unknown value "v".</u>

$2^v = 8$ _____

$2^v = 2^3$ _____

$v = 3$ _____

$\therefore \log_2 8 = 3$ _____

_____

Class Ex. #1

Evaluate the following logarithms.

a) $\log_3 81$ **b)** $\log_4 64$ **c)** $\log_7 7$ **d)** $\log_{12} 1$

Class Ex. #2 Determine the value of

a) $\log_b 1$ **b)** $\log_b b$

Class Ex. #3 Evaluate.

a) $2 \log_8 512$ **b)** $\log_2\left(\dfrac{1}{32}\right)$ **c)** $\log_5 \sqrt{125}$

Class Ex. #4 **a)** Evaluate. **i)** $5^{\log_5 25}$ **ii)** $7^{\log_7 49}$ **iii)** $3^{\log_3 27}$

b) Based on your observations from a) to c), what is the value of $a^{\log_a n}$?
Use inverses to explain your answer.

c) Determine the value of $\log_a a^n$.

Complete Assignment Questions #1 - #3

Evaluating Logarithms by Changing the Base

a) Try to evaluate $\log_5 50$. What problem do you encounter?

b) Choose the correct alternative. The exact value of $\log_5 50$ is
   i) between 1.5 and 2   **ii)** between 2 and 2.5   **iii)** between 2.5 and 3

At the moment we are unable to evaluate $\log_5 50$ by converting to exponential form.

We can, however, evaluate the logarithm using a calculator by changing the base to a base the calculator recognizes.

To do this, we introduce **Common Logarithms** and **Natural Logarithms**.

Common Logarithms

Common logarithms are logarithms in base 10, eg. $\log_{10} 1000$.

These logarithms are in such common use that when a base is not given the logarithm is understood to be in base ten. For instance,

$$\log_{10} 1000 \text{ is often written as } \log 1000$$

On a graphing calculator, this can be evaluated using the $\boxed{\text{LOG}}$ key.

Class Ex. #5

Evaluate log 1000 by

a) converting to exponential form   **b)** using the $\boxed{\text{LOG}}$ key on a calculator.

Class Ex. #6

In each of the following,
   i) estimate the value, to the nearest whole number, without using technology and explain the reasoning
   ii) approximate the value to the nearest hundredth using technology

a) $\log_{10} 89$ **b)** log 2000

Natural Logarithms

Natural logarithms are logarithms in base e eg. $\log_e 15$.

e is an irrational number, the value of which will be determined in the enrichment below.

$\log_e 15$ is often written as ln 15

On a graphing calculator, this can be evaluated using the [LN] key.

Class Ex. #7

Evaluate the following logarithms to one decimal place where necessary.

a) ln 5   **b)** $\log_e 5$ **c)** ln e

Enrichment   *Approximating the Value of e*

Although not required for this course, the enrichment may give students a greater understanding in preparation for higher level math courses.

The formal definition of the irrational number e is the limit as x approaches infinity of the function $f(x) = \left(1 + \dfrac{1}{x}\right)^x$.

Complete the following table to determine the value of this function as x gets very large. Use the [TABLE] feature of a graphing calculator and work to 4 decimal places.

x	10	100	1000	10 000	100 000	1 000 000
$\left(1 + \dfrac{1}{x}\right)^x$						

Estimate for e is _____.

A more accurate estimate can be determined by pressing the [e] key on a graphing calculator.

The value of e to 9 decimal places is _____ .

Investigating the Change of Base Identity

a) i)   Evaluate $\log_5 25$ by converting to exponential form.

ii)   Evaluate $\dfrac{\log 25}{\log 5}$ and $\dfrac{\ln 25}{\ln 5}$ using a calculator.

iii)   Comment on your answers from i) and ii).

b) i)   Evaluate $\log_3 243$ by converting to exponential form.

ii)   Evaluate $\dfrac{\log 243}{\log 3}$ and $\dfrac{\log_e 243}{\log_e 3}$ using a calculator.

iii)   Comment on your answers from i) and ii).

c)   In the first page of this lesson, we learned that $\log_2 8 = 3$.
Write $\log_2 8$ in a form which can be evaluated using a calculator and verify the answer.

d) Write $\log_2 64$ in a form which can be evaluated using a calculator.

Change of Base Identity

$$\log_b c = \frac{\log_a c}{\log_a b}$$

We have seen that the above identity is true for converting logarithms to base 10 or base *e*.
In fact it holds true for converting logarithms to any base. The example below supports this.

i) Evaluate $\log_4 1024$

ii) Evaluate $\dfrac{\log_2 1024}{\log_2 4}$

Class Ex. #8

Evaluate the following logarithms to the nearest hundredth by changing the base.

a) $\log_5 221$

b) $\log_2 \dfrac{1}{1000}$

c) $3 \log_7 512$

Class Ex. #9   Convert the following logarithms to the base indicated.

     a) $\log_6 216$ to base 3   **b)** $\log 300$ to base 5

Class Ex. #10   Find the exact value of the following.

     a) $-\log_7\left(\dfrac{1}{343}\right)$ **b)** $6^{\log_6 216}$ **c)** $\log_2\sqrt{\dfrac{1}{1024}}$ **d)** $\log_7 49^{-5}$

> **Complete Assignment Questions #4- #15**

Assignment

1. Evaluate.

     a) $\log_{10} 1000$ **b)** $\log_{12} 144$ **c)** $\log_6 36$ **d)** $\log_{36} 6$

     e) $\log_5 \sqrt{5}$ **f)** $4\log_{10} 0.001$ **g)** $\log_2\sqrt{\dfrac{1}{512}}$ **h)** $-4\log_8 8^{-4}$

2. State the value of

     a) $\log_b 1$ **b)** $\log_c c$ **c)** $\log_x x^z$ **d)** $b^{\log_b 10}$

3. Solve for x.

     a) $\log_x 125 = 3$ **b)** $\log_{125} 5 = x$ **c)** $\log_4 x = -8$

4. Evaluate each of the following logarithms.

     a) $\log 100$ **b)** $\log 10^6$ **c)** $\log \sqrt{10}$ **d)** $\log 0.01$

5. Evaluate the following logarithms to the nearest tenth.

  a) $\ln 20$ **b)** $\log_e 8$ **c)** $\ln e^2$

6. Convert the following logarithms to the base indicated.

  a) $\log_8 35$ to base 7   **b)** $\log \dfrac{1}{2}$ to base 6   **c)** $\log_3 50$ to base e

7. Evaluate, to the nearest hundredth, using the change of base identity.

  a) $\log_5 17$ **b)** $\log_{0.5} 5.9$ **c)** $\dfrac{1}{\log_5 3}$ **d)** $-2 \log_{12} 6$ **e)** $\log_8 8$

8. Evaluate each expression:

  a) $4^{\log_4 4}$ **b)** $10^{\log_{10} 1000}$

9. Describe how to graph $y = \log_3 x$ using a graphing calculator. Sketch the graph and determine the x-intercept.

10. In each of the following

  i) estimate the value, to the nearest whole number, without using technology and explain the reasoning
  ii) approximate the value to the nearest hundredth using technology

  a) $\log_3 26$ **b)** $\log_2 100$ **c)** $\log_4 60$

Multiple Choice

11. Which of the following has a negative value?

  A. $-\log_4(0.1)$ **B.** $\log_4\left(\dfrac{5}{2}\right)$ **C.** $\log_{\frac{1}{2}}\left(\dfrac{2}{3}\right)$ **D.** $\log_4\left(\dfrac{2}{3}\right)$

12. Without using a calculator, an estimate of the value of $\log_2 30 - \log_3 30$ is

  A. 5.0   **B.** 2.4

  C. 1.8   **D.** −1.9

13. The value of the expression $\log_{\sqrt{2}} 8 + 2\log_9 3$, to the nearest tenth, is _____ .

(Record your answer in the numerical response box from left to right.)

14. Given the equation $\log_7 x = \log_4 60$, the value of x to the nearest whole number is _____ .

(Record your answer in the numerical response box from left to right.)

15. If $\log_x 27 = \log_{12} 3$, the value of x to the nearest whole number is _____ .

(Record your answer in the numerical response box from left to right.)

Answer Key

1. a) 3 **b)** 2 **c)** 2 **d)** $\dfrac{1}{2}$ **e)** $\dfrac{1}{2}$ **f)** –12 **g)** $-\dfrac{9}{2}$ **h)** 16

2. a) 0 **b)** 1 **c)** z **d)** 10 **3. a)** 5 **b)** $\dfrac{1}{3}$ **c)** $4^{-8} = 0.0000153$

4. a) 2 **b)** 6 **c)** $\dfrac{1}{2}$ **d)** –2 **5. a)** 3.0 **b)** 2.1 **c)** 2.0

6. a) $\dfrac{\log_7 35}{\log_7 8}$ **b)** $\dfrac{\log_6\left(\frac{1}{2}\right)}{\log_6 10}$ **c)** $\dfrac{\log_e 50}{\log_e 3}$

7. a) 1.76 **b)** –2.56 **c)** 1.46 **d)** –1.44 **e)** 1.00

8. a) 4 **b)** 1000 **9.** Graph $y = \dfrac{\log x}{\log 3}$, x-intercept is 1

10. a) i) $\log_3 26$ is slightly less than $\log_3 27$ which equals 3. Therefore the estimate for $\log_3 26$ is 3.
ii) 2.97
b) i) $\log_2 100$ is greater than $\log_2 64$ (equal to 6) and smaller than $\log_2 128$ (equal to 7).
Therefore an estimate for $\log_2 100$ is 7.
ii) 6.64
c) i) $\log_4 60$ is slightly less than $\log_4 64$ which equals 3. Therefore the estimate for $\log_4 60$ is 3.
ii) 2.95

11. D **12.** C

13. | 7 | . | 0 | | **14.** | 3 | 1 | 3 | | **15.** | 1 | 7 | 2 | 8 |

Exponential and Logarithmic Functions Lesson #6: Laws of Logarithms

Investigating the Product Law

a) Evaluate the following.

  i) $\log_2 16 + \log_2 8$

  ii) $\log_2 [(16)(8)]$

b) Evaluate the following.

  i) $\log_3 27 + \log_3 3$

  ii) $\log_3 [(27)(3)]$

c) Comment on the answers from a) and b).

Investigating the Quotient Law

a) Evaluate the following.

  i) $\log_2 16 - \log_2 8$

  ii) $\log_2 \dfrac{16}{8}$

b) Evaluate the following.

  i) $\log_3 27 - \log_3 3$

  ii) $\log_3 \dfrac{27}{3}$

c) Comment on the answers from a) and b).

Product and Quotient Laws of Logarithms

The above investigations are examples of the following laws.

$$\log_a (M \times N) = \log_a M + \log_a N \qquad \textbf{The Product Law}$$

$$\log_a \left(\frac{M}{N} \right) = \log_a M - \log_a N \qquad \textbf{The Quotient Law}$$

Class Ex. #1

Evaluate the following using the product law or quotient law.

a) $\log_2 12 - \log_2 3$

b) $\log_6 9 + \log_6 8 - \log_6 2$

Class Ex. #2

a) Use the laws of logarithms to write $\log_x 10 + \log_x 75 - (\log_x 2 + \log_x 3)$ as a single logarithm.

b) Evaluate a) if $x = 5$.

Class Ex. #3

a) Use the laws of logarithms to write $\log_b 2 + \log_b 3 - \log_b 6 - \log_b 8$ as a single logarithm.

b) Evaluate a) if $b = 2$.

Class Ex. #4

The expression $\log_2 x + \log_2 2x - \log_2 x^2 - \log_2 y$ is equivalent to

A. $2 + \log_2 y$

B. $1 + \log_2 y$

C. $2 - \log_2 y$

D. $1 - \log_2 y$

Class Ex. #5

Determine the value of $3 \log_2 p - 3 \log_2 q$ if $\dfrac{p}{q} = 8$.

Complete Assignment Questions #1 - #4

Investigating the Power Law

a) By writing $2 \log x$ as $\log x + \log x$, show that $2 \log x = \log x^2$.

b) Prove that $3 \log_2 a = \log_2 a^3$.

c) Write an expression equivalent to $a \log_b c$.

The Power Law of Logarithms

The above investigation is an example of the power law of logarithms.

$$\log_a M^n = n \log_a M \qquad \textbf{The Power Law}$$

Class Ex. #6

Without using a calculator, evaluate each of the following.

a) $\log_4 16^{12}$ **b)** $\log 10^{21}$

Class Ex. #7

Simplify the following.

a) $\log_6 6^n$ **b)** $6^{\log_6 n}$

Note

Class Ex. #7 is an example of the following logarithmic identities:

$$\log_b b^n = n \qquad \text{and} \qquad b^{\log_b n} = n$$

These identities follow from the fact that the logarithmic and exponential functions are inverses.

Complete Assignment Questions #5 - #14

Assignment

1. Without using a calculator, evaluate each of the following.

a) $\log_4 8 + \log_4 0.5$ **b)** $\log_5 100 - \log_5 4$ **c)** $\log_6 9 + \log_6 8 - \log_6 2$

d) $\log 2 + \log 10 - \log \dfrac{1}{5}$ **e)** $\log 8 - \log \dfrac{2}{5} + \log 5$ **f)** $\log 3 + \log 4 + \log \dfrac{1}{2} + \log \dfrac{1}{6}$

2. In each case, use laws of logarithms to write each expression as a single logarithm and evaluate for the given value of the variable.

a) $\log_x\left(\dfrac{4}{3}\right) + \log_x 768$, for $x = 2$ **b)** $\log_a\left(\dfrac{7}{2}\right) - \log_a 56$, for $a = 4$

c) $\log_b 9 - \log_b\left(\dfrac{1}{3}\right)$, for $b = 3$ **d)** $\log_n 3 + \log_n 2 - \log_n 27 - \log_n 6$, for $n = 3$

3. Use the laws of logarithms to identify which of the following statements are true for logarithms to *every base*. Do not use a calculator.

a) $\log_b 2 + \log_b 3 = \log_b 5$

b) $\log_b 3 + \log_b 4 = \log_b 12$

c) $\log_b 8 = \log_b 4 + \log_b 2$

d) $\log_b 10 + \log_b 10 = \log_b 100$

e) $\log_b 2 \times \log_b 3 = \log_b 6$

f) $\dfrac{\log_b 8}{\log_b 2} = \log_b 4$

g) $\log_b 3^2 + \log_b 3^{-2} = 0$

h) $\log_b \dfrac{5}{3} = \dfrac{\log_b 5}{\log_b 3}$

i) $\log_b \dfrac{1}{8} = -\log_b 8$

4. a) Determine the value of $\log_2 p - \log_2 q$ if $\dfrac{p}{q} = 64$.

b) Determine the value of $4 \log_3 a + 4 \log_3 b$ if $ab = 81$.

c) Determine the value of $5 \log_5 Q - 5 \log_5 R$ if $Q = 5R$.

5. Without using a calculator, evaluate each of the following.

a) $\log_2 8^{15}$

b) $\log_7 49^{20}$

c) $\log_{49} 7^{20}$

d) $\log 10^{15}$

6. Use the laws of logarithms to identify which of the following statements are true for logarithms to *every base*. Do not use a calculator.

a) $\log 5^{-2} = -2 \log 5$

b) $\log 4 = \dfrac{2}{3} \log 8$

c) $\log 125 = \dfrac{3}{2} \log 25$

d) $\dfrac{1}{3} \log 11 = \log \dfrac{11}{3}$

e) $\log 5 = \dfrac{1}{2} \log 10$

f) $\log 2 - \log \sqrt{2} = \log \sqrt{2}$

g) $\log \dfrac{1}{5} - \log 5 = -\log 25$

h) $\dfrac{\log \sqrt{2}}{\log \sqrt{8}} = \dfrac{1}{3}$

7. a) Explain why $\log 81 = 4 \log 3$.

b) Hence simplify: **(i)** $\log 81 - \log 27$ **(ii)** $\dfrac{\log 81}{\log 27}$

8. Determine the greatest of $\dfrac{1}{3} \log x, \ \dfrac{2}{3} \log x, \ \dfrac{4}{3} \log x$ if

a) $x = 2$ **b)** $x = 1$?   **c)** $x = \dfrac{1}{2}$

9. State the value of the following without the use of a calculator.

a) $\log_5 5^7$ **b)** $10^{\log 6}$ **c)** $\ln e^4$ **d)** $\log_c c^t$ **e)** $e^{\ln 7}$

Use the following information to answer the next question.

Three students were asked to find an alternative expression for $\log\left(\dfrac{1}{x}\right)$, $x > 0$.

- Alex gave the answer as $-\log x$.
- Bahman gave the answer as $\log(-x)$.
- Connor gave the answer as $\log\left(x^{-1}\right)$.

Multiple Choice

10. The correct alternative was given by

A. Connor only

B. Alex and Connor only

C. Bahman and Connor only

D. some other combination of the students

11. $\log x + \log(x + 4)$ is equal to

A. $\log(2x + 4)$ **B.** $\log(x^2 + 4x)$

C. $\log(x^2 + 4)$ **D.** $\log(x)\log(x + 4)$

12. $\log(x^2 - 4) - \log(x - 2)$ is equal to

A. $\log(x + 2)$

B. $\log(x^2 - x - 2)$

C. $\log(x - 2)$

D. $\dfrac{\log(x^2 - 4)}{\log(x - 2)}$

13. $(\log 2x)^2$ is equivalent to

A. $2 \log 2x$

B. $\log 4x^2$

C. $2 \log 4x$

D. $(\log 2)^2 + 2 \log 2 \log x + (\log x)^2$

14. The value of $\dfrac{3^{\log_2 4\sqrt{5}}}{3^{\log_2 \sqrt{5}}}$ to the nearest tenth is _____ .

(Record your answer in the numerical response box from left to right.)

Answer Key

1. **a)** 1   **b)** 2   **c)** 2   **d)** 2   **e)** 2   **f)** 0

2. **a)** $\log_x 1024, 10$ **b)** $\log_a\left(\frac{1}{16}\right), -2$ **c)** $\log_b 27, 3$ **d)** $\log_n\left(\frac{1}{27}\right), -3$

3. **a)** F   **b)** T   **c)** T   **d)** T   **e)** F   **f)** F   **g)** T   **h)** F   **i)** T

4. **a)** 6   **b)** 16   **c)** 5

5. **a)** 45   **b)** 40   **c)** 10   **d)** 15

6. **a)** T   **b)** T   **c)** T   **d)** F   **e)** F   **f)** T   **g)** T   **h)** T

7. **a)** $\log 81 = \log 3^4 = 4 \log 3$ **b)** **(i)** $\log 3$ **(ii)** $\dfrac{4}{3}$

8. **a)** $\dfrac{4}{3} \log x$ **b)** none because each of these equals zero.   **c)** $\dfrac{1}{3} \log x$

9. **a)** 7   **b)** 6   **c)** 4   **d)** t **e)** 7

10. B   **11.** B   **12.** A   **13.** D   **14.**

9	.	0	

Exponential and Logarithmic Functions Lesson #7:
Combining the Laws of Logarithms

Review

In the previous lesson we learned three laws of logarithms.

The Product Law $\qquad \log_a(M \times N) = \log_a M + \log_a N$

The Quotient Law $\qquad \log_a\left(\dfrac{M}{N}\right) = \log_a M - \log_a N$

The Power Law $\qquad \log_a M^n = n \log_a M$

In this lesson we will study examples which combine the Power Law with the Product and Quotient Laws.

Class Ex. #1

Recall Class Ex. #5 from Lesson 6 shown below.

"Determine the value of $3 \log_2 p - 3 \log_2 q$ if $\dfrac{p}{q} = 8$."

Show how this problem can be solved using a combination of the Laws of Logarithms without removing a common factor.

Class Ex. #2

a) Use laws of logarithms to write $\dfrac{1}{2} \log_a 16 - \dfrac{1}{3} \log_a 8$ as a single logarithm.

b) Evaluate a) if $a = 32$.

Class Ex. #3 Evaluate the following without the use of a calculator.

a) $3 \log x - \log x^3$

b) $2 \log 5 + 2 \log 2$

c) $\log_3 \dfrac{27^3}{81^4}$

Class Ex. #4 If $\log_2 x = a$, determine an expression for $\log_2 16x^2$.

Class Ex. #5 Write the following expression as a single logarithm.

$$\log B + \log D - 5 \log E - \log A^2 + \frac{1}{2} \log A$$

Complete Assignment Questions #1 - #11

Assignment

1. Write each expression as a single logarithm:

   a) $\log x - 3 \log y - 2 \log z$

   b) $\frac{1}{3} \log_a p + 3 \log_a q - 4 \log_a p$

2. Simplify the following without using a calculator.

   a) $\log 2 + 2 \log 3 - \log 18$

   b) $2 \log_4 2 - 2 \log_4 4 - \log_4 \frac{1}{4}$

3. Use the laws of logarithms to simplify and evaluate the following expressions.

   a) $\log_2 \sqrt{6} - \frac{1}{2} \log_2 3$

   b) $\frac{1}{2} \log_{10} 10 + 3 \log_{10} \sqrt{10}$

4. Simplify the following:

a) $\log x^4 - 3 \log x + \log \dfrac{1}{x}$

b) $\log x^{\frac{1}{2}} + \log y^{\frac{1}{2}} - \dfrac{1}{2} \log xy$

c) $\log_a a^{2x+1} - \log_a a^{x-7}$

d) $\log_2 a^{x+5} + 2 \log_2 a^{x-3}$

5. Show that $\log_a y^{2x-3} + \log_a y^{5x-2} - \log_a y^{x-5} - 2 \log_a y^{3x+1}$ can be written as $\log_a\left(\dfrac{1}{y^2}\right)$.

6. Determine the value of the following.

   a) $(5^{\log_5 2})(5^{\log_5 3})$

   b) $\dfrac{\left(\sqrt{2}^{\ \log_6 27}\right)\left(\sqrt{2}^{\ \log_6 16}\right)}{\sqrt{2}^{\ \log_6 12}}$

Multiple Choice

7. The expression $3\log_x 4 + \log_x 8 - \dfrac{1}{4}\log_x 16$, where $x > 0$, is equal to

   A. $\log_x 384$

   B. $\dfrac{3}{4}\log_x 512$

   C. $\log_x 256$

   D. $\dfrac{1}{4}\log_x\left(\dfrac{1}{2}\right)$

8. $\log_p(p^6 q^2) - \log_p(p^2 q^2)$ is equivalent to

   A. 3

   B. 4

   C. $4p$

   D. p^4

9. If $\log_3 A = t$, then $\log_3 27A^3 =$

   A. $3 + 3t$

   B. $3 + t^3$

   C. $9t^2$

   D. $3t^3$

10. If $\log_3 x^2 = 2$ and $2 \log_k \sqrt{x} = \dfrac{1}{3}$, then the value of k is _____ .

(Record your answer in the numerical response box from left to right.)

11. If $\log_3 x^2 = 4$, $\log_2 y^3 = 6$, and $\log_b x + \log_b y = \dfrac{1}{2}$, where $x, y > 0$,

then the value of b is _____ .

(Record your answer in the numerical response box from left to right.)

Answer Key

1. a) $\log\left(\dfrac{x}{y^3 z^2}\right)$ **b)** $\log_a\left(\dfrac{q^3}{p^{\frac{11}{3}}}\right)$ **2. a)** 0   **b)** 0   **3. a)** $\dfrac{1}{2}$ **b)** 2

4. a) 0   **b)** 0   **c)** $x + 8$ **d)** $\log_2 a^{3x-1}$ or $(3x-1)\log_2 a$

6. a) 6   **b)** 2   **7.** C   **8.** B   **9.** A

10. | 2 | 7 | | | **11.** | 1 | 2 | 9 | 6 |

Exponential and Logarithmic Functions Lesson #8: Graphing Logarithmic Functions

Exploring the Value of b in $y = \log_b x$

We will investigate how changing the value of b affects the graph of $y = \log_b x$.
Notice that every graph of this form must pass through the point $(1, 0)$ because $\log_b 1 = 0$.

Part 1 The graph of $y = \log_3 x$ is shown. The graph passes through the point $(3, 1)$
because $\log_3 3 = 1$.

a) In each of the following, complete the statement and sketch the graph on the grid.
Use a graphing calculator with window format $x\text{:}[-1, 11, 1]$ $y\text{:}[-4, 4, 1]$.

i) $y = \log_{10} x$ passes
through (, 1).

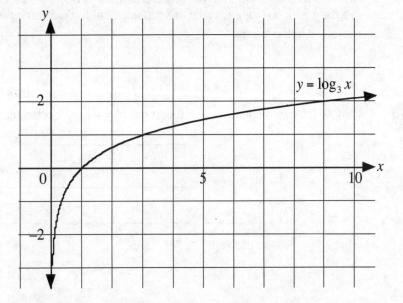

ii) $y = \log_{\frac{1}{3}} x$ passes
through (, 1).

iii) $y = \log_{\frac{1}{10}} x$ passes
through (, 1).

b) Without using a graphing calculator, make a sketch of the graphs of the following
and verify with a graphing calculator.

   i) $y = \log_5 x$ **ii)** $y = \log_{\frac{1}{5}} x$

c) Complete the table.

Function	Domain	Range	x-int	y-int	Asymptote	x-value when $y = 1$
$y = \log_3 x$	X > 0	y ∈ R	1	NONE	X = 0	
$y = \log_{10} x$	X > 0	y ∈ R	1	NONE	X = 0	
$y = \log_{\frac{1}{3}} x$	X > 0	y ∈ R	1	NONE	X = 0	
$y = \log_{\frac{1}{10}} x$	X > 0	y ∈ R	1	NONE	X = 0	
$y = \log_b x$						

d) How do the graphs of $y = \log_3 x$ and $\log_{\frac{1}{3}} x$ compare with each other?

e) How do the graphs of $y = \log_{10} x$ and $\log_{\frac{1}{10}} x$ compare with each other?

f) Complete the following statement.

"The graph of $y = \log_{\frac{1}{b}} x$ is _____ of the graph of $y = \log_b x$."

g) In the transformation unit, the replacement for reflection in the x-axis is $y \rightarrow -y$. Starting with $y = \log_b x$, make this replacement to determine the equation of the graph reflected in the x-axis.

 Note   We now have two equations for the graph of $y = \log_b x$ reflected in the x-axis. Hence

$$\log_{\frac{1}{b}} x = - \log_b x$$

Class Ex. #1   **a)** If $\log_4 x = 8$, state the value of $\log_{\frac{1}{4}} x$.

b) Prove the result in a) by converting to exponential form.

Part 2   The partial graphs of $y = \log_2 x$, $y = \log_4 x$, and $y = \log_8 x$ are shown.

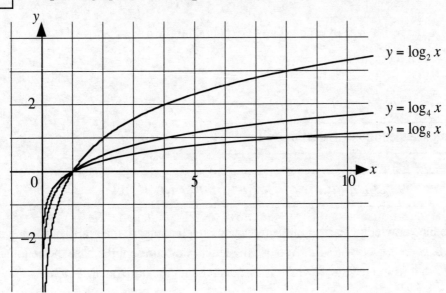

a) Complete the following statements.   **i)** $y = \log_2 x$ passes through $(8,\ \ )$.

ii) $y = \log_4 x$ passes through $(8,\ \ )$.   **iii)** $y = \log_8 x$ passes through $(8,\ \ )$.

b) The graph of $y = \log_4 x$ is a vertical stretch of the graph of $y = \log_2 x$ about the x-axis. State the stretch factor and complete the statement $\log_4 x =$ ___$\log_2 x$.

c) The graph of $y = \log_8 x$ is a vertical stretch of the graph of $y = \log_2 x$ about the x-axis. State the stretch factor and complete the statement $\log_8 x =$ ___$\log_2 x$.

d) i) Use the results above to determine the transformation which would map the graph of $y = \log_2 x$ to the graph of $y = \log_{64} x$.

ii) Complete the statement $\log_{64} x =$ ___$\log_2 x$.

 The above is an example of the general rule.

> The transformation which maps $y = \log_b x$ to $y = \log_{b^n} x$ is a vertical stretch
> about the x-axis by a factor of $\dfrac{1}{n}$, so $\log_{b^n} x = \dfrac{1}{n}\log_b x$

Class Ex. #2   **a)** Describe the transformation which would map the graph of
    i) $y = \log_3 x$ to the graph of $y = \log_{81} x$ **ii)** $y = \log_{16} x$ to the graph of $y = \log_4 x$

b) Complete the statements: **i)** $\log_{81} x =$ ___$\log_3 x$ **ii)** $\log_4 x =$ ___$\log_{16} x$

Class Ex. #3

a) If $\log_5 x = 6$, state the value of $\log_{125} x$.

b) Prove the result in a) by converting to exponential form.

Complete Assignment Questions #1 - #5

Further Transformations of Logarithmic Functions

We use the knowledge learned in *Transformations* to compare the graph of $y = \log_c x$ to the graph of $y = a \log_c b(x - h) + k$. We use the letter c to represent the base of the logarithm to distinguish it from the letter b which is associated with the horizontal stretch.

Class Ex. #4

The graph of $y = \log_3 x$ is shown.

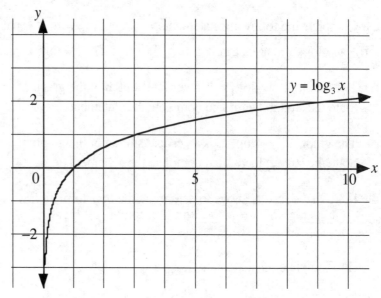

a) Write the transformation associated with each of the following and sketch the graph on the grid.

   i) $y = 2 \log_3 x$ **ii)** $y = \log_3(x - 2)$ **iii)** $y = \log_3 x - 2$

b) Do any of the above transformations result in a change in the original domain or range?

c) State the equation of the asymptote for each part of a).

> ### *Investigating the Graphs of $y = \log x^n$ and $y = n \log x$*

One of the laws of logarithms states that $\log x^n = n \log x$.

However, are the graphs of $y = \log x^n$ and $y = n \log x$ identical?

Investigate by considering odd and even values for n.

> **Complete Assignment Questions #6 - #17**

Assignment

1. a) Complete the following table.

Function	Domain	Range	Asymptote
$f(x) = \log_4 x$			
$f(x) = \log_{\frac{1}{4}} x$			

b) Describe how the graph of $y = \log_4 x$ is related to the graph of $y = \log_{\frac{1}{4}} x$.

c) Hence write $y = \log_{\frac{1}{4}} x$ in the form $y = a \log_4 x$.

2. a) Describe the transformation which maps the graph of $\log_9 x$ to the graph of

   i) $\log_{\frac{1}{9}} x$

   ii) $\log_{81} x$

   iii) $\log_3 x$

b) Complete the statements

   i) $\log_{\frac{1}{9}} x$ = ___$\log_9 x$ **ii)** $\log_{81} x$ = ___$\log_9 x$ **iii)** $\log_3 x$ = ___$\log_9 x$

3. a) Describe the transformation which maps the graph of $\log_8 x$ to the graph of

   i) $\log_2 x$

   ii) $\log_{64} x$

   iii) $\log_{\frac{1}{8}} x$

b) Complete the statements

   i) $\log_2 x$ = ___$\log_8 x$ **ii)** $\log_{64} x$ = ___$\log_8 x$ **iii)** $\log_{\frac{1}{8}} x$ = ___$\log_8 x$

4. a) If $\log_6 x = 6$, state the values of $\log_{\frac{1}{6}} x$, $\log_{36} x$, and $\log_{\sqrt{6}} x$.

b) Prove the results in a) by converting to exponential form.

Use the following information to answer the next question.

The equations of six logarithmic functions are given below.

$$y = \log_b x , \quad y = -\log_b x , \quad y = \log_{\frac{1}{b}} x , \quad y = -\log_{\frac{1}{b}} x , \quad y = \log_b\!\left(\frac{1}{x}\right) , \quad y = \log_{\frac{1}{b}}\!\left(\frac{1}{x}\right)$$

When graphed, the six functions can be arranged into two groups of three identical graphs.

5. Which functions are in each group?

6. Describe how the graphs of the following functions relate to the graph of $y = \log x$.

    a) $y = 5 \log x - 2$

    b) $\frac{1}{7}y = \log 2(x - 3)$

    c) $y = \log \frac{1}{3}x + 1$

    d) $y = \log(3x + 1)$

7. Complete the following table .

Function	Domain	Range	Asymptote
$f(x) = \log x$			
$f(x) = 5 \log x + 2$			
$f(x) = 5 \log (x + 2)$			
$f(x) = -\log x$			
$f(x) = \log (-x)$			
$f(x) = 2 \log 3(x - 6) - 1$			
$f(x) = \log(3x - 6)$			

8. Consider the graph of the function $f(x) = a \log_c b(x - h) + k$, with $a, b > 0$
    Which of the parameters a, b, c, h, k, affect the
    a) domain   **b)** range   **c)** asymptote

9. Consider the graph of the function $f(x) = a \log_c b(x - h) + k$, with $a, b > 0$.

   a) If a is changed to a negative value, does this affect the domain, range, or asymptote?

   b) If b is changed to a negative value, does this affect the domain, range, or asymptote?

Use the following information to answer the next question.

Two students, Andy and Holly, were given the following question on an exam.

" A transformation is applied to the graph of $y = \log x$ and a sketch of both graphs is shown. Write the equation of the graph which represents the transformed image."

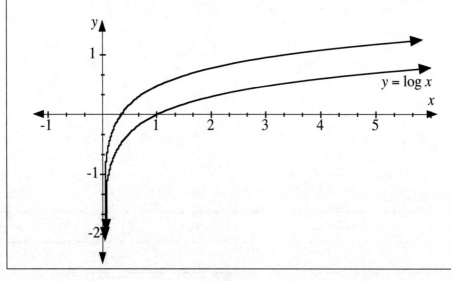

10. **a)** Andy correctly answered the question with the equation of the transformed image as $y = \log 3x$. Explain from the given sketch how Andy arrived at his solution.

   b) Holly also correctly answered the question, but with an equation in the form $y = \log x + k$. Find the value of k.

11. Explain why $2\log_b x = \log_b x^2$, but the graphs of $y = 2\log_b x$ and $y = \log_b x^2$ are not identical.

12. The *x*-intercept of the graph of the function $f(x) = \log_a(x - d)$ is

    A. d **B.** $-d$

    C. $1 + d$ **D.** $1 - d$

13. The graph of $y = \log x$ is transformed to the graph of $y = \log(2x + 5)$ by a horizontal stretch about the *y*-axis by a factor of p followed by a horizontal translation of q units left. The value of $p + q$ is

    A. 3

    B. 4.5

    C. 5.5

    D. 7

14. If $\log_6 x = k \log_{216} x$, then the value of k is

    A. 3   **B.** -3

    C. $\dfrac{1}{3}$ **D.** 36

15. An equation of the asymptote of $y = 3 \log_4(x + 2) - 6$ is

    A. $x = -6$ **B.** $y = -6$

    C. $x = -2$ **D.** $y = -2$

16. If the graph of $y = \log_7 x$ is reflected in the *x*-axis, the equation of the image can be written in the form $y = \log_c x$. The value of c, to the nearest hundredth, is _____ .

(Record your answer in the numerical response box from left to right.)

17. The graph of $y = \log_5 x$ is translated 2 units down. A student writes the equation of the transformed image in the form $y = \log_5 kx$.
The value of k, to the nearest hundredth, is _____ .

(Record your answer in the numerical response box from left to right.)

Answer Key

Function	Domain	Range	Asymptote
$f(x) = \log_4 x$	$\{x \mid x > 0, x \in R\}$	$y \in R$	$x = 0$
$f(x) = \log_{\frac{1}{4}} x$	$\{x \mid x > 0, x \in R\}$	$y \in R$	$x = 0$

1. a) See the table at the side.
   b) reflection in the x-axis
   c) $y = -\log_4 x$

2. a) i) reflection in the x-axis
   ii) vertical stretch by a factor of $\frac{1}{2}$ about the x-axis
   iii) vertical stretch by a factor of 2 about the x-axis

   b) i) -1
   ii) $\frac{1}{2}$
   iii) 2

3. a) i) vertical stretch by a factor of 3 about the x-axis
   ii) vertical stretch by a factor of $\frac{1}{2}$ about the x-axis
   iii) reflection in the x-axis

   b) i) 3
   ii) $\frac{1}{2}$
   iii) -1

4. a) $-6, 3, 12$

5. • $y = \log_b x$, $y = -\log_{\frac{1}{b}} x$, $y = \log_{\frac{1}{b}}\left(\frac{1}{x}\right)$ are in one group

   • $y = -\log_b x$, $y = \log_{\frac{1}{b}} x$, $y = \log_b\left(\frac{1}{x}\right)$ are in another group

6. a) vertical stretch about the x-axis by a factor of 5, then a vertical translation 2 units down
   b) vertical stretch about the x-axis by a factor of 7 and horizontal stretch about the y-axis by a factor of $\frac{1}{2}$, then a horizontal translation 3 units right
   c) horizontal stretch by a factor of 3 about the y-axis and a vertical translation 1 unit up
   d) horizontal stretch by a factor of $\frac{1}{3}$ about the y-axis, then a horizontal translation $\frac{1}{3}$ unit left

7. See the table at the side.

Function	Domain	Range	Asymptote
$f(x) = \log x$	$\{x \mid x > 0, x \in R\}$	$y \in R$	$x = 0$
$f(x) = 5 \log x + 2$	$\{x \mid x > 0, x \in R\}$	$y \in R$	$x = 0$
$f(x) = 5 \log (x + 2)$	$\{x \mid x > -2, x \in R\}$	$y \in R$	$x = -2$
$f(x) = -\log x$	$\{x \mid x > 0, x \in R\}$	$y \in R$	$x = 0$
$f(x) = \log (-x)$	$\{x \mid x < 0, x \in R\}$	$y \in R$	$x = 0$
$f(x) = 2 \log 3(x - 6) - 1$	$\{x \mid x > 6, x \in R\}$	$y \in R$	$x = 6$
$f(x) = \log(3x - 6)$	$\{x \mid x > 2, x \in R\}$	$y \in R$	$x = 2$

8. a) h
   b) none
   c) h

9. a) no
   b) domain,
      and asymptote if $h \neq 0$

10. a) Since the x-intercept of the image is $\frac{1}{3}$ of the original intercept, there is a horizontal stretch by a factor of $\frac{1}{3}$ about the y-axis; therefore Andy is correct by writing $y = \log 3x$.
   b) $k = \log 3$

11. $2\log_b x = \log_b x^2$ because of the product law of logarithms.
   $y = 2\log_b x$ has a domain of $x > 0, x \in R$ and $y = \log_b x^2$ has a domain of $x \neq 0, x \in R$.
   Since the domains are different, the graphs are not identical.

12. C   **13.** A   **14.** A   **15.** C   **16.** | 0 | . | 1 | 4 | **17.** | 0 | . | 0 | 4 |

Exponential and Logarithmic Functions Lesson #9: Practice Test

1. The graph that best represents $y = ab^x$, where $a < 0$ and $b > 1$, is

A.
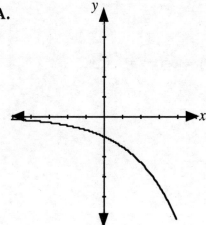

B.
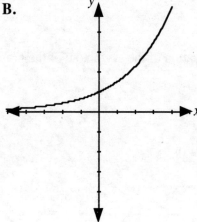

C.
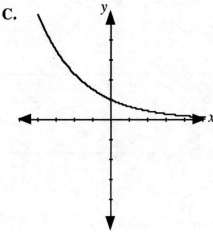

D.
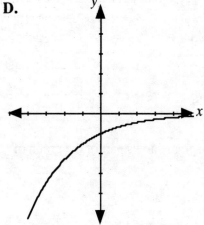

2. The exact value of $\log_4 16$ is

A. 0.5

B. 2

C. 4

D. none of A, B, or C

3.   The domain of the function $g(x) = \log_3(x + 4) + 2$ is

    A. $x > 0, x \in R$

    B. $x > 2, x \in R$

    C. $x > -4, x \in R$

    D. $x \in R$

4.   The equation of the asymptote of the graph of $y = \log(x - 5) + 6$ is

    A. $x = 6$

    B. $x = 5$

    C. $x = 0$

    D. $x = -5$

5.   The approximate value of $\log_5 31$ is

    A.   0.2

    B.   2.1

    C.   6.1

    D.   26

 1.   The diagram shows part of the graph of $y = \log_b(x - a)$ where $a, b \in N$.

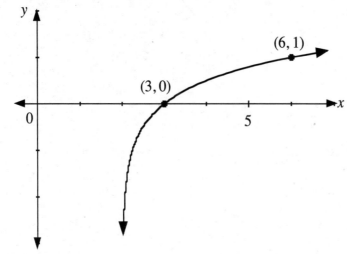

The value of $a + 3b$ is _____ .

(Record your answer in the numerical response box from left to right.)

A graphing calculator may be used for the remainder of the test.

6.   Solve for x. $(n^3)^{3x-1} = \left(\sqrt{n}\right)^{4x+6}$

   A. $\dfrac{9}{7}$

   B. 1

   C. $\dfrac{6}{7}$

   D. $-\dfrac{5}{7}$

    2.   If $\dfrac{p}{q} = 25$, then the value of $\log_6 p - \log_6 q$, to the nearest tenth, is

   (Record your answer in the numerical response box from left to right.)

7.   At which of these points is the relation $\log_3(x+1) + \log_3(x-y) = \log_3 6$ **not** defined?

   A. $(0,-6)$

   B. $(2,0)$

   C. $(5,4)$

   D. $(-4,-2)$

8.   The range of the function $f(x) = 3^{x+c} - d$ is

   A. $y > c$

   B. $y > -d$

   C. $y > d$

   D. $y > 0$

9. If $\log_6 y = t$, the value of $\log_6 36y$ is

   A. $36t$

   B. $t + 36$

   C. $2t$

   D. $t + 2$

10. Expressed as a single logarithm, $\log P - 4 \log Q - \log R$ is

   A. $\log \dfrac{P}{Q^4 R}$ **B.** $\log \dfrac{PR}{4Q}$

   C. $\log \dfrac{P}{4QR}$ **D.** $\log \dfrac{PR}{Q^4}$

11. If $\log_6 p = \log_6 q + r$, where $p > 0$ and $q > 0$, then q is equal to

   A. $\dfrac{p}{r^6}$

   B. $\dfrac{6^3}{p}$

   C. $\dfrac{p}{6^r}$

   D. $p - r$

12. If $3^{\log_2 a + \log_2 6} = \dfrac{1}{81}$, then a is equal to

   A. -10

   B. $\dfrac{1}{486}$

   C. $\dfrac{1}{96}$

   D. $\dfrac{8}{3}$

3.   If $\log_b p = 4$ and $\log_b q = 2$, then $\log_b (pq^3)$ is equal to

(Record your answer in the numerical response box from left to right.)

13.   The domain of the function $g(x) = 2 + \log_x(10 - x)$ is

    A. $x < 10, x \neq 1, x \in R$

    B. $x < 12, x \neq 1, x \in R$

    C. $0 < x < 10, x \neq 1, x \in R$

    D. $2 < x < 12, x \neq 1, x \in R$

14.   If $\log_a\left(\dfrac{1}{16}\right) = -\dfrac{1}{4}$, then a is equal to

    A.   2   **B.** $\dfrac{1}{2}$

    C. $\dfrac{1}{65\,536}$ **D.**   65 536

 4.   To the nearest hundredth, the y-intercept, of the graph of $y = \log_5(x + 4)$ is _____ .

(Record your answer in the numerical response box from left to right.)

15.   If $\log_{16} x = A$, then $\log_2 x =$

    A. $4A$ **B.** $\dfrac{1}{4}A$

    C. $8A$ **D.** $\dfrac{1}{8}A$

16. If $\dfrac{2}{3}\log_n x = 5$, then x^2 is equal to

   A. n^{15}

   B. 15^n

   C. $n^{\frac{20}{3}}$

   D. $n^{\frac{5}{3}}$

17. $12\log_{64} x - 6\log_{16} x$ is equivalent to

   A. $\log_2 x$

   B. $\log_4 x$

   C. $\log_{16} x$

   D. $\log_{64} x$

18. In the diagram, P is on the partial graph of $y = \log x$.

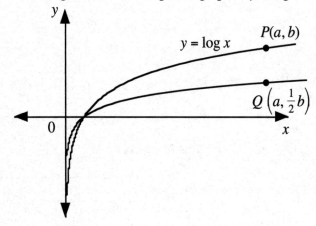

The point Q is on the partial graph of

   A. $y = \log x^{\frac{1}{2}}$

   B. $y = (\log x)^{\frac{1}{2}}$

   C. $y = \log \dfrac{1}{2}x$

   D. $y = \log x^2$

5.   In the equation $\log_x 64 = \dfrac{2}{3}$, the value of x, to the nearest whole number, is _____.

(Record your answer in the numerical response box from left to right.)

19.   When solving the equation $\log_x(2x + 3) + \log_x(x - 2) = 2$, an equation that could arise is

   A. $2x^2 - x - 6 = 0$

   B. $2x^2 - x - 8 = 0$

   C. $x^2 + x - 6 = 0$

   D. $x^2 - x - 6 = 0$

20.   The expression $\log_{\frac{1}{2}} x$ is equivalent to which one or more of the following expressions?

   I. $\log_2\left(\dfrac{1}{x}\right)$ **II.** $-\log_2 x$

   A.   **I** only

   B.   **II** only

   C.   **I** and **II**

   D.   neither **I** nor **II**

6.   If $\log_5 x = -0.02$, then the exact value of $\log_{\frac{1}{5}} x$ is equal to _____.

(Record your answer in the numerical response box from left to right.)

Written Response

Students are investigating logarithmic functions with base 2.

- The graph of $y = 4 \log_2 x$ is shown.

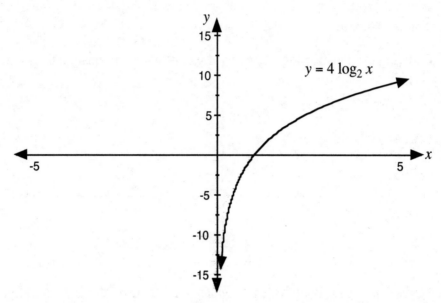

Complete the table which describes some of the features of the graph of $y = 4 \log_2 x$.

Domain	
Range	
***x*-intercept**	
***y*-intercept**	

- Determine, in the form $y = \ldots$, the equation of the inverse of the graph of $y = 4 \log_2 x$.

• A student identifies the following law of logarithms on the formula sheet:

$$\log_a M^n = n \log_a M.$$

The student assumes that, because of this law, the graph of $y = \log_2 x^4$ will be identical to the graph of $y = 4 \log_2 x$.

Sketch a partial graph of $y = \log_2 x^4$ on the grid below to show that the student's assumption is **not** correct.

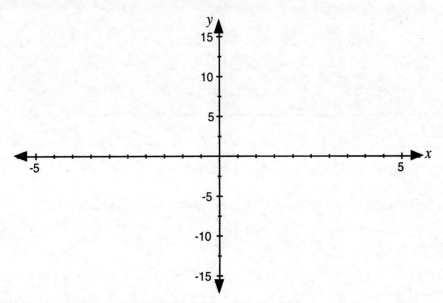

Explain why the difference occurs.

• If $\log_2 x = P$, write expressions for $\log_{\frac{1}{2}} x$, $\log_2 x^2$, and $\log_8 x$.

Answer Key

Multiple Choice

1. A   2. B   3. C   4. B   5. B   6. C   7. D   8. B

9. D   10. A   11. C   12. C   13. C   14. D   15. A   16. A

17. B   18. A   19. D   20. C

Numerical Response

1. | 1 | 4 | | |

2. | 1 | . | 8 | |

3. | 1 | 0 | |

4. | 0 | . | 8 | 6 |

5. | 5 | 1 | 2 | |

6. | 0 | . | 0 | 2 |

Written Response

- Domain: $\{x \mid x > 0, x \in R\}$, Range: $\{y \mid y \in R\}$, x-intercept = 1, no y-intercept

- $y = 2^{\frac{x}{4}}$

- The domain of $y = 4 \log x$ is $x > 0$. The domain of $y = \log x^4$ is $x \neq 0$.

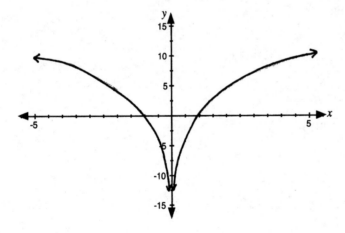

- $-P, \ 2P, \ \dfrac{1}{3}P$

Applications of Exponential and Logarithmic Functions
Lesson #1: Solving Exponential Equations

Overview

In this unit, we will learn how to solve exponential and logarithmic equations and apply this to real life problems involving exponential growth and decay, including compound interest, loans, investments, half-life, etc. We will also solve problems involving logarithmic scales, such as the Richter scale, the pH scale, and the Bell scale.

Review | Solving Exponential Equations with a Common Base

In the last unit we solved exponential equations involving a common base.

Solve the following exponential equations by converting to a common base.

a) $4^x = 2^{x+3}$

b) $27^{2x-1} = 9(3)^{2x-1}$

Solving Exponential Equations without using a Common Base

Consider the exponential equation $2^x = 50$.

a) Explain why the solution cannot be determined by the above method.

b) i) Determine, by considering powers of 2, the two integers between which the solution must lie.

ii) Estimate the solution to the nearest tenth.

c) The equation $2^x = 50$ can be solved by taking the logarithm (base 10) of each side and solving the resulting equation.

Complete the work started below and give
i) the exact solution and, **ii)** an approximation to the nearest tenth.

$$2^x = 50$$

$$\log 2^x = \log 50$$

$$x \log 2 = \log 50$$

Class Ex. #1

Solve the following equations, expressing the solution

i) as an exact value in the form $\dfrac{\log M}{\log N}$ ii) to three decimal places

a) $4^x = 12$

b) $8^x + 4 = 40$

c) $6^{3x} = 3^{2x-1}$

d) $2(3)^{x-2} = 7^x$

Class Ex. #2

In simple cases, such as $2^x = 50$ or $4^x = 12$, the equation can also be solved by converting to logarithmic form. For example $2^x = 50 \Rightarrow x = \log_2 50 = \dfrac{\log 50}{\log 2}$.

Solve $4^x = 12$ by converting to logarithmic form.

Class Ex. #3

According to Statistics Canada, in the 21st century, Canada's population has been growing at an average annual rate of 1.0%. The exponential equation $P = P_o(1.01)^n$ can be used to predict the population, P, n years after a known population P_o.
(http://www.statcan.gc.ca/pub/91-003-x/2007001/4129907-eng.htm)

If the Canadian population at the beginning of 2001 was approximately 30 million, estimate in which year the Canadian population will reach 50 million assuming the same average annual rate of growth.

Note • We can take the logarithm of each side of any exponential equation to any base, but it is simpler to use a calculator base.

• If the base of the exponential equation is e, it is simpler to use natural logarithms (ln) to solve the exponential equation as in the example below.

Class Ex. #4

Solve the equation $7e^{-2x} + 9 = 12$ expressing the solution
i) as an exact value   **ii)** to three decimal places

Complete Assignment Questions #1 - #8

Solving Exponential Equations Using a Graphing Calculator

In previous math courses we learned two methods to solve equations by graphing calculator.
Intersect Method:
    Insert the left side of the equation into Y_1. Insert the right side of the equation into Y_2.
    Graph Y_1 and Y_2 and determine the x-coordinate of the point(s) of intersection using
    the intersect feature of the calculator.

Zero Method
    Rearrange the original equation so that all terms are on the left hand side and zero is
    on the right side. Insert the rearranged left side into Y_1, graph and determine the
    x-intercept(s) of the graph using the zero feature of the calculator.

Class Ex. #5

Consider the equation $4^x = 7$.

a) Use the intersection method to solve the equation to the nearest tenth. Show this method on the grid.

b) Use the zero method to solve the equation to the nearest tenth. Show this method on the grid.

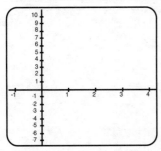

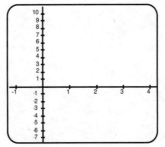

c) Solve the equation algebraically.

Complete Assignment Questions #9 - #15

Assignment

1. Solve the following equations, expressing the solution

    i) as an exact value in the form $\dfrac{\log M}{\log N}$ ii) to two decimal places

    a) $4^x = 60$ **b)** $3^x = 90$ **c)** $7^{x+2} + 3 = 444$

2. Show that the solution to the equation $5^{x-2} = 4^{x+1}$ can be written as $\dfrac{2}{\log 1.25}$.

3. Determine the exact value of x in the form $\dfrac{\log M}{\log N}$.

    a) $5^{x-3} = 40$ **b)** $0.5^{x+2} = 6^{x-1}$

    c) $2^{2x} = 6^{x-3}$

4. Algebraically determine, to the nearest hundredth, the solution to the equation $3(2^x) = 6^{x-2}$.

5. A sports car priced at \$60 000 depreciates at a rate of 14% per year. The value after n years is given by $A = 60\,000(0.86)^n$ where A is the amount after depreciation. How long, to the nearest year, will it take for the value of the car to depreciate to \$18 000?

6. The number, N, of throat swab bacteria being grown in a culture after t hours, is given by the formula $N = N_0(10^{0.43t})$, where N_0 is the original number of bacteria. If there are initially 500 bacteria in the culture, determine how long it would take, to the nearest tenth of an hour, for the number of bacteria to grow to 1 million.

7. Solve the following equations expressing the solution
   i) as an exact value   **ii)** to three decimal places
   a) $e^x = 5$ **b)** $6 + 0.5e^{2x} = 13$ **c)** $5e^{-x} - 4 = 6$

8. Over the last ten years, the amount of money, M (in billions of dollars), spent in North America by car dealerships advertising their product can be modelled by the equation $M = 0.15e^{0.3t} + 0.78$, where $t = 0$ represents the year 2000.
   In what year was about 3 billion dollars spent by car dealerships on advertising?

9. Describe **two** graphing methods to determine the value of x if $5^x = 30$. State an appropriate window. Determine the solution graphically to the nearest hundredth and verify algebraically.

10. Use a graphing calculator to solve each equation to the nearest hundredth.

    a) $4^{x + 2} = 7^{2x + 5}$

    b) $2^{x - 5} + 10 = 9^{x - 3} - 15$

11. If $21 = 6^{3x}$, then the value of x is

    A. $\dfrac{\log 21}{\log 216}$

    B. $\dfrac{\log 21}{3}$

    C. $\dfrac{\log 3}{3}$

    D. $\dfrac{\log 21}{\log \sqrt[3]{6}}$

Numerical
Response **12.** A current, I_0 amperes, falls to I amperes after t seconds according to the formula $I = I_0 e^{-kt}$. The value of the constant, k, to the nearest whole number, if a current of 25 amperes falls to 2.5 amperes in 0.01 seconds is _____ .

(Record your answer in the numerical response box from left to right.)

13. The price of a famous brand name camera lens can be found by the equation $P = 14(1.1)^c$, where c is the circumference of the lens in centimetres and P is the price of the lens in dollars. The diameter, to the nearest tenth of a centimetre, of a camera lens which costs \$2500 is _____ .

(Record your answer in the numerical response box from left to right.)

14. Kyle determined the exact solution to the exponential equation $5^{2-x} = 2$. He wrote the answer as the quotient of two logarithms in the form $\dfrac{\log M}{\log 5}$. The value of M is _____ .

(Record your answer in the numerical response box from left to right.)

15. The solution to the equation $4^{x-3} = 5(2)^{x+1}$ can be written as $\dfrac{\log P}{\log 2}$, where P is a whole number. The value of P is _____ .

(Record your answer in the numerical response box from left to right.)

Answer Key

1. a) i) $\dfrac{\log 60}{\log 4}$ **ii)** 2.95 **b) i)** $\dfrac{\log 90}{\log 3}$ **ii)** 4.10 **c) i)** $\dfrac{\log 9}{\log 7}$ **ii)** 1.13

3. a) $\dfrac{\log 5000}{\log 5}$ **b)** $\dfrac{\log 1.5}{\log 12}$ **c)** $\dfrac{\log 216}{\log 1.5}$

4. 4.26 **5.** 8 years **6.** 7.7 hours

7. a) i) $\ln 5$ **ii)** 1.609 **b) i)** $\frac{1}{2} \ln 14$ or $\ln\sqrt{14}$ **ii)** 1.320 **c) i)** $-\ln 2$ or $\ln 0.5$ **ii)** -0.693

8. 2009

9. Intersect Method: Insert 5^x into Y_1. Insert the 13 into Y_2. Graph Y_1 and Y_2 and determine the x-coordinate of the point of intersection by using the intersect feature of a graphing calculator.
x:$[-4, 4, 1]$ y:$[-10, 40, 10]$
Zero Method: Rearrange the original equation into $5^x - 30 = 0$. Insert $5^x - 30$ into Y_1, graph and determine the x-intercept(s) of the graph using the zero feature of a graphing calculator.
x:$[-4, 4, 1]$ y:$[-30, 20, 10]$
The solution is $x = 2.11$.

10. a) -2.78 **b)** 4.48   **11.** A

12.
2	3	0	

13.
1	7	.	3

14.
1	2	.	5

15.
6	4	0	

Applications of Exponential and Logarithmic Functions
Lesson #2: Applications in Finance

Investing Money

If you deposit money in a financial institution, such as a bank, you are in effect lending money to the bank. In exchange the bank pays you interest. There are two types of interest: **simple interest** and **compound interest**.

Simple Interest

Simple Interest is usually applicable to short term investments of one year or less or to longer term investments where the annual interest is paid to the investor and not reinvested.

a) If you invest $500 which earns interest at a rate of 6% per year, how much interest would you earn in:

    i) one year   **ii)** half a year   **iii)** one month?

b) If r is the annual interest rate (expressed as a decimal) and P is the initial investment, calculate how much interest would be earned in:

    i) one year   **ii)** half a year   **iii)** t years.

The formula to calculate simple interest is $\boxed{I = Prt}$

where
    I represents the amount of interest
    P represents the principal (the initial investment)
    r represents the <u>annual</u> rate of interest - expressed as a decimal
    t represents the time in years for which the money is invested

Class Ex. #1   Millie invests $2350.00 at 7% per year for six months. Calculate, after six months,
a) the simple interest on Millie's investment   **b)** the value of Millie's investment

Compound Interest

In simple interest the principal at the beginning of the second year is the same as the principal at the beginning of the first year.

In compound interest the interest earned during the first year is added to the original principal to form a new principal.

To understand the comparison between simple interest and compound interest, do the investigation on the next two pages.

Exploring Simple Interest and Compound Interest

A bank offers two types of savings bond:

- Regular Savings Bond which pays simple interest at 9% p.a. (per year, or per annum).

- Compound Savings Bond which pays interest at 9% p.a. compounded annually.

Simple Interest

a) The simple interest each year

is 9% of $5000 = _____ .

b) Find the value of the bond at the end of each of the first 8 years, and complete the table.

End of Year	Amount($)
1	5450
2	5900
3	
4	
5	
6	
7	
8	

Compound Interest

c) Complete the following to determine the compound interest and the value of the bond.

End of Year 1:   Value of Bond = Principal + Interest

$$= 5000 + 5000(0.09)$$
$$= 5000(1 + 0.09) \qquad \text{factor out 5000}$$
$$= 5000(1.09)$$

End of Year 2:   Value of Bond = Principal + Interest

$$= 5000(1.09) + 5000(1.09)(0.09)$$
$$= 5000(1.09)(1 + 0.09) \qquad \text{factor out } 5000(1.09)$$
$$= 5000(1.09)(1.09)$$
$$= 5000(1.09)^2$$

End of Year 3:   Value of Bond = Principal + Interest

$$=$$

$$=$$

$$=$$

$$=$$

d) The value for the bond at the end of each year is 1.09 times the value at the end of the previous year. Complete the table below.

End of Year	Value of Bond	Amount ($)
1	$5000(1.09)$	5450
2	$5000(1.09)^2$	
3		
4		
5		
6		
7		
8		
n		

The value at the end of n years is $= 5000(1.09)^n$.

e) In general, if A = the final amount (or the value of the bond), P = the initial principal, i = the annual interest rate, and n = the number of years, we have the formula:

$$A=$$

f) Plot the data from the simple interest and compound interest tables.
Do not join the points.

g) The graph shows that the simple interest bond is growing in a **linear** pattern and the compound interest bond is growing more quickly, or **exponentially**.

Write the formula for the exponential function shown on the grid in the form $y = ab^n, n \in N$.

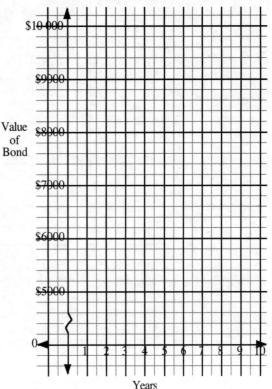

Value of Bond

Years

Note In the previous explorations, interest is compounded on an annual basis. In practice, compounding can take place over any period of time, eg semi-annually, monthly, daily, continuously, etc.

Compound Interest Formula

The formula which can be used to calculate compound interest is an exponential function of the form $y = ab^x$, where the domain of the function is discrete (not continuous).

$$A = P(1 + i)^n$$

where, A represents the final amount
P represents the initial principal
i represents the interest rate per compounding period
n represents the number of compounding periods.

Note • Note that i does **NOT** always represent the annual interest rate.
• Note that n does **NOT** always represent the number of years.

Class Ex. #2 $1000 is invested for 5 years at an annual interest rate of 6%. Complete the table to calculate the final value of the investment if interest is compounded according to the period of time given in the table.

Compounding Period	Number of Compounding Periods Per Year	Total Number of Compounding Periods	Interest Rate per Compounding Period	Formula A =	Amount
Annually					
Semi-Annually					
Quarterly					
Monthly					

Class Ex. #3 $7000 is invested in a 6 year GIC compounded quarterly at a rate of 5% per annum. Determine the value of the investment at the end of the term.

$A =$

$P =$

$i =$

$n =$

Class Ex. #4 Christine invested $2500 for 4 years compounded semi-annually and received $843.26 interest. What was the annual rate of interest?

$A =$

$P =$

$i =$

$n =$

Class Ex. #5 Barbara invests $8000 in an account which pays compound interest of 6% per annum compounded monthly. How long would it take, in years and months, for her investment to double in value ?

$A =$

$P =$

$i =$

$n =$

Borrowing Money

When an amount of money is borrowed, interest is charged for the use of that money for a certain fixed period of time. If the loan is paid off in one payment at the end of the loan period, then the compound interest formula can be used.

If repayments are made on a regular basis during the period of the loan, the compound interest formula cannot be used.

Class Ex. #6 Andrea borrows $7500 from her parents to buy new car. Her parents charge her interest at the rate of 4% p.a. compounded quarterly. When she pays off the loan, she has to pay $785 interest. What was the length of the loan?

Complete Assignment Questions #1 - #11

Assignment

1. Calculate the simple interest in each case.
   a) $740 is invested at 6% per annum for six months.

   b) $1500 is invested at 8%/a for 3 months.

2. If the annual rate of interest is 9% per annum, state the interest rate per compounding period and the total number of compounding periods in each case:

   a) compounded semi-annually for 4 years   b) compounded quarterly for 3 years

   c) compounded monthly for $4\frac{1}{2}$ years   d) compounded annually for 6 years

3. $4000 is invested for 4 years at an annual interest rate of 7.2%.

   a) Complete the table to calculate the final value of the investment if interest is compounded according to the period of time given in the table.

Compounding Period	Number of Compounding Periods Per Year	Total Number of Compounding Periods	Interest Rate per Compounding Period	Formula A =	Amount
Annually					
Semi-Annually					
Quarterly					
Monthly					

   b) If the interest is compounded continuously, then the formula $A = Pe^{kt}$ can be used, where P is the initial amount invested, A is the final amount at the end of t years, and k is the annual interest rate.

   i) Calculate the final amount if $4000 is invested for 4 years at an annual interest rate of 7.2% compounded continuously.

   ii) Use the formula in b) i) to determine the annual interest rate, to the nearest tenth of a percent, if an investment, compounded continuously, doubles in value in 11 years.

4. The function represented by the compound interest formula is an exponential function.

   a) What is the base of the exponential function represented by the compound interest formula?

   b) How does the exponent in the compound interest formula compare with the exponent in the exponential function $y = ab^x, x \in R$?

5. If a student's summer job savings of $3000 is invested at 12% per year compounded monthly, how many months will it take to earn at least $600 in interest?

6. The value of an investment is given by $f(x) = 2600(1.062)^x$, where x is the number of years for which the investment is held.

   a) What is the annual interest rate if interest is compounded annually?

   b) Determine the number of complete years until the investment is worth at least $6000.

7. A student borrows $6000. Interest is charged at 5% per year compounded semi-annually. The loan is paid off in one final payment of $6958. What was the length of the loan?

8. Find the interest rate per annum (to one decimal place) at which a $3000 investment, compounded quarterly, will double in value over a period of 5 years.

9. Mary-Ann invested $3500 in a Canada Savings Bond at an interest rate of 5.4% per year compounded monthly. Carlos invested $3000 in a G.I.C. at an interest rate of 6.8% per year, compounded annually. After how many years will the two investments be approximately equal in value?

Multiple Choice 10. A student invests $100 @ 8% per year compounded semi-annually. The amount of money that the student will have at the end of each year is increased from the amount at the end of the previous year by a factor of

   A. 1.04   **B.** 1.08

   C. 1.0816   **D.** 1.16

Numerical Response 11. George invests $2500 in an account which pays compound interest of 8.1% per annum compounded quarterly. The number of quarters it will take George's investment to at least double in value is _____ .

(Record your answer in the numerical response box from left to right.)

Answer Key

1. **a)** $22.20   **b)** $30   **2.** **a)** 4.5%, 8 **b)** 2.25%, 12 **c)** 0.75%, 54   **d)** 9%, 6

3.a) see table below   **b)** **i)** $5335.03   **ii)** 6.3%

Compounding Period	Number of Compounding Periods Per Year	Total Number of Compounding Periods	Interest Rate per Compounding Period	Formula	Amount
Annually	1	4	7.2%	$A = 4000(1.072)^4$	$5282.50
Semi-Annually	2	8	3.6%	$A = 4000(1.036)^8$	$5308.09
Quarterly	4	16	1.8%	$A = 4000(1.018)^{16}$	$5321.38
Monthly	12	48	0.6%	$A = 4000(1.006)^{48}$	$5330.44

4. **a)** $1 + i$

   b) The exponent n in the compound interest formula is equal to x, but the set of values for n is discrete, whereas the set of values for x is continuous, i.e. the domains of the functions are not the same.

5. 19   **6.** **a)** 6.2% **b)** 14   **7.** 3 years   **8.** 14.1%   **9.** 13

10. C   **11.** 3 5

Applications of Exponential and Logarithmic Functions
Lesson #3: Applications of Exponential Growth or Decay

Review

- An **exponential function** is a function whose equation is of the form

$$y = ab^x \quad \text{where } a \neq 0, b > 0, x \in R$$

- For $a > 0$,
    - when $b > 1$, the function represents a growth function.
    - when $0 < b < 1$, the function represents a decay function.

Writing an Equation Using $y = ab^x$

There are many applications of exponential functions in real life. In some cases, the function $y = ab^x$ can be written in "disguised" form. For example, $A = P(1 + i)^n$ is an exponential function whose base is $1 + i$. In this lesson, we will meet further real life applications of exponential growth and decay.

We can use variations of the formula $y = ab^x$ (such as $A = P(1 + i)^n$) to solve problems involving population growth, growth of bacteria, radioactive decay etc.

Class Ex. #1

In 2012 the university population of a country was 160 000 and was increasing at an annual rate of 4.5%.

a) If the function representing the population is of the form $y = ab^x$, state the values for a and b.

b) Write an equation to represent the university population, P, of the country as a function of the number of years, n, since 2012.

c) Determine the population in the year 2015.

d) If the population continues to grow at this rate, determine the number of years, to the nearest year, for the population to double from its 2012 size.

Class Ex. #2 The number of fish in a lake is decreasing by 5% each year as a result of overfishing.

a) If the number of fish present is an exponential function of time, state the base of the exponential function.

b) Write an equation to represent the number of fish present after t years.
   Use N_0 to represent the initial population and $N(t)$ to represent the final population.

c) If there were 2500 fish present in June 2012, how many would you expect to be present in June 2017?

d) How many years, to the nearest tenth, would it take for the fish population to reduce to half of the number in June 2012?

Class Ex. #3 The intensity, I_0, of a light source is reduced to I after passing through d metres of a fog, according to the formula $I = I_0 e^{-0.12d}$. At what distance, to the nearest hundredth of a metre, will the intensity be reduced to one quarter of its original value?

Complete Assignment Questions #1 - #7

Developing an Exponential Formula for Half-Life, Doubling Time, etc.

Half-Life

Radioactive substances decay by changing into non-radioactive substances. The amount of radioactive substance present at any given time is an exponential function of time.

After an interval of time, H, called the **half-life** of the radioactive substance, only half the original amount will still be radioactive.

Let A represent the amount of a radioactive substance present at time, t, and let A_0 represent the amount present initially.

For some base, b, we can write the exponential function of time as $A = A_0 b^t$.

Complete the following to determine the base in terms of the half-life.

$A = A_0 b^t$ When $t = H$, only half the substance will be radioactive, so $A = \dfrac{1}{2} A_0$.

$\dfrac{1}{2} A_0 = A_0 b^H$ Solve for b to determine the base.

The exponential function is now of the form $A = A_0\left(\left(\dfrac{1}{2}\right)^{\frac{1}{H}}\right)^t$, which can be written

as $A = A_0\left(\dfrac{1}{2}\right)^{\frac{t}{H}}$.

Doubling Time

The time is takes for an exponential function to double in value is called the **doubling time**.

The base in the formula for doubling time is $2^{\frac{1}{D}}$, where D is the doubling time, and the exponential function is of the form $A = A_0((2)^{\frac{1}{D}})^t$, which can be written as $A = A_0(2)^{\frac{t}{D}}$.

Use a similar procedure to the one above to develop this formula.

Formula

The formulas on the previous page are examples of the following general formula which can be used for solving problems involving doubling time, tripling time, half-life, etc.

$$A = A_0((C)^{\frac{1}{P}})^t, \text{ which can be written as } A = A_0(C)^{\frac{t}{P}} \text{ or in function form } A(t) = A_0C^{\frac{t}{p}}$$

where,

A_0 = initial amount

A = amount at time t

C = a constant, for example, 2 for doubling, 3 for tripling, $\dfrac{1}{2}$ for half life

t = time

p = period of time for doubling, tripling, halving, etc.

Note that the base of the exponential function is $C^{\frac{1}{p}}$.

 Class Ex. #4 A patient feeling ill had a sample of bacteria taken from her throat. The sample contained 387 cells. Twenty-four hours later the sample was recounted and was found to contain 8012 cells. Find the doubling period of the bacteria to the nearest tenth of an hour.

 Class Ex. #5 In April 1986, the nuclear accident at Chernobyl contaminated the atmosphere with quantities of radioactive iodine-131. If the half-life of radioactive iodine-131 is 8.1 days, determine the number of days, to the nearest day, it took for the level of radiation to reduce to 2% of the original level.

Class Ex. #6

A radioactive isotope has a half-life of 7 years.

a) Use the formula $A = A_0 C^{\frac{t}{p}}$, with $C = \frac{1}{2}$, to determine how much of the isotope must initially be present to decay to 60 grams in 14 years.

b) Write an equivalent formula with $C = 2$ which would solve the problem in a).

c) In this particular example, explain how the solution to the problem in a) could be found without using any formula.

Complete Assignment Questions #8 - #15

Assignment

1. A truck bought for \$35 000 depreciates at a rate of 12% per year.

a) If the value of the truck is an exponential function of time, state the base of the exponential function.

b) Write an equation to represent the value, V, of the truck after t years.

c) Determine, to the nearest hundred dollars, the value of the truck after 4 years.

d) How many years, to the nearest tenth, would it take for the value of the truck to reduce to one quarter of its purchase price?

2. In 2008 the world population was approximately 6.7 billion and was increasing at an annual rate of 1.3%.

   a) If the function representing the population, in billions, is of the form $y = ab^x$, state values for a and b.

   b) Write an equation to represent the world population, W billions, as a function of the number of years, n, since 2008.

   c) Assuming the same growth rate, determine, to the nearest tenth of a billion, the expected world population in the year 2025.

   d) If the population continues to grow at this rate, determine the number of years, to the nearest year, for the population to double from its 2008 size.

   e) Estimate the world population in 1950. State any assumptions you have made. How does your answer compare with the actual world population in 1950? Give a reason for any discrepancy.

3. The value of a type of robotic technology depreciates 25% per year.

   a) Write an exponential function to represent the value of this robotic technology after t years.

   b) How many years, to the nearest year, would it take for the value of the robotic technology, which initially cost $575\,000$, to depreciate to $25\,000$?

4. A town in southern British Columbia is growing at a rate of 3.5% per annum. If the town continues to grow at this rate, it is projected that the population will reach 20 000 in 5 years.

  a) Determine, to the nearest ten people, the current population of the town.

  b) Assuming the same growth rate, determine how many years from now the population will reach 30 000. Answer to the nearest year.

5. A quantity of water contains 500 g of pollutants. Each time the water passes through a filter, 18% of the pollutants are removed. How many filters are needed to reduce the mass of pollutants to less than 150 g?

6. An x-ray beam of intensity, I_0, in passing through absorbing material x millimeters thick, merges with an intensity, I, given by $I = I_0 e^{-kx}$. When the material is 9 millimetres thick, 50% of the intensity is lost.

  a) Calculate the value of the constant k to the three decimal places.

  b) What percentage intensity, to one decimal place, remains if the material is 20 millimetres thick?

7. A hot piece of metal loses heat according to the formula $T = T_0 e^{-0.2t}$, where T is the temperature difference between the metal and the surrounding air after t minutes and T_0 is the initial temperature difference.

a) If the initial temperature of the metal was 330°C and of the air 30°C, find the temperature of the metal, to the nearest degree, after 5 minutes.

b) A different piece of hot metal cools to a temperature of 200°C after 8 minutes. What was the original temperature of the metal, to the nearest degree, if the air temperature was 27°C?

8. How much of a radioactive substance must be present to decay to 30 grams in 12 years if the half–life of the substance is 5.2 years? Round the answer to the nearest gram.

9. A radioactive isotope has a half–life of approximately 45 minutes. How long would it take for 480 mg of the isotope to decay to 15 mg?

10. A lab technician placed a bacterial cell into a vial at 5 a.m. The cells divide in such a way that the number of cells doubles every 4 minutes. The vial is full one hour later.

 a) How long does it take for the cells to divide to produce 4096 cells?

 b) At what time is the vial half full?

 c) At what time is the vial $\frac{1}{16}$ full?

11. The population of germs in a dirty bathtub doubles every 20 minutes. How long, to the nearest minute, would it take for the population to triple?

12. A radioactive isotope has a half–life of approximately 25 weeks. How much of a sample of 50 grams of the isotope would remain after 630 days?
 (Round the answer to the nearest hundredth of a gram.)

13. What is the half–life, to the nearest month, of a radioactive isotope if it takes 7 years for 560 grams to decay to 35 grams?

Numerical
Response **14.** The tripling period, to the nearest tenth of an hour, of a bacterial culture which grows from 500 cells to 64 000 cells in 50 hours is _____ .

(Record your answer in the numerical response box from left to right.)

15. Radioactive material decays to 40% of its original mass in 5 years. The half-life of the radioactive material, to the nearest hundredth of a year, is _____ .

(Record your answer in the numerical response box from left to right.)

Answer Key

1. **a)** 0.88   **b)** $V = 35\ 000(0.88)^t$ **c)** \$21 000   **d)** 10.8

2. **a)** $a = 6.7,\ b = 1.013$ **b)** $W = 6.7(1.013)^n$ **c)** 8.3 billion   **d)** 54 years
   e) 3.2 billion assuming a growth rate of 1.3% since 1950. The actual population was 2.55 billion, so the average growth rate since 1950 must have been greater than 1.3%.

3. **a)** $V_t = V_0(0.75)^t$ **b)** 11   **4.** **a)** 16 840   **b)** 17 years   **5.** 7 filters

6. **a)** 0.077   **b)** 21.4%   **7.** **a)** 140°C   **b)**   884°C   **8.** 149 grams

9 225 min   **10.a)** 48 min   **b)** 5:56 a.m.   **c)** 5:44 a.m.

11. 32 min   **12.** 4.12 g   **13.** 21 months

17. | 1 | 1 | . | 3 | **18.** | 3 | . | 7 | 8 |

Applications of Exponential and Logarithmic Functions
Lesson #4: Solving Logarithmic Equations

There are many techniques for solving logarithmic equations. Much of the work will involve using the laws of logarithms so that we arrive at one of two possible positions shown.

Either   1) $\log_b P = \log_b Q$ in which case $P = Q$

or   2) $\log_b P = Q$ in which case $P = b^Q$

Exploration

Alice is solving the equation $\log_5(x + 1) + \log_5(x - 3) = 1$.
Part of her solution (including explanation) is shown below

$$\log_5(x + 1) + \log_5(x - 3) = 1$$

- Use the product law

$$\log_5[(x + 1)(x - 3)] = 1$$

- Convert to exponential form

$$(x + 1)(x - 3) = 5^1$$

a) Complete the solution by solving for x.

b) Explain what happens when you try to verify the values of x in a) in the original equation.

c) Circle the correct alternative:

In solving this equation, Alice arrived at one of the two positions shown in the introduction. The position Alice arrived at is $\log_b P = \log_b Q$ / $\log_b P = Q$.

Note When attempting to verify the solution $x = -2$ in the previous example, we reached the situation of the logarithm of a negative number.

We know that logarithmic expressions are only defined for positive values of the argument. So in this case, $x = -2$ is an **extraneous solution**.

Notice that it is not the fact x is negative that makes the solution extraneous. It is the fact that the argument of the logarithm is negative that makes the solution extraneous.

Solving Logarithmic Equations using the Laws of Logarithms

A logarithmic expression is defined only for positive values of the argument.

When we solve a logarithmic equation, it is essential to verify that the solutions do not result in the logarithm of a negative number. Solutions that would result in the logarithm of a negative number are called **extraneous**, and are not valid solutions.

Values obtained by solving logarithmic equations may be extraneous and must be verified. There are two verifications required when the solution is replaced in the <u>original</u> equation:

- All the arguments of the logarithms must be positive.
- If the base is variable, it too must be positive.

Class Ex. #1

a) Solve the following logarithmic equations.

  i) $\log x^2 = \log 16$

  ii) $2 \log x = \log 16$

b) Solve the equations in a) using a graphing technique. Illustrate the solutions on the grids provided.

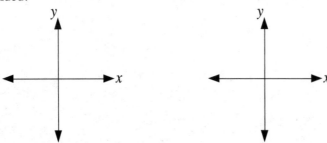

c) Explain why the solutions to the logarithmic equations are not the same even though $2 \log x$ can be written as $\log x^2$.

Class Ex. #2 Solve for x in the following equations.

a) $\log_4(x + 1) - \log_4(2x - 3) = \log_4 8$

b) $\log_6(x + 4) = 1 - \log_6(x + 3)$

Class Ex. #3 Solve $2 \log_3 x - \log_3(x + 3) - 3 = 0$ to two decimal places.

> **Complete Assignment Questions #1 - #6**

> *Solving More Complex Logarithmic Equations*

Class Ex. #4 Solve the equation $\log_2(\log_x(3x + 4)) = 1$ by twice converting to exponential form.
Remember to check for extraneous solutions.

Class Ex. #5

Solve and verify.

a) Solve the equation $\log x^2 - 3 \log x = 10$ by using the laws of logarithms.

b) Explain why the equation $(\log x)^2 - 3 \log x = 10$ cannot be solved using the laws of logarithms.

c) Solve the equation in b) using the following steps:

   1. Replace $\log x$ by a new variable A.

   2. Solve for A.

   3. Replace A by $\log x$ and solve for x.

   4. Check for extraneous solutions.

d) A student is solving the logarithmic equation $(\log x)^2 - \log x^3 = 0$. Her work is shown.

$$(\log x)^2 - \log x^3 = 0 \qquad \text{Let } A = \log x.$$

$$A^2 - A^3 = 0$$

$$A^2(1 - A) = 0$$

$$A = 0 \quad \text{or} \quad A = 1$$

$$\log x = 0 \quad \text{or} \quad \log x = 1$$

$$x = 10^0 \quad \text{or} \quad x = 10^1$$

$$x = 1, 10 \implies \text{No extraneous solutions.}$$

There is an error in the student's work because $x = 10$ does not satisfy the original equation. Identify her error, and provide the correct solution in the space above.

Complete Assignment Questions #7 - #12

Assignment

1. Solve for the variable in each equation. Remember to check for extraneous solutions.

   a) $\log_3 x + \log_3 3 = \log_3 30$ **b)** $\log_3 3y - \log_3 4 = \log_3 6$ **c)** $2 \log y = \log 25$

2. Solve for x.

   a) $\log_9 x - \log_9 3 = 1$ **b)** $\log_4(x - 5) + \log_4(x - 2) = 1$

3. Solve for the variable in each equation.

   a) $\log_5 x - \log_5(x - 1) = \log_5 3$ **b)** $\log_3(3x - 1) - \log_3(x - 1) = 4$

   c) $\log(2x + 3) + \log(x + 2) - 1 = 0$

4. Solve each logarithmic equation for the given variable.
State, and explain the reason for, any extraneous roots.

a) $\log_{49}(m + 4) + \log_{49}(m - 2) = \dfrac{1}{2}$

b) $\log_8(-x) + \log_8(3 - x) = \log_8 10$

c) $\log_5(7x - 1) - \log_5 x = \log_5 4$

d) $\log_2 3a + \log_2 2 = \log_2 8 - \log_2 4$

e) $\log_2 x = 2 + \dfrac{1}{2}\log_2(x - 3)$

5. The number of students in a school t years after the school opens can be modelled by the equation $S = S_0[\log_2(t + 1) + 1]$, where S_0 is the original number of students in the school.

a) If there were initially 100 students in the school, how many would be expected after 10 years?

b) How many years will it take for the number of students to reach 800 if the original number of students in the school was 200?

6. Determine the root(s) of the following equations.

a) $\dfrac{1}{2}\log_4(y + 4) + \dfrac{1}{2}\log_4(y - 4) = \log_4 3$ **b)** $\log_2(1 - w) - \log_2(3 - w) = -1$

7. Solve for x. State, and explain the reason for, any extraneous roots.

a) $\log_5(\log_x(2x - 3)) = 0$ **b)** $\log_2(\log_x(20 - x)) = 1$ **c)** $\log_3(\log_2(x^2 - 2x)) = 1$

8. Solve.

   a) $\log x + (\log x)^2 = 0$

   b) $(\log x)^2 - \log x^5 = 14$

9. Solve each logarithmic equation.

   a) $(\log x)^2 + \log x^{-1} - 12 = 0$

   b) $2(\log_3 n)^3 - (\log_3 n)^2 = 0$

   c) $3(\log_3 x)^2 - 36 = \log_3 x^{23}$

Multiple Choice **10.** If $\log_4(2x + 1) + \log_4(x - 1) = \dfrac{1}{2}$, then the value(s) of x is/are

    A. $\dfrac{3}{2}, -1$

    B. $\dfrac{3}{2}$ only

    C. 3 only

    D. $\dfrac{1}{2}, 3$

Numerical Response **11.** The equation $2 \log x - \log 25 = \log 9 + \log x, x > 0,$ has an integral solution.

The value of x is _____ .

(Record your answer in the numerical response box from left to right.)

12. If $\dfrac{1}{3} \log \sqrt{x} + \log x^3 = n \log x$ for all values of x, then the value of n,
to the nearest tenth, is _____ .

(Record your answer in the numerical response box from left to right.)

Answer Key

1. **a)** 10   **b)** 8   **c)** 5   **2.** **a)** 27   **b)** 6

3. **a)** $\dfrac{3}{2}$ **b)** $\dfrac{40}{39}$ **c)** $\dfrac{1}{2}$

4. **a)** $m = 3$. -5 is an extraneous root because it leads to the logarithm of a negative number.
    b) $x = -2$. 5 is an extraneous root because it leads to the logarithm of a negative number.
    c) $c = \dfrac{1}{3}$ **d)** $a = \dfrac{1}{3}$ **e)** $x = 4, 12$

5. **a)** 446   **b)** 7   **6.** **a)** 5   **b)** -1

7. **a)** $x = 3$ **b)** $x = 4$ -5 is an extraneous root because it leads to a negative base.
    c) $x = -2, 4$

8. **a)** $1, \dfrac{1}{10}$ **b)** $\dfrac{1}{100}$, 10 000 000

9. **a)** 10 000, $\dfrac{1}{1000}$ **b)** $1, \sqrt{3}$ **c)** $3^{-\frac{4}{3}}$ or ≈ 0.2311, 3^9 or 19 683

10. B   **11.**

2	2	5	

12.

3	.	2	

Applications of Exponential and Logarithmic Functions
Lesson #5: Logarithmic Scales and Applications

Earthquakes

The Richter scale, named after the American seismologist Charles Richter (1900-85), is used to measure the magnitude of an earthquake. The magnitude of an earthquake is a measure of the amount of energy released. It is determined from the logarithm of the amplitude of waves recorded by seismographs.

The Richter scale is logarithmic – a difference in one unit in magnitude corresponds to a factor of ten difference in intensity. This means that each whole number step represents a ten-fold increase in intensity. Therefore a magnitude 9 earthquake is ten times larger than a magnitude 8 earthquake, one hundred times larger then a magnitude 7 earthquake, and one thousand times larger than a magnitude 6 earthquake.

A magnitude of 1.0 on the Richter Scale is equivalent to a large blast at a construction site using approximately 14 kg of TNT. It is 10 times as intense as the zero reference point.

An earthquake with magnitude 2.0 is 10^2 times as intense as the zero reference point, etc.

Any earthquakes having magnitudes in excess of 6.0 are considered dangerous. The largest yet recorded, the Chilean earthquake of 1960, registered 9.4 on the Richter scale. The most powerful recorded in North America, the Alaska quake of 1964, reached 8.4 on the Richter scale.

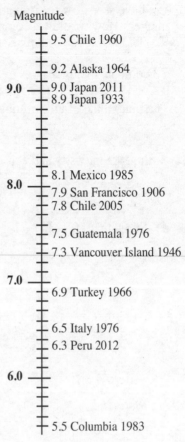

The Richter Scale

Magnitude

- 9.5 Chile 1960
- 9.2 Alaska 1964
- 9.0 — 9.0 Japan 2011
- 8.9 Japan 1933

- 8.1 Mexico 1985
- 8.0 — 7.9 San Francisco 1906
- 7.8 Chile 2005

- 7.5 Guatemala 1976
- 7.3 Vancouver Island 1946

- 7.0 —
- 6.9 Turkey 1966

- 6.5 Italy 1976
- 6.3 Peru 2012

- 6.0 —

- 5.5 Columbia 1983

Class Ex. #1

Complete the following:

a) An earthquake of magnitude 8 is __10__ times as intense as an earthquake of magnitude 7.

b) An earthquake of magnitude 7 is __10^4__ times as intense as an earthquake of magnitude 3.

c) An earthquake of magnitude 4 is __10__ times $10^{-2} = \frac{1}{100}$ as intense as an earthquake of magnitude 6.

d) An earthquake of magnitude 4.8 is __10^{-2}__ times as intense as an earthquake of magnitude 6.8.

e) The 1960 earthquake in Chile was __10^3__ times as intense as the 1976 earthquake in Italy and __10^4__ times as intense as the 1983 earthquake in Colombia.

f) The 1966 earthquake in Turkey was __10^{-2}__ times as intense as the 1933 earthquake in Japan.

Comparing Earthquake Intensities

We have seen how to compare the intensity of earthquakes whose magnitude differs by an integer. How would we compare the intensities of the 1960 earthquake in Chile (magnitude 9.5) and the 2005 earthquake in Chile (magnitude 7.8)?

To compare the intensities of magnitude M_1 and M_2, consider the following:

The magnitude of an earthquake is given by the formula $M = \log\left(\dfrac{I}{I_0}\right)$, where I is the

earthquake intensity and I_0 is a reference intensity, e.g., $M_1 = \log\left(\dfrac{I_1}{I_0}\right)$ and $M_2 = \log\left(\dfrac{I_2}{I_0}\right)$.

a) Show that $M_1 - M_2 = \log\left(\dfrac{I_1}{I_2}\right)$.　　　　**b)** Hence, show that $\dfrac{I_1}{I_2} = 10^{M_1 - M_2}$.

> The intensities of two earthquakes can be compared using $\dfrac{I_1}{I_2} = 10^{M_1 - M_2}$

Class Ex. #2　　How many times more intense was the 1960 earthquake in Chile (magnitude 9.5) than the 2005 earthquake in Chile (magnitude 7.8)? Answer to the nearest whole number.

Class Ex. #3　　A major earthquake of magnitude 7.5 is 375 times as intense as a minor earthquake. Find the magnitude, to the nearest tenth, of the minor earthquake.

Loudness of Sound

The loudness of a sound was originally measured in **Bels**, named after Alexander Graham Bell.

The current unit used is the **decibel (dB)**, which is equal to one tenth of a Bel.

The Bel scale, like the Richter scale, is logarithmic – a difference of 1 Bel, or 10 decibels, corresponds to a factor of ten difference in sound intensity.

A leaf rustling (10 decibels or 1 Bel) is 10 times as loud as the threshold of hearing.

A whisper (30 decibels or 3 Bels) is 10^3, or 1000, times as intense as the threshold of hearing and 10^2, or 100, times as loud as a leaf rustling.

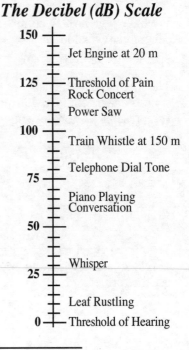

The Decibel (dB) Scale

- 150
- Jet Engine at 20 m
- 125 — Threshold of Pain
  - Rock Concert
  - Power Saw
- 100
  - Train Whistle at 150 m
  - Telephone Dial Tone
- 75
  - Piano Playing
  - Conversation
- 50
  - Whisper
- 25
  - Leaf Rustling
- 0 — Threshold of Hearing

Class Ex. #4

Complete the following using the chart above.

a) A power saw (120 dB) is __10^4__ times as loud as a telephone dial tone (80 dB).

b) A jet engine at 20 m (145 dB) is __10^2__ times as loud as the threshold of pain (125 dB).

c) A whisper (30 dB) is __10^{-3}__ times as loud as a conversation (60 dB).

Comparing Loudness of Sounds

We have seen how to compare the loudness of sounds whose Bels differ by an integer. To compare the loudness of sounds when the Bels are not integers, we suggest the following approach.

The loudness, or intensity, of sound can be measured in dB or Bels. The intensity of two sounds can be compared using the following formulas where I represents sound intensity, and I_0 represents a reference sound intensity (threshold of hearing):

<table>
<tr><td align="center"><u>For dB</u></td><td align="center"><u>For Bels</u></td></tr>
<tr><td align="center">$$dB = 10 \log\left(\frac{I}{I_0}\right)$$</td><td align="center">$$Bels = \log\left(\frac{I}{I_0}\right)$$</td></tr>
<tr><td>To compare the loudness, or intensity, of two sounds measured in **decibels**, use the formula

$$\frac{I_1}{I_2} = 10^{\frac{dB_1 - dB_2}{10}}$$</td><td>To compare the loudness, or intensity, of two sounds measured in **Bels**, use the formula

$$\frac{I_1}{I_2} = 10^{B_1 - B_2}$$</td></tr>
</table>

We can derive the above formulas in a way similar to the one used in the previous section.

Class Ex. #5

Given that $dB = 10 \log\left(\frac{I}{I_0}\right)$, show that the decibel level for the threshold of pain (125 dB) has a sound intensity $10^{12.5} I_0$.

Class Ex. #6

How many times more intense is the sound of a piano playing (67 dB) than a whisper (22 dB)?

Class Ex. #7

Two telephones in a home ring at the same time with a loudness of 80 decibels each. Does this mean that the total loudness is 160 dB? Explain why or why not using sound intensities and the properties of logarithms.

pH Scale

In 1909, Sören Sörenson, a Dutch chemist, introduced the term **pH**, representing the expression "the power of hydrogen", to measure the extreme wide range of hydrogen ion concentration in substances.

The pH scale measures the range of hydrogen ion concentration by determining the acidity or the alkalinity of a solution. The scale measures from 0 to 14 with values below 7 representing increasing acidity, and values above 7 representing increasing alkalinity. The value 7 represents the neutral level on the pH scale where the solution is neither acidic nor alkaline.

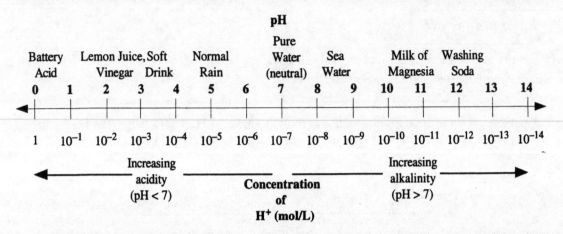

Similar to the Richter scale, the pH scale is logarithmic – a difference in one unit of pH corresponds to a factor of ten difference in intensity. This means that each whole number step represents a ten-fold increase in intensity.

Therefore, if vinegar has a pH of 3, then it is ten times as **acidic** as tomato juice (pH of 4), and one hundred times as acidic as normal rain (pH of 5).

On the other hand, household ammonia (pH of 11.5), is ten times as **alkaline** as milk of magnesia (pH of 10.5) and one thousand times as alkaline as sea water (pH of 8.5).

Class Ex. #8

Complete the following, using the <u>approximate</u> pH values given.

a) Tomato juice is _____ times as acidic as pure water.

b) Eggs are _____ times as alkaline as pure water.

c) Milk of magnesia is _____ times as _____ as blood.

d) _____ is 100 times as acidic as normal rain.

e) Eggs are _____ times as alkaline as washing soda.

Solution	pH
Battery Acid	0.5
Lemon Juice	2.5
Vinegar	3
Tomato Juice	4
Normal Rain	5
Pure Water	7
Blood	7.5
Eggs	8
Milk of Magnesia	10.5
Washing Soda	12

Comparing Acidity and Alkalinity of Solutions

To find how much more **acidic** or **alkaline** one solution is to another, use $10^{pH_1 - pH_2}$.

Class Ex. #9

Pure water, swimming pool water, and sea water have pH levels of 7, 7.5, and 8.4 respectively.

a) How many times as alkaline is sea water than pure water?

b) How many times as alkaline as swimming pool water is sea water?

Formula for pH

The pH of a solution is defined as $pH = -\log [H^+]$, where the H^+ is the hydrogen ion concentration (expressed as moles/litre).

Class Ex. #10

A patient gave a urine sample which was found to have a pH of 5.7. What was the hydrogen ion concentration? Answer in scientific notation using one decimal place.

Class Ex. #11

Determine the pH of a solution, to the nearest tenth, if the hydrogen ion concentration is 3.4×10^{-4} mol/L.

Complete Assignment Questions #1 - #11

Assignment

1. How many times more intense was the 2011 earthquake in Japan (magnitude 9.0) than the 2012 earthquake in Peru (magnitude 6.3)? Answer to the nearest whole number

2. At 2:45 pm on March 11, 2011, a major earthquake of magnitude 9.0 hit the east coast of Japan. Half an hour later, a second earthquake of magnitude 7.9 hit the same region. How many times more intense, to the nearest whole number, was the first earthquake than the second one?

3. An earthquake in Peru had a magnitude of 7.7 on the Richter Scale. The following day a second earthquake with one third of the intensity of the first hit the same region. Determine the magnitude of the second earthquake to the nearest tenth.

4. How many times more intense is the sound of a referee's whistle (125 dB) than a train whistle at 200 m (90 dB)? Answer to the nearest whole number.

5. How many times louder is a clarinet (95 dB) than a flute (89 dB)? Answer to the nearest whole number.

6. Use the chart to answer the following to the nearest whole number.

   a) Eggs are how many times as alkaline as blood?

   b) Black coffee is how many times as acidic as milk?

Solution	pH
Black Coffee	5.1
Milk	6.6
Pure Water	7
Blood	7.5
Eggs	8

7. A river has a pH value of 6.4 upstream from a chemical factory and a pH value of 5.8 downstream of the factory. Compare the acidity levels.

8. The pH of a solution is defined as pH $= -\log(H^+)$, where H^+ is the hydrogen ion concentration (expressed as mol/L).

   a) If a solution has a hydrogen ion concentration of 1.21×10^{-2} mol/L, determine the pH value, to the nearest tenth, of the solution.

   b) A vinegar solution has pH of 3.2. Determine its hydrogen ion concentration in scientific notation to one decimal place.

   c) A weaker vinegar solution is 25% as acidic as the solution in b).
   Determine its pH value to the nearest tenth.

9. **a)** The ionization of pure water is given by the equations:

$$[H^+][OH^-] = 1.0 \times 10^{-14} \text{ and } [H^+] = [OH^-]$$

If the pH of a solution is defined as pH = $-\log [H^+]$, prove the pH of pure water is 7.0.

b) Determine the pH, to the nearest tenth, of an acidic solution whose $[OH^-]$ concentration is 3.98×10^{-10} mol/L if $[H^+][OH^-] = 1.0 \times 10^{-14}$.

10. The loudness of sound can be modelled by the formula dB = $10 \log \left(\dfrac{I}{I_0} \right)$,

where I represents sound intensity, and I_0 represents a reference sound intensity.

If two different jets are flying together at an air show, each with a sound level of 120 decibels, then the approximate total decibel level is

A. 12.3 decibels

B. 24.0 decibels

C 123 decibels

D. 240 decibels

11. A major earthquake of magnitude 8.2 is 110 times as intense as a minor earthquake. The magnitude, to the nearest tenth, of the minor earthquake is _____ .

(Record your answer in the numerical response box from left to right.)

Answer Key

1. 501   **2.** 13   **3.** 7.2   **4.** 3162   **5.** 4   **6. a)** 3   **b)** 32

7. Downstream is 4 times as acidic as upstream.   **8. a)** 1.9   **b)** 6.3×10^{-4} **c)** 3.8

9. b) 4.6   **10.** C   **11.**  6 . 2

Applications of Exponential and Logarithmic Functions
Lesson #6: Practice Test

No calculator may be used for this section of the test.

Use the following information to answer the first question.

A teacher gave his class the following logarithmic equation to solve.

$$2\log_3 n - \log_3 2n = 2$$

The three most common solutions submitted by the students were

1. $n = 0$ **2.** $n = 16$ **3.** $n = 18$

1. The correct solution to the equation is

   A. 0 only

   B. 16 only

   C. 18 only

   D. none of the above

1. The root of the equation $5^{\log_3 x - \log_3 2} = 125$ is _____ .

(Record your answer in the numerical response box from left to right.)

2. The magnitude of an earthquake that is 100 times as intense as an earthquake of magnitude 5.5 on the Richter scale is

   A. 5.7

   B. 7.5

   C. 11

   D. 550

3.   If $\log_2[\log_x(x + 12)] = 1$, then x is equal to

    A.   3 only

    B.   4 only

    C.   3 or –4

    D.   4 or –3

4.   The population of an Alberta town is decreasing at the rate of 5% per annum. The current population is 25 000 . Which equation can be used to determine the number of years, n, for the population to reduce to 15 000?

    A. $25\,000 = 15000(0.95)^n$ **B.** $15\,000 = 25000(0.95)^n$

    C. $15\,000 = 25000(0.05)^n$ **D.** $25\,000 = 15000(0.05)^n$

5.   If $\log_6(4a) = \log_6(a - 2) + 2$, then a is equal to

    A.   –2

    B.   2

    C. $\dfrac{9}{4}$

    D. $1 + \sqrt{10}$

Section B   *A graphing calculator may be used for the remainder of the test.*

6.   The exact solution to the equation $5(2^{4x}) = 3^{x+1}$ is

    A. $\dfrac{\log 3 - \log 5}{4 \log 2 - \log 3}$

    B. $\dfrac{\log 3}{4 \log 10 - \log 3}$

    C. $\dfrac{\log 3 - \log 5}{4 \log 2 - 1}$

    D. $\dfrac{\log 3}{4 \log 10 - 1}$

2. A privately owned music store is selling all of its compact discs so it can focus on selling DVDs. During the first week of the sale all compact discs are priced at $18 and each week the compact discs are reduced by 12% of the previous week's price.

During the 7th week of the sale, the price of compact discs, in dollars rounded to the nearest cent, will be _____.

(Record your answer in the numerical response box from left to right.)

Use the following information to answer the next two questions.

A ball is dropped from a height of five metres. After each bounce, the ball rises to 75% of its previous height.

7. The maximum height of the ball, in metres, after it hits the ground for the sixth time is

A. 0.001

B. 0.667

C. 0.890

D. 1.187

3. The number of bounces it would take for the ball to reach a maximum height of approximately 5 cm is _____.

(Record your answer in the numerical response box from left to right.)

8. Jane would like to visit her family in Australia. She figures that she will need at least $9000 for the plane ticket and expenses. She goes to a local bank in Calgary to open a savings account. After some thought she decides to deposit $7500 into an account that pays interest at 8% per annum compounded quarterly.

The number of compounding periods it will take her to reach her goal is

A. 9

B. 10

C. 11

D. 12

9.   A population is growing continuously according to the formula $A = A_0e^{kt}$, where A_0 is the
initial population, A is the population at the end of t years, and k is the annual growth rate.
If the initial population is 6000 and the population at the end of 6 years is 7000, the
annual growth rate is

   A.   1.1%

   B.   2.4%

   C.   2.6%

   D.   2.8%

Use the following information to answer the next question.

> A student is attempting to solve the equation $5^{4x-2} = 3^{3x+2}$.
> The student's work is shown below.
>
> $$\log 5^{4x-2} = \log 3^{3x+2}$$
>
> **Line A:** $4x - 2\log 5 = 3x + 2\log 3$
>
> **Line B:** $4x - 3x = 2\log 3 + 2\log 5$
>
> **Line C:** $x = \log 3^2 + \log 5^2 = \log 9 + \log 25 = \log 225$

10.   The student's work may contain one or more errors.
In which line does the first error appear?

   A.   Line A

   B.   Line B

   C.   Line C

   D.   The student's solution is correct.

11.   In the process of solving $\log_5(2x + 1) + \log_5(x - 4) = 2$, a correct equation
that can arise is

   A. $(2x + 1)(x - 4) = 2$

   B. $(2x + 1)(x - 4) = 10$

   C. $(2x + 1)(x - 4) = 25$

   D. $(2x + 1)(x - 4) = 32$

12. The solution to the equation $\log_3(3 - 4y) - \log_3(y - 2) = \log_3 3$ is

A. $y = \dfrac{9}{7}$

B. $y = 1$

C. $y = \dfrac{2}{5}$

D. no solution

13. Josh borrowed $2000. Interest was charged at the rate of 3% per annum compounded semi-annually. He did not make any interim payments and paid off the loan in full at the end of the term of the loan.

If the interest he was charged was $253, then the length of the loan was

A. 2 years

B. 4 years

C. 6 years

D. 8 years

4. An earthquake in Tokyo measured 5.6 on the Richter scale. An aftershock was one-quarter as intense as the original earthquake. To the nearest tenth, the magnitude of the aftershock on the Richter scale was _____ .

(Record your answer in the numerical response box from left to right.)

14. The formula $\dfrac{I_1}{I_2} = 10^{\frac{dB_1 - dB_2}{10}}$ can be used to compare the intensity (I) of two sounds measured in decibels (dB).

How many times more intense is the sound of a student talking (60 dB) than a student whispering (30 dB)?

A. 2

B. 3

C. 100

D. 1000

Use the following information to answer the next two questions.

The pH scale is used to measure the acidity or alkalinity of a solution.
The scale is logarithmic in base 10. Thus, a difference of 1 unit in pH corresponds
to a factor of 10 difference in intensity. Vinegar (pH of 3) is 10 times as acidic as
tomato juice (pH of 4) and 100 times as acidic as rain (pH of 5).

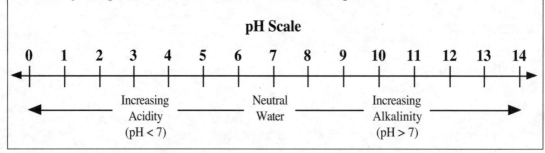

pH Scale

 5.   If lemon juice has a pH value of 2.5, then, to the nearest whole number, how many times
more acidic is lemon juice than tomato juice?

(Record your answer in the numerical response box from left to right.)

15.   Solution *X* has a pH of 9.2. Solution *Y* is twenty times more alkaline than solution *X*.
The pH of solution *Y* is

  A.   7.2

  B.   7.9

  C.   10.5

  D.   11.2

16.   University tuition will be approximately $25 000 in six years' time. Money invested
now will earn interest at 8% per annum compounded semi-annually. The amount of
money that should be invested now to have a value of $25 000 in six years' time is
approximately

  A. $19 758

  B. $16 016

  C. $15 754

  D. $15 615

17. A radioactive substance loses 90% of its radioactivity in 200 days.
An equation which can be used to determine the half-life, p days, of the substance is

A. $10 = 100\left(\dfrac{1}{2}\right)^{\frac{200}{p}}$

B. $10 = 100\left(\dfrac{1}{2}\right)^{\frac{p}{200}}$

C. $90 = 100\left(\dfrac{1}{2}\right)^{\frac{200}{p}}$

D. $90 = 100\left(\dfrac{1}{2}\right)^{\frac{p}{200}}$

Numerical
Response **6.** In a population of insects, 32 insects increase to 500 insects in 25 weeks. The doubling time for this population of insects, to the nearest tenth of a week, is _____.

(Record your answer in the numerical response box from left to right.)

18. The value of a painting doubles every 20 years. If the value was $40 000 on July 1, 2011, then the approximate value on July 1, 1999 was

A. $12 599

B. $24 000

C. $26 390

D. $60 629

19. The complete solution to the equation $\log_5(x-2) = 1 - \log_5(x+2)$ is $x =$

A. 3

B. ± 3

C. $\sqrt{5}$

D. $\pm\sqrt{5}$

20. The solution to the equation $p^{x+1} = q^x$ is

A. $\dfrac{1}{\log q - \log p}$

B. $\dfrac{\log p}{\log q - \log p}$

C. $\dfrac{1}{\log p - \log q}$

D. $\dfrac{\log p}{\log p - \log q}$

Written Response

A Pre-Calculus student correctly solves each of the following exponential equation problems as a review for an examination.

Problem #1	Problem #2	Problem #3
$2(4^x) = 32$	$9^{x+2} = \left(\dfrac{1}{27}\right)^x$	$2^{x-3} = 27$
Only solution: $x = 2$	Only solution: $x = -\dfrac{4}{5}$	Only Solution: $x = 7.75$ (correct to the nearest hundredth)

- In the student's original attempt to solve Problem #1, **one error** was made. The student's original solution is shown below. State the step in which the error was made and explain the error.

Problem #1: $2(4^x) = 32$

Step #1	$8^x = 32$
Step #2	$x \log 8 = \log 32$
Step #3	$x = \dfrac{\log 32}{\log 8}$
Step #4	$x = 1.67$ (correct to the nearest hundredth)

- Algebraically, **using logarithms**, show that $x = 2$ is the **only** correct solution to Problem #1.

- Algebraically, **without the use of logarithms**, show that $x = -\dfrac{4}{5}$ is the **only** correct solution to Problem #2.

- Problem #3 was solved graphically by the student. **Explain** clearly how this problem can be solved using a graphical technique. Include an appropriate graphical window setting for the problem in the form $x:[x_{min}, x_{max}, x_{scl}]$, $y:[y_{min}, y_{max}, y_{scl}]$.

Answer Key

Multiple Choice

1. C	**2.** B	**3.** B	**4.** B	**5.** C	**6.** A	**7.** C	**8.** B
9. C	**10.** A	**11.** C	**12.** D	**13.** B	**14.** D	**15.** C	**16.** D
17. A	**18.** C	**19.** A	**20.** B				

Numerical Response

1. | 5 | 4 | | | **2.** | 8 | . | 3 | 6 | **3.** | 1 | 6 | | |

4. | 5 | . | 0 | | **5.** | 3 | 2 | | | **6.** | 6 | . | 3 | |

Written Response

1. • In step #1, $2(4^x) \neq 8^x$.

• $\log 2(4^x) = \log 32$ $\Rightarrow$ $\log 2 + x \log 4 = \log 32$ $\Rightarrow$ $x \log 4 = \log 32 - \log 2$

$\Rightarrow$ $x \log 4 = \log 16$ $\Rightarrow$ $x = \dfrac{\log 16}{\log 4}$ $\Rightarrow$ $x = 2$

• $9^{x+2} = \left(\dfrac{1}{27}\right)^x$ $\Rightarrow$ $(3^2)^{x+2} = (3^{-3})^x$ $\Rightarrow$ $3^{2x+4} = 3^{-3x}$ $\Rightarrow$ $2x + 4 = -3x$ $\Rightarrow$ $5x = -4 \Rightarrow x = -\dfrac{4}{5}$

• Graph $y_1 = 2^{x-3}$. Graph $y_2 = 27$
Use the intersect feature of a graphing calculator to determine the x-coordinate of the point of intersection of the two graphs.
Possible window x:[0, 10, 2] y:[0, 40, 10]

Polynomial Functions and Equations Lesson #1:
Polynomial Functions

Overview

In this unit, we will use long division and synthetic division to divide polynomial expressions by binomial expressions, and use these processes as a means to factor polynomial expressions, and to determine the zeros of polynomial functions. We will also establish relationships between the equations of polynomial functions and their graphs.

Polynomial Function

A polynomial function is a function in the form

$$f(x) = a_n x^n + a_{n-1} x^{n-1} + a_{n-2} x^{n-2} + ... + a_2 x^2 + a_1 x + a_0,$$

where: $a_0, a_1, a_2, ... a_n$ are real numbers, $a_n \neq 0$, and $n \in W$.

- The values, $a_1, a_2, ... a_n$ are called **coefficients**.
- The coefficient of the highest power of x, which is a_n, is called the **leading coefficient**.
- The term independent of x, which is a_0, is the **constant term**.
- The value of n is the **degree** of the polynomial.

Class Ex. #1

Consider the polynomial $f(x) = x^4 + 7x^3 - 8x^2 + 5$. State:
a) the degree of the polynomial   **b)** the leading coefficient   **c)** the constant term

Recognizing a Polynomial Function

Expressions containing roots of variables, negative or fractional powers of a variable, or any coefficient which is non-real are **NOT** polynomial functions.

Class Ex. #2

State whether or not the following are polynomial functions. If they are not polynomial functions, explain why not.

a) $f(x) = -5x^3 + x^{\frac{1}{2}} - 4$

b) $f(x) = 2x^2 - 7x^{-1} - 3$

c) $f(x) = x^4 + 9029x^3 - \sqrt{17}\, x^2 + 3897$

d) $f(x) = \sqrt{5x^3} - 3x^2 + 2x - 4$

e) $f(x) = 5x^3 - \sqrt{3x^2} + 2x - 4$

f) $f(x) = \sqrt{3}\, x^3 - \sqrt{-3}\, x$

Degree, Leading Coefficient, and Constant Term

Sometimes a polynomial function can be in a "disguised" form.

Class Ex. #3

State the degree, the leading coefficient, and the constant term of each polynomial function.

a) $f(x) = 34x^2 - 25x^3 + 2x - 39$

    degree→

    leading coefficient→

    constant→

b) $f(x) = (5x - 1)(2x + 7)$

    degree→

    leading coefficient→

    constant→

Class Ex. #4

In the following polynomial functions,

  i) determine the degree, the leading coefficient, and the constant term without expanding

  ii) verify the results in i) by expanding and simplifying the polynomial.

a) $P(x) = 2(3x - 1)^2(5x^2 - x + 1)$

    degree→

    leading coefficient→

    constant→

b) $P(x) = 2(3x - 1)^2 + (5x^2 - x + 1)$

    degree→

    leading coefficient→

    constant→

Class Ex. #5

Consider the polynomial function $P(x) = 7$.

a) Explain why the polynomial function $P(x) = 7$ has a degree of zero.

b) Explain why this type of function is called a constant function.

Classifying Polynomial Functions

Polynomial functions can be classified in several ways.

By Number of Terms

In previous courses we have used the classification **monomial** (one term), **binomial** (two terms), and **trinomial** (three terms). Polynomials with four or more terms are not usually given a classification other than polynomial.

By Degree

Polynomial functions can also be classified according to degree, such as:
constant (degree zero), **linear** (degree one), **quadratic** (degree two), **cubic** (degree three), **quartic** (degree four), etc.

Class Ex. #6

a) Complete the chart.

Polynomial Function	Degree	Type
$P(x) = c$		
$P(x) = ax + b, \qquad a \neq 0$		
$P(x) = ax^2 + bx + c, \qquad a \neq 0$		
$P(x) = ax^3 + bx^2 + cx + d, \qquad a \neq 0$		
$P(x) = ax^4 + bx^3 + cx^2 + dx + e, \qquad a \neq 0$		

b) Research the names for polynomials of degrees five through ten.

By Type of Coefficients

Polynomial functions can also be classified according to their coefficients. For example,

- $3x^4 - 5x^2 + x + 7$ is an **integral** polynomial function

- $3x^4 - \dfrac{2}{5}x^2 + x + 7$ is a **rational** polynomial function

- $\sqrt{3}\, x^4 - \dfrac{2}{5}x^2 + x + 7$ is a **real** polynomial function

Class Ex. #7 In each case, write a polynomial $P(x)$ satisfying the following conditions.

a) trinomial, quartic, and integral

b) binomial, linear, and real

c) monomial, quadratic, and rational

> ## *Evaluating Unknowns in a Polynomial Function*

Class Ex. #8 If $P(x) = -3x^2 + ax + 8$ and $P(1) = -9$, then find the value of a.

Class Ex. #9 Determine the values of a and b in $P(x) = -2x^2 + ax + b$ if $P(2) = -18$ and $P(-3) = -13$.

> **Complete Assignment Questions #1 - #14**

Assignment

1. Which of the following are not polynomial functions of x? Explain.

   a) $f(x) = \dfrac{1}{2}x^2 + 5x$ **b)** $f(x) = x^{-4} + x^3$ **c)** $f(x) = \sqrt{x} + 3x - 1$ **d)** $f(x) = 3^x + 1$

   e) $f(x) = 4(\sqrt{x} - 1)(\sqrt{x} + 1)$ **f)** $f(x) = \sqrt{10x^4} + 3x$ **g)** $f(x) = \sqrt{x^2 + 4}$

2. State the degree, leading coefficient and constant term for each of the following polynomial functions.

   a) $P(x) = 5x^3 - 7x^4 + 2$ **b)** $P(x) = 4x^2 - x^4 + 2x^3 + x^4$

   degree→   degree→
   leading coefficient→   leading coefficient→
   constant→   constant→

   c) $P(x) = 4(4x + 1)^2(2x^2 - x + 5)$ **d)** $P(x) = 3(4x + 1)^2 - (4x^2 + x - 1)$

   degree→   degree→
   leading coefficient→   leading coefficient→
   constant→   constant→

   e) $P(x) = (x + 1)(x + 2)(x - 3)$ **f)** $g(x) = -5(2x^3 + 3x - 2)^4$

   degree→   degree→
   leading coefficient→   leading coefficient→
   constant→   constant→

3. Which of the following is a polynomial of degree 5?

   a) $5x^4 + 5x$ **b)** $\dfrac{3}{x^5} + 5$ **c)** $x^2 - 3x^5 + x - 4$

   d) $x^5 - 2x^7$ **e)** $2x^5 + 3x - 7x^{-3}$ **f)** $(x^2 + 3)(x^3 + 4)$

4. For each polynomial, use substitution to find the indicated value.

a) $P(x) = 3x^3 - 5x^2 - 2$; $P(-3)$

b) $P(x) = 4x^4 - x^3 - x + 3$; $P\left(\dfrac{1}{2}\right)$

5. Some of the following functions are polynomial functions when simplified. For those which are, answer the following.

i) Write the expression in simplest polynomial form in descending powers of x.

ii) Name the type of polynomial (integral, rational, real) according to its coefficients.

iii) State the degree, leading coefficient, and constant term.

a) $f(x) = 3x^{-4} + 2x^3 - 3x^{-4} + 2x^3$

b) $g(x) = \left(\sqrt{3}\,x - \sqrt{2}\right)\left(\sqrt{3}\,x + \sqrt{2}\right)$

c) $h(x) = 8x^5 - \sqrt{36x} + 2$

d) $f(x) = 3 - \sqrt{10x^2} + 3x^4$

e) $g(x) = \dfrac{7x^3 - 3x^2 + 2x}{2}$

f) $g(x) = 2x^2 - 3x^{-1} + 5x^2 + 7x^{-1}$

6. Determine the values of a and b in $P(x) = ax^3 + bx^2 + 3x - 4$ if $P(1) = -2$ and $P(2) = 2$.

7. Determine the values of $a, b,$ and c in $P(x) = ax^2 + bx + c$ if $P(0) = 1, P(1) = 6,$ and $P(-1) = 2$.

Multiple Choice

8. Which of the following is an integral polynomial of degree 4?

A. $2x^4 - \dfrac{1}{3}x^2 + 1$

B. $x + x^2 + 3x^4$

C. $\dfrac{x^4 + 2x}{x}$

D. $3x^6 + 2x^4 + 2x + 1$

Use the following functions to answer questions #9 - #12.

A. $f(x) = (x - 1)(2x + 3)^2(4 - x)$

B. $g(x) = 2x^4 - 3x^5 + x^3 - \sqrt{7x^2} + 2x - 3$

C. $h(x) = 3x^3 - 2x^2 + 4x^{-1} + 14$

D. $P(x) = -5x^2 + \dfrac{1}{2}x + 3x^3 + 36$

9. Which one of these functions is a polynomial function with a leading coefficient of 3?

10. Which one of these functions is a polynomial function with a degree of 4?

11. Which one of these functions would be classified as an integral polynomial function?

12. Which one of these functions has a constant term of -36?

13. Consider the polynomial function $P(x) = px^3 + qx + r$, where $P(0) = 1$, $P(1) = 3$, and $P(-2) = -33$. The value of p, to the nearest tenth, is _____ .

(Record your answer in the numerical response box from left to right.)

14. The degree of the polynomial $4(x + 1)^3 + (x^3 - 2)^2 - x^2(x^4 + 12)$ is _____ .

(Record your answer in the numerical response box from left to right.)

Answer Key

1. No to b, c, d, g

2. a) 4, –7, 2   **b)** 3, 2, 0   **c)** 4, 128, 20
     d) 2, 44, 4   **e)** 3, 1, –6   **f)** 12, –80, –80

3. c, f   **4. a)** –128   **b)** $\dfrac{21}{8}$

5. a) (i) $f(x) = 4x^3$ (ii) integral   (iii) 3, 4, 0
   b) (i) $g(x) = 3x^2 - 2$ (ii) integral   (iii) 2, 3, –2
   c) not a polynomial function
   d) (i) $f(x) = 3x^4 - \sqrt{10}\,x + 3$ (ii) real   (iii) 4, 3, 3
   e) (i) $g(x) = \dfrac{7}{2}x^3 - \dfrac{3}{2}x^2 + x$ (ii) rational   (iii) 3, $\dfrac{7}{2}$, 0
   f) not a polynomial function

6. $a = 1, b = -2$ **7.** $a = 3, b = 2, c = 1$ **8.** B   **9.** D   **10.** A

11. A   **12.** A   **13.** | 5 | . | 0 | | **14.** | 1 | | | |

Polynomial Functions and Equations Lesson #2:
Using Long Division to Divide a Polynomial by a Binomial

Review | *Dividing a Polynomial by a Monomial*

Complete the following division: $\dfrac{15x^3 - 10x^2 + 5x}{5x} = \dfrac{15x^3}{5x} - \dfrac{10x^2}{5x} + \dfrac{}{5x} =$

In this example:
the **dividend** is $15x^3 - 10x^2 + 5x$, the **divisor** is $5x$, and the **quotient** is $3x^2 - 2x + 1$.

Dividing a Polynomial by a Binomial

In the example above, the divisor divided the polynomial exactly. This is not always the case.

Consider the division of 20 by 3. Complete the following.
The **dividend** is ___ , the **divisor** is ___, the **quotient** is ___ , and the **remainder** is ___.

The result of the division can be written in two ways. $20 = 3 \times 6 + 2$ **or** $\dfrac{20}{3} = 6 + \dfrac{2}{3}$

In other words, **i)** dividend = divisor × quotient + remainder.

ii) $\dfrac{\text{dividend}}{\text{divisor}} = \text{quotient} + \dfrac{\text{remainder}}{\text{divisor}}$.

In the case where the dividend is a polynomial, we have the following:

i) polynomial = **divisor × quotient + remainder.** $\qquad P = DQ + R$

ii) $\dfrac{\textbf{polynomial}}{\textbf{divisor}} = \textbf{quotient} + \dfrac{\textbf{remainder}}{\textbf{divisor}}$. $\qquad \dfrac{P}{D} = Q + \dfrac{R}{D}$

Class Ex. #1

A student used **long division** to divide 739 by 35 and wrote the result of the division in two ways. The work is shown below. Use the student's method to divide 5773 by 25 and show the result in two ways.

Student's Work

$$
\begin{array}{r}
21 \\
35 \overline{\smash{)}739} \\
70 \\
\hline
39 \\
35 \\
\hline
4
\end{array}
$$

$$739 = 35(21) + 4$$

or

$$\dfrac{739}{35} = 21 + \dfrac{4}{35}$$

Long division may also be used to divide polynomials.

Class Ex. #2

Three partially completed long divisions are shown.
In each case, complete the division and write the result in the form $P = D \cdot Q + R$.

i) $\dfrac{x^2 + 3x + 18}{x}$

$$
\begin{array}{r}
x + \\
x\,\overline{\big)\,x^2 + 3x + 18} \\
\underline{x^2} \\
0
\end{array}
$$

ii) $(x^3 - 5x + 6) \div (x)$

$$
\begin{array}{r}
x^2 + 0x \\
x\,\overline{\big)\,x^3 + 0x^2 - 5x + 6} \\
\underline{x^3} \\
0 + 0x^2 \\
0x^2 \\
0 - 5x
\end{array}
$$

iii) $\dfrac{2x^2 - x - 18}{x + 2}$

$$
\begin{array}{r}
2x \\
x+2\,\overline{\big)\,2x^2 - x - 18} \\
\underline{2x^2 + 4x}
\end{array}
$$

Note

• A video demonstration of polynomial long division can be found at
http://www.mathsisfun.com/algebra/polynomials-division-long.html

Class Ex. #3

Divide $y^3 - 6y + 20$ by $y - 3$. Express the answer in the form $\dfrac{P}{D} = Q + \dfrac{R}{D}$.

The Division Algorithm

When a polynomial $P(x)$ is divided by a polynomial $D(x)$, there exist unique polynomials $Q(x)$ and $R(x)$ such that

$$P(x) = D(x) \cdot Q(x) + R(x).$$

- If $R(x) = 0$, then $D(x)$ and $Q(x)$ are both factors of $P(x)$.
- If $R(x) \neq 0$, then $D(x)$ and $Q(x)$ are **not** factors of $P(x)$.
- The degree of the divisor, $D(x)$, must not be greater than the degree of the polynomial, $P(x)$.
- The degree of the remainder, $R(x)$, must be less than the degree of the divisor, $D(x)$.

Class Ex. #4

Consider the polynomial $P(x) = 1 + 5x^3 - 4x + 6x^4$.

a) Write the polynomial in descending order of the powers of x.

b) Divide the polynomial by $2x - 1$ and write the result in the form $P(x) = D(x) \cdot Q(x) + R(x)$.

c) Is $2x - 1$ a factor of $1 + 5x^3 - 4x + 6x^4$? Explain.

Class Ex. #5

Consider the long division shown.

a) State the divisor, quotient, and remainder.

b) Use the division algorithm to determine $P(x)$.

$$2x - 3 \overline{\smash{)}\ P(x)} \quad \genfrac{}{}{0pt}{}{x^2 + 4}{}$$

$$-2$$

Complete Assignment Questions #1 - #11

Assignment

1. Divide the following polynomials. Express the answer in the form $P = DQ + R$.

a) $\dfrac{x^2 + 5x + 4}{x + 2}$ **b)** $\dfrac{2x^2 - 5x + 2}{x - 3}$ **c)** $\dfrac{6x^2 - 5x - 3}{x - 1}$

2. Divide the following polynomials. Express the answer in the form $\dfrac{P}{D} = Q + \dfrac{R}{D}$.

a) $\dfrac{a^3 - a^2 - 4a + 12}{a - 2}$ **b)** $\dfrac{3x^3 - x^2 + 2x + 4}{x + 4}$

3. Determine the quotient and remainder when the following polynomials are divided.

a) $\dfrac{6x^2 - 5x + 7}{2x - 3}$

b) $\dfrac{9x^2 - 9}{3x + 1}$

c) $\dfrac{12x^3 - 5x^2 + x}{4x - 3}$

4. a) Explain how to determine if $x + 5$ is a factor of $x^3 + 125$.

b) Use the process in a) to determine if $x + 5$ is a factor of $x^3 + 125$.

5. Given that the degree of $D(x) = 4$, state the possible degrees of $R(x)$ in
$P(x) = D(x) \cdot Q(x) + R(x)$.

6. A rectangular carpet has an area of $x^3 - 5x + 12$ square metres.

   a) If the width of the carpet is $x + 3$ metres, determine an expression for the length of the carpet.

   b) If the width of the carpet is 8 metres, determine the length of the carpet.

7. The division shows a polynomial expression in x, written as $P(x)$, being divided by a binomial.

$$3x - 2 \overline{\smash{\big)}\ \begin{matrix} x^2 - 3x + 2 \\ \hline P(x) \end{matrix}}$$

$$\overline{17}$$

   a) Write $P(x)$ in the form $D(x) \cdot Q(x) + R(x)$.

   b) Write $P(x)$ in the form $ax^3 + bx^2 + cx + d$.

8. When a third degree polynomial is divided by $x + 5$, the quotient is $x^2 - 2x - 1$ and the remainder is 7. Express the polynomial in the form $ax^3 + bx^2 + cx + d$.

Multiple Choice **9.** When $(3z^4 + 6z^3 - 18z)$ is divided by $(z + 3)$, the remainder is

    A. -45

    B. 45

    C. -135

    D. 135

Numerical Response **10.** A rectangle has an area of $8x^2 - 14x - 15$ cm^2 and a length of $4x + 3$ cm. The perimeter of the rectangle can be written in the form $ax + b$ cm.

The value of $a + b$ is _____.

(Record your answer in the numerical response box from left to right.)

11. When the polynomial $ax^3 + bx^2 + cx + d$ is divided by $3x - 2$, the quotient is $2x^2 + 2x + 3$ and the remainder is 7.

Record the value of a in the first box.
Record the value of b in the second box.
Record the value of c in the third box.
Record the value of d in the fourth box.

Answer Key

1. a) $x^2 + 5x + 4 = (x + 2)(x + 3) - 2$ **b)** $2x^2 - 5x + 2 = (x - 3)(2x + 1) + 5$

    c) $6x^2 - 5x - 3 = (x - 1)(6x + 1) - 2$

2. a) $\dfrac{a^3 - a^2 - 4a + 12}{a - 2} = a^2 + a - 2 + \dfrac{8}{a - 2}$ **b)** $\dfrac{3x^3 - x^2 + 2x + 4}{x + 4} = 3x^2 - 13x + 54 - \dfrac{212}{x + 4}$

3. a) Quotient $= 3x + 2$, remainder $= 13$ **b)** Quotient $= 3x - 1$, remainder $= -8$

    c) Quotient $= 3x^2 + x + 1$, remainder $= 3$

4. a) Divide $x^3 + 125$ by $x + 5$. If the remainder is zero, then $x + 5$ is a factor of $x^3 + 125$.

    b) $x + 5$ is a factor of $x^3 + 125$.

5. 0, 1, 2, 3

6. a) $x^2 - 3x + 4$ metres   **b)** 14 metres

7. a) $P(x) = (3x - 2)(x^2 - 3x + 2) + 17$ **b)** $P(x) = 3x^3 - 11x^2 + 12x + 13$

8. $x^3 + 3x^2 - 11x + 2$ **9.** D   **10.**

8			

    11.

6	2	5	1

Polynomial Functions and Equations Lesson #3:
Using Synthetic Division to Divide a Polynomial by a Binomial

Review

The work shows the process of long division used by a student to divide the polynomial $3x^3 - 7x - 9$ by $x - 2$.

State

a) the dividend

b) the quotient

c) the divisor

d) the remainder

$$
\begin{array}{r}
3x^2 + 6x + 5 \\
x-2{\overline{\smash{\big)}\,3x^3 + 0x^2 - 7x - 9}} \\
\underline{3x^3 - 6x^2}\phantom{{}-7x-9} \\
6x^2 - 7x \\
\underline{6x^2 - 12x} \\
5x - 9 \\
\underline{5x - 10} \\
1
\end{array}
$$

$$\underline{3x^3 - 7x - 9 = (x-2)(3x^2 + 6x + 5) + 1}$$

Exploring Synthetic Division

A student who was repeating this course showed his friend a much quicker method for determining the above result. His work is shown.

$$
\begin{array}{r|rrrr}
2 & 3 & 0 & -7 & -9 \\
  & \downarrow & 6 & 12 & 10 \\
\hline
  & 3 & 6 & 5 & \circled{1}
\end{array}
$$

$$\underline{3x^3 - 7x - 9 = (x-2)(3x^2 + 6x + 5) + 1}$$

a) By looking at both sets of work, explain how the following parts of the synthetic division are related to the long division.

  i)   the 2 on the left side

  ii) the numbers $3, 0, -7, -9$, in the top row

  iii) the 1 which is circled

  iv) the numbers $3, 6, 5$ in the bottom row

b) Can you identify how the sets of numbers $6, 12, 10$, and $3, 6, 5, 1$ are obtained?

Class Ex. #1   Complete the following synthetic division to determine the quotient and remainder when $2x^3 - 3x^2 - 8x + 15$ is divided by $x - 1$. Express the answer in the form $\dfrac{P}{D} = Q + \dfrac{R}{D}$.

$$1 \,\big|\, \begin{array}{cccc} 2 & -3 & -8 & 15 \end{array}$$

Class Ex. #2   Consider the polynomial $5x^5 - 6x^4 + 3x^2 - 2x + 1$.

a) Use synthetic division to find the quotient and remainder when
$5x^5 - 6x^4 + 3x^2 - 2x + 1$ is divided by $x + 2$.

b) Find the value of the polynomial when x is replaced by -2.

c) Comment on your answers in **a)** and **b)**.

Class Ex. #3   If $x + 3$ is the divisor in the following synthetic division, calculate the values of m and p.

$$\big|\, \begin{array}{cccc} 2 & 2 & -m & 16 \\ & & & n \\ \hline 2 & & 2m & p \end{array}$$

Class Ex. #4

When $2x^3 - 4x^2 + ax + 3$ is divided by $x + 2$, the remainder is 3. Determine the value of a.

Complete Assignment Questions #1 - #7

Synthetic Division by $ax - b$

Use synthetic division to determine the quotient and remainder when the polynomial $2x^3 + x^2 + 5x - 1$ is divided by $2x - 1$.

Note that $2x - 1 = 2\left(x - \dfrac{1}{2}\right)$.

We divide first by $x - \dfrac{1}{2}$.

$$\begin{array}{c|cccc} & 2 & 1 & 5 & -1 \\ \hline & & & & \end{array}$$

$P = DQ + R.$

so
$$P = \left(x - \frac{1}{2}\right)(2x^2 + 2x + 6) + 2$$

$$= \left(x - \frac{1}{2}\right)(2)(x^2 + x + 3) + 2$$

$$= (2x - 1)(\qquad\qquad) + \qquad\qquad$$

Quotient is _____

Remainder is _____

Class Ex. #5

Divide $6x^3 - 8x^2 - 5x + 5$ by $3x + 2$ using synthetic division and write the division in the form $P = DQ + R$.

Complete Assignment Questions #8 - #11

Assignment

1. In the partially completed synthetic division below, a polynomial $P(x)$ is divided by $x - 2$.

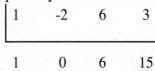

$$\begin{array}{r|rrrr} & 1 & -2 & 6 & 3 \\ \hline & 1 & 0 & 6 & 15 \end{array}$$

a) State the polynomial $P(x)$.   b) State the quotient.   c) State the remainder.

d) Write the above synthetic division in the form of the division algorithm.

2. Use synthetic division to divide the polynomial by the binomial and express each in the form $P(x) = D(x) \cdot Q(x) + R(x)$.

a) $x^3 + 2x^2 + 3x + 6; \quad x - 2$

b) $2x^3 - 4x^2 - 5x + 9; \quad x + 2$

c) $x^4 - x^2 + 7; \quad x + 1$

d) $2y^4 - y^5 - y^3 + 4y; \quad y - 3$

3. Determine $p, q,$ and r in the partially completed synthetic division below in which the divisor is $x - 1$.

$$\begin{array}{r|rrrr} & 2 & 3 & q & 1 \\ \hline & 2 & p & 7 & r \end{array}$$

4. Determine m and n in the partially completed synthetic division below in which the divisor is $x + 2$.

$$
\begin{array}{c|cccc}
2 & & m & -3 & n \\
  & & & -4 & & m \\
\hline
\end{array}
$$

5. Find the remainder on dividing $x^3 - 3x^2 + x + 8$ by $x - 2$. Compare this with $f(2)$ where $f(x) = x^3 - 3x^2 + x + 8$.

6. Find the remainder on dividing $12 - 5x + 3x^2 + 2x^3$ by $x + 3$. Compare this with $P(-3)$ where $P(x) = 12 - 5x + 3x^2 + 2x^3$.

7. When $2x^3 + ax^2 - 3x + 4$ is divided by $x + 1$, the remainder is 8. Determine the value of a.

8. Divide $9x^3 + 18x^2 - 13x + 5$ by $3x - 1$ using synthetic division and write the division in the form $P = DQ + R$.

9. Divide $4x^3 + 11x^2 - 14x - 9$ by $4x + 3$ using synthetic division and write the division in the form $P = DQ + R$.

10. When the polynomial $2a^3 - 7a + 6$ is divided by $a - 4$, the remainder is

    A. -94

    B. 10

    C. 66

    D. 106

11. When the polynomial $3y^3 - 4y^2 + by + 6$ is divided by $y + 2$, the remainder is -40. The value of b is _____.

(Record your answer in the numerical response box from left to right.)

Answer Key

1. a) $x^3 - 2x^2 + 6x + 3$ **b)** $x^2 + 6$ **c)** 15 **d)** $x^3 - 2x^2 + 6x + 3 = (x - 2)(x^2 + 6) + 15$

2. a) $x^3 + 2x^2 + 3x + 6 = (x - 2)(x^2 + 4x + 11) + 28$
    b) $2x^3 - 4x^2 - 5x + 9 = (x + 2)(2x^2 - 8x + 11) - 13$
    c) $x^4 - x^2 + 7 = (x + 1)(x^3 - x^2) + 7$
    d) $-y^5 + 2y^4 - y^3 + 4y = (y - 3)(-y^4 - y^3 - 4y^2 - 12y - 32) - 96$

3. $p = 5, q = 2, r = 8$ **4.** $m = 0, n = 10$ **5.** $6, 6$ **6.** $0, 0$ **7.** 3

8. $9x^3 + 18x^2 - 13x + 5 = (3x - 1)(3x^2 + 7x - 2) + 3$

9. $4x^3 + 11x^2 - 14x - 9 = (4x + 3)(x^2 + 2x - 5) + 6$ **10.** D   **11.** $\boxed{3}$

Polynomial Functions and Equations Lesson #4:
The Remainder Theorem and the Factor Theorem

Review

a) Use synthetic division to divide
$P(x) = x^3 - 2x^2 - 4$ by $x + 1$.

Calculate $P(-1)$ in
$P(x) = x^3 - 2x^2 - 4$.

b) Use synthetic division to divide
$P(x) = x^2 - 2x - 5$ by $x - 2$.

Calculate $P(2)$ in
$P(x) = x^2 - 2x - 5$.

c) Complete the following statements based on your observations in a) and b).

• When $P(x) = x^3 - 2x^2 - 4$ is divided by $x + 1$, the ___remainder___ is equal to $P(-1)$.

• When $P(x) = x^2 - 2x - 5$ is divided by $x - 2$, the ___remainder___ is equal to $P(2)$.

The Remainder Theorem

When a polynomial function, $P(x)$, is divided by a binomial, $(x - a)$, the remainder obtained is equal to the value of the polynomial when $x = a$, i.e. the remainder is $P(a)$.

Proof:

The division algorithm states $P(x) = D(x) \cdot Q(x) + R(x)$

Using $x - a$ as the divisor, we get $P(x) = (x - a) \cdot Q(x) + R(x)$

To find $P(a)$ we can substitute a for x to get

$$P(a) = (a - a) \cdot Q(a) + R$$

$$= 0 \cdot Q(a) + R$$

$$= 0 + R$$

$\therefore P(a) = R$ which is what the remainder theorem states.

Class Ex. #1

Use the remainder theorem to find the remainder when $P(x) = 6x^3 - 4x^2 + 8x + 6$ is divided by

i) $x + 1$ **ii)** $2x - 1$

Class Ex. #2

Find a if the remainder is 131 when $P(x) = 2x^4 - x^3 - ax + 8$ is divided by $x - 3$;

a) using synthetic division   **b)** using the remainder theorem

Class Ex. #3

Find the coefficients d and c in $P(x) = 2x^4 + dx^3 - cx^2 + 5x - 8$ if the remainder is -41 when divided by $x + 3$ and the remainder is 74 when divided by $x - 2$.

Complete Assignment Questions #1 - #5

The Factor Theorem

The binomial $x - a$ is a **factor** of the polynomial function $P(x)$ if, and only if, $P(a) = 0$.
Note that a is then a **zero** of the polynomial function $P(x)$.

Class Ex. #4   Show that $x - 4$ is a factor of $P(x) = x^2 + 2x - 24$ by using

a) synthetic division   **b)** the factor theorem

_____

Class Ex. #5   Write a binomial factor with integral coefficients of the polynomial $P(x)$ if

a) $P(3) = 0$ **b)** $P\left(-\dfrac{2}{3}\right) = 0$

_____

Class Ex. #6   If $P(5) = P(-2) = 0$, determine a second degree factor of the polynomial $P(x)$.

_____

Class Ex. #7   Use the factor theorem to determine which of the following is a factor of $4x^3 - 16x^2 - x + 4$.

a) $x + 2$ **b)** $2x - 1$

_____

Class Ex. #8   Show that 1 is a root of the equation $x^3 - 9x^2 + 20x - 12 = 0$ and find the other roots.

Note Class Ex. #8 shows that if the sum of the coefficients of a polynomial function is equal to zero, then 1 is a zero of the function.

Complete Assignment Questions #6 - #20

Assignment

1. Use the remainder theorem to find the remainder when each of the following polynomials is divided by the binomial.

    a) $P(x) = 3x^3 - x^2 + 2x + 1$
    is divided by $x + 5$

    b) $P(x) = x^4 + x^2 - 8x + 5$
    is divided by $x - 4$

2. Find the values of p and q if $x^3 + px + q$ yields remainders of -3 and 2 when divided by $x - 2$ and $x + 1$ respectively.

3. When $P(x) = x^4 + mx^3 - nx^2 + 28x - 24$ is divided by $x - 3$, the remainder is 6. If $P(1) = -4$, find the values of m and n.

4. When $x^4 + ax^2 - 16$ is divided by $x + 1$, the remainder is -14.
   What is the remainder when $x^4 + ax^2 - 16$ is divided by $x - 2$?

5. $P(x)$ is a polynomial which has a remainder of 2 when it is divided by $x + 3$.
   Find the remainder when the following polynomials are divided by $x + 3$.

   (i) $P(x) - 1$ (ii) $P(x) + 2x + 6$ (iii) $3P(x)$

6. If $x - a$ is a factor of the polynomial $P(x)$, what is the remainder obtained when $P(x)$ is divided by $x - a$?

7. Determine which of the following binomials are factors of $P(x) = x^3 - 4x^2 - x + 4$.

   a) $x - 1$ b) $x - 2$

   c) $x + 2$ d) $x - 4$

8. Find the value of a so that $x + 1$ is a factor of $x^4 + 4x^3 + ax^2 + 4x + 1$.

9. When $P(x) = 2x^3 + ax^2 + bx + 6$ is divided by $x + 2$, the remainder is -12. If $x - 1$ is a factor of the polynomial, find the values of a and b.

10. If $P(x) = x^3 + kx^2 - x - 2$ and $P(-2) = 0$, determine the complete factoring of $P(x)$.

11. Show that -4 is a zero of $P(x) = 6x^3 + 25x^2 + 2x - 8$ and find the other zeros.

12. Given that $x^2 + 2x - 3$ is a factor of $f(x) = x^4 + 2x^3 - 7x^2 + ax + b$, find a and b and hence factor $f(x)$ completely.

13. Find the remainder when

a) $2x^4 + x^3 - 3x^2 + 3x - 4$ is divided by $2x - 1$ **b)** $3t^3 - 2t + 2$ is divided by $3t + 1$

14. For $P(x) = x^2 - x + 1$, find a if $P(a) = 3$.

Multiple Choice **15.** When a polynomial $P(x)$ is divided by $x - 2$, the remainder is 3. If the polynomial $A(x) = 2P(x)$ is divided by $x - 2$, the remainder will be

A. 1.5

B. 2

C. 3

D. 6

16. If a polynomial $P(x)$ has $P(0) = 8$, then which of the following statements **must** be true?

    A. The constant term in $P(x)$ is 8.   **B.** The constant term in $P(x)$ is –8.
    C. A factor of $P(x)$ is $x + 8$.   **D.** A factor of $P(x)$ is $x – 8$.

17. If a polynomial $P(x)$ has $P(8) = 0$, then which of the following statements **must** be true?

    A. The constant term in $P(x)$ is 8.   **B.** The constant term in $P(x)$ is –8.
    C. A factor of $P(x)$ is $x + 8$.   **D.** A factor of $P(x)$ is $x – 8$.

18. When a polynomial $P(x)$ is divided by $x + 5$, the remainder is –2.
Which of the following statements is true?

    A. $P(-2) = -5$ **B.** $P(-2) = 5$ **C.** $P(5) = -2$ **D.** $P(-5) = -2$

19. The polynomial $P(x) = 2x^3 - ax^2 - 11x + 2a$ has a remainder of 126 when divided by $x - 5$. The value of a, to the nearest tenth, is _____ .

(Record your answer in the numerical response box from left to right.)

20. When $x^3 - 4x^2 + 3$ and $x^3 - 3x^2 - 8x + 19$ are each divided by $x - a$, the remainders are equal. To the nearest tenth, the value of a is _____ .

(Record your answer in the numerical response box from left to right.)

Answer Key

1. a) –409   **b)** 245   **2.** $p = -\frac{14}{3}, q = -\frac{5}{3}$ **3.** $m = -3, n = 6$
4. 4   **5. (i)** 1   **(ii)** 2   **(iii)** 6   **6.** 0   **7.** a and d
8. $a = 6$ **9.** $a = -3, b = -5$ **10.** $(x + 2)(x + 1)(x - 1)$
11. $-\frac{2}{3}, \frac{1}{2}$ **12.** $a = -8, b = 12$ $(x + 3)(x - 1)(x + 2)(x - 2)$
13. a) –3   **b)** $\frac{23}{9}$ **14.** $a = -1$ or $a = 2$ **15.** D   **16.** A
17. D   **18.** D   **19.** | 3 | . | 0 | | **20.** | 4 | . | 0 | |

Polynomial Functions and Equations Lesson #5:
Factoring Polynomial Expressions - Part One

In this lesson we will focus on factoring polynomial expressions where the leading coefficient is 1.

Review

Consider the polynomial function $f(x) = x^2 - x - 6$. The function can be expressed in factored form as $f(x) = (x + 2)(x - 3)$.

a) Fill in the blanks in the illustration below.

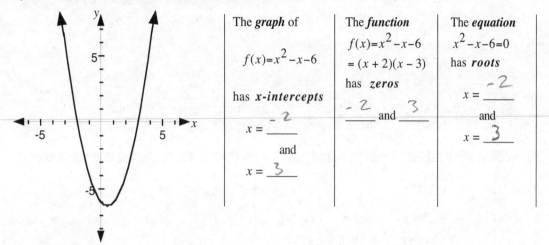

The **graph** of	The **function**	The **equation**
$f(x) = x^2 - x - 6$ has **x-intercepts** $x = \underline{-2}$ and $x = \underline{3}$	$f(x) = x^2 - x - 6$ $= (x + 2)(x - 3)$ has **zeros** $\underline{-2}$ and $\underline{3}$	$x^2 - x - 6 = 0$ has **roots** $x = \underline{-2}$ and $x = \underline{3}$

b) Fill in the blanks in the following statement regarding the function with equation $y = f(x)$.

" The _____ of the function, the _____ of the graph of the function, and

the _____ of the corresponding equation $y = 0$, are the _____ numbers."

Investigating the Integral Zero Theorem

a) The factors of the polynomial, $P(x) = x^2 + 5x - 24$ are $(x + 8)$ and $(x - 3)$.

   i) State the zeros of the polynomial function.

   ii) What do you notice about the constant term in the polynomial and the zeros of the polynomial?

b) The factors of the polynomial, $P(x) = x^3 - 2x^2 - x + 2$ are $(x - 2), (x - 1),$ and $(x + 1)$.

   i) State the zeros of the polynomial function.

   ii) What do you notice about the constant term in the polynomial and the zeros of the polynomial?

The examples on the previous page are illustrations of the **Integral Zero Theorem** which states that **the zeros of an integral polynomial function with a leading coefficient of 1 must be factors of the constant term**.

Consider $P(x) = x^3 - 7x - 6$.

- The integral zero theorem tells us that zeros of $P(x)$ must be factors of –6 and so must come from the list $\pm 1, \pm 2, \pm 3, \pm 6$.
- This list contains all **potential zeros** of the polynomial.

Class Ex. #1

Consider the polynomial $P(x) = x^3 - 7x - 6$.

a) List the potential zeros of the polynomial.

b) List the potential factors of the polynomial.

c) Students were asked to identify one of the actual factors of the polynomial.
Luke used the factor theorem, and Nicole used synthetic division. Their work is shown.

<u>Luke's Work Using the Factor Theorem</u>

- Try $x - 1$ as a factor.

  $P(1) = (1)^3 - 7(1) - 6 = -12$

  $P(1) \neq 0$, therefore $x - 1$ is <u>not</u> a factor.

- Try $x + 1$ as a factor.

  $P(-1) = (-1)^3 - 7(-1) - 6 = 0$

  $P(1) = 0$, therefore $x + 1$ <u>is</u> a factor.

- use $x + 1$ as a factor in synthetic division to find a quadratic quotient

```
-1 | 1    0    -7   -6
   |     -1    1    6
   ------------------------
     1    -1   -6   ( 0 )
```

<u>Nicole's Work Using Synthetic Division</u>

- Try $x - 1$ as a factor.

```
1 | 1    0    -7   -6
  |      1    1    -6
  ----------------------
    1    1    -6   (-12)
```

Since the remainder is –12, then $x - 1$ is <u>not</u> a factor.

- Try $x + 1$ as a factor.

```
-1 | 1    0    -7   -6
   |      -1    1    6
   ----------------------
     1    -1   -6   ( 0 )
```

Since the remainder is 0, then $x + 1$ <u>is</u> a factor.

Complete the factoring of the polynomial $x^3 - 7x - 6$.

Class Ex. #2

Consider the polynomial $P(x) = x^4 + 2x^3 - 7x^2 - 8x + 12$.

a) List the potential zeros of the polynomial.

b) Express the polynomial in factored form.

c) State the zeros of $P(x)$.

d) State the roots of the equation $x^4 + 2x^3 - 7x^2 - 8x + 12 = 0$.

Complete Assignment Questions #1 - #8

Class Ex. #3

Consider the polynomial function $P(x) = x^3 - 3x^2 - 3x + 1$.

a) Find the zeros of $P(x)$, to the nearest hundredth, using a graphing calculator.

b) Use the integral zero in a) and synthetic division to determine the exact value of the zeros.

Complete Assignment Questions #9 - #13

Assignment

1. Consider the polynomial $P(x) = x^3 + x^2 - 4x - 4$

   a) List the potential zeros of the polynomial.

   b) List the potential factors of the polynomial.

   c) Express the polynomial in factored form.

2. Consider the polynomial $P(x) = x^3 - 2x^2 - 5x + 6$

   a) List the potential zeros of the polynomial.

   b) List the potential factors of the polynomial.

   c) Express the polynomial in factored form.

   d) State the zeros of $P(x)$.   e) State the roots of the equation $x^3 - 2x^2 - 5x + 6 = 0$.

3. Determine the smallest positive value of k if the possible integral zeros
   of $P(x) = x^3 - 7x^2 + k$ are
   a) $\pm 1, \pm 2, \pm 7$ b) $\pm 1, \pm 2, \pm 5,$ and ± 10

4. Factor the following polynomials algebraically.

  a) $P(x) = x^3 + x^2 - 5x + 3$ **b)** $P(x) = x^3 + x^2 + 2x + 2$

5. Algebraically determine the zeros of the function $f(x) = x^4 + x^3 - 7x^2 - x + 6$.

6. Algebraically determine the x-intercepts of the graph of $y = x^4 - 2x^3 - 9x^2 + 2x + 8$.

7. Factor the polynomial $x^5 + 2x^4 - 12x^3 - 14x^2 + 11x + 12$.

Use the following information to answer the next question.

A horizontal beam 8 metres long has its left end built into a wall and its right end resting on a support. A pile of bricks is placed on the beam and the beam sags downward according to the formula $y = f(x) = x^4 - 26x^3 + 224x^2 - 640x$, where x is the distance in metres from the wall and y is the sag in hundredths of a millimetre.

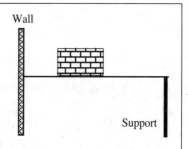

8. **a)** State a suitable domain for x.

   b) Determine the sag at the midpoint of the beam.

   c) The function has a zero when $x = 10$. Determine the other zeros of the function and explain what the zeros represent in the context of the question.

9. Consider the polynomial function $P(x) = x^3 + 10x^2 + 8x - 16$.
   a) Find the zeros of $P(x)$, to the nearest hundredth, using a graphing calculator.

   b) Use the integral zero in a) and synthetic division to determine the exact value of the zeros.

10. Determine the exact roots of the following equations.

    a) $x^3 + 4x^2 + 3x - 2 = 0$ **b)** $x^4 - 12x^2 + 4x + 15 = 0$.

11. Which of the following is not a potential zero of $P(x) = x^5 - 3x^3 - 6x - 27$.

    A. 1   **B.** −3
    C. −6   **D.** −27

12. Which of the following is not a root of the equation $x^4 - 8x^3 + 13x^2 + 12x - 18 = 0$?

    A. 1

    B. 3

    C. $2 + 2\sqrt{5}$

    D. $2 - \sqrt{10}$

13. The polynomial function $P(x) = x^3 - 7x^2 + 16x - 12$ can be written in the form $P(x) = (x - a)(x - b)^2$ where a and b are integers. The value of b is _____ .

(Record your answer in the numerical response box from left to right.)

Answer Key

1. a) $\pm1, \pm2, \pm4$ **b)** $x - 1, x + 1, x - 2, x + 2, x - 4, x + 4$ **c)** $P(x) = (x - 2)(x + 2)(x + 1)$

2. a) $\pm1, \pm2, \pm3, \pm6$ **b)** $x - 1, x + 1, x - 2, x + 2, x - 3, x + 3, x - 6, x + 6$
c) $P(x) = (x - 1)(x + 2)(x - 3)$ **d)** $-2, 1, 3$ **e)** $-2, 1, 3$

3. a) 14 **b)** 10 **4. a)** $P(x) = (x - 1)^2(x + 3)$ **b)** $(x + 1)(x^2 + 2)$

5. $-3, -1, 1, 2$ **6.** $-2, -1, 1, 4$ **7.** $(x - 1)(x + 1)^2(x - 3)(x + 4)$

8. a) $\{x \mid 0 \le x \le 8, x \in R\}$ **b)** 3.84 mm
c) The zeros are 0, 8 (twice), and 10. The zeros at 0 and 8 indicate that there is no sag where the beam is attached to the wall and where it is supported. The zero at 10 is outside the domain and has no meaning in the context of this question.

9. a) $-8.90, -2.00, 0.90$ **b)** $-2, -4 - 2\sqrt{6}, -4 + 2\sqrt{6}$

10. a) $-2, -1 - \sqrt{2}, -1 + \sqrt{2}$ **b)** $-1, 3, -1 - \sqrt{6}, -1 + \sqrt{6}$

11. C   **12.** C   **13.** 2

Polynomial Functions and Equations Lesson #6:
Factoring Polynomial Expressions - Part Two

In this lesson we extend the factoring of polynomial expressions to examples where the leading coefficient is not 1. **Some of the examples in this lesson require an understanding of the Rational Zero Theorem. These examples can be regarded as enrichment for students following the Alberta Curriculum.**

Investigating the Rational Zero Theorem

a) The factors of the polynomial $P(x) = 15x^2 - 34x + 16$ are $(3x - 2)$ and $(5x - 8)$.

  i) State the zeros of the polynomial function.

  ii) What do you notice about the constant term in the polynomial and the constant terms in the factors?

  iii) What do you notice about the leading coefficient in the polynomial and the leading coefficients in the factors?

  iv) How do the zeros relate to the coefficients in the polynomial?

b) The factors of the polynomial $P(x) = 10x^3 + 81x^2 - 298x + 231$ are $(2x - 3), (5x - 7)$, and $(x + 11)$.

  i) State the zeros of the polynomial function.

  ii) What do you notice about the constant term in the polynomial and the constant terms in the factors?

  iii) What do you notice about the leading coefficient in the polynomial and the leading coefficients in the factors?

  iv) How do the zeros relate to the coefficients in the polynomial?

The examples above are illustrations of the **Rational Zero Theorem** which states that **the zeros of an integral polynomial function $P(x)$ are of the form $\dfrac{p}{q}$, where the numerator p is a factor of the constant term, and the denominator q is a factor of the leading coefficient**.

$$\text{i.e.} \quad \frac{p}{q} = \frac{\text{Factor of the constant term}}{\text{Factor of the leading coefficient}}$$

Consider the polynomial $P(x) = 5x^3 - 51x^2 + 55x - 9$.

- The factors of the constant term, -9, are: $\pm1, \pm3, \pm9$.
- The factors of the leading coefficient, 5, are: $\pm1, \pm5$.

- $\dfrac{p}{q} \Rightarrow \dfrac{\text{Factors of the constant term}}{\text{Factors of the leading coefficient}} \Rightarrow \dfrac{\pm1, \pm3, \pm9}{\pm1, \pm5}$

- **Potential zeros** of $P(x)$ are $\pm1, \pm3, \pm9, \pm\dfrac{1}{5}, \pm\dfrac{3}{5}, \pm\dfrac{9}{5}$.

Class Ex. #1

Consider the function $P(x) = 5x^3 - 51x^2 + 55x - 9 = 0$.
a) Use the potential zeros above to list the potential binomial factors of $P(x)$ in the form $ax - b$, where $a \in N$ and $b \in I$.

b) Show that $x = 1$ is a zero of $P(x)$, and hence determine all the zeros of $P(x)$.

c) Solve the equation $5x^3 - 51x^2 + 55x - 9 = 0$.

Class Ex. #2

Determine all real solutions to the equation $2x^3 - x^2 - x - 3 = 0$.

Complete Assignment Questions #1 - #12

Assignment

1. Emma is determining the zeros of the integral polynomial $P(x) = 4x^5 - 2x + 10$.
   Which of the following rational numbers are potential zeros ?

   i) $\dfrac{5}{4}$ ii) $\dfrac{5}{2}$ iii) $\dfrac{2}{5}$ iv) -5 v) 10 vi) $-\dfrac{1}{2}$ vii) $\dfrac{1}{4}$

2. Consider the polynomial $g(x) = 6x^3 + 13x^2 + x - 2$

   a) List the potential zeros of the polynomial.

   b) List the potential binomial factors of the polynomial in the form $ax - b$, where $a \in N$
   and $b \in I$.

   c) Express the polynomial in factored form.

   d) State   **i)** the zeros of $g(x)$ **ii)** the roots of the equation $6x^3 + 13x^2 + x - 2 = 0$

3. The volume of a bar of gold is $3x^3 + 23x^2 + 45x + 25$ cm^3. The
   length, width, and height of the bar can all be expressed in the
   binomial form $px + q$, where p and q are natural numbers.

   a) Determine binomial expressions for the dimensions of the bar.

   b) State the dimensions of the bar if $x = 5$.

4. Express $3x^4 - 5x^3 - 17x^2 + 13x + 6$ in factored form.

5. Consider the function $f(x) = 2x^3 - 9x^2 + 6x - 1$.

a) State the potential zeros of the polynomial.

b) Given that there are no integral zeros, determine a rational zero of the polynomial.

c) The zero in b) is the only rational zero. Use the quadratic formula to determine the two irrational zeros.

d) State the roots as exact values of the equation $2x^3 - 9x^2 + 6x - 1 = 0$.

6. State the zeros of the polynomial function $g(x) = (2x - 5)(x - 7)(3x + 1)$.

7. The function $P(x) = 12x^3 - 16x^2 - 7x + 6$ has no integral zeros.

    a) State all possible rational zeros of the function.

    b) Express the function in factored form.

8. Solve the equation $8x^4 - 12x^3 + 6x^2 - x = 0$.

9. Jenny is attempting to algebraically find the factors of $P(x) = 6x^3 - 7x^2 - x + 2$.
    Which of the following factors should she **NOT** consider as a possible factor?

      A. $x - 1$

      B. $x - 6$

      C. $x + 1$

      D. $x + 2$

10. The zeros of the function $f(x) = 2x^3 - x^2 - 18x + 9$ are

    A. $\dfrac{1}{2}, -3, 3$

    B. $\dfrac{1}{2}, 3, 3$

    C. $-\dfrac{1}{2}, 3, 3$

    D. $-\dfrac{1}{2}, -3, 3$

11. If $P(x) = 6x^3 - 11x^2 - x + 6$ and $P\left(\dfrac{3}{2}\right) = 0$, then the factorization of $P(x)$ is

    A. $(2x - 3)(3x + 2)(x - 1)$

    B. $(3x - 2)(2x + 3)(x - 1)$

    C. $((2x + 3)(3x - 2)(x + 1)$

    D. $(3x + 2)(2x - 3)(x + 1)$

 12. The trinomial $x^2 - 3x - 4$ is a factor of the polynomial $2x^3 - 12x^2 + cx + d$, where c and d are integers. The value of $c + d$ is _____ .

(Record your answer in the numerical response box from left to right.)

Answer Key

1. i), ii), iv), v), vi), vii)

2. **a)** $\pm 1, \pm 2, \pm\dfrac{1}{2}, \pm\dfrac{1}{3}, \pm\dfrac{2}{3}, \pm\dfrac{1}{6}$

    b) $x - 1, x + 1, x - 2, x + 2, 2x - 1, 2x + 1, 3x - 1, 3x + 1, 3x - 2, 3x + 2, 6x - 1, 6x + 1$

    c) $g(x) = (x + 2)(2x + 1)(3x - 1)$ **d)** $-2, -\dfrac{1}{2}, \dfrac{1}{3}$ **e)** $-2, -\dfrac{1}{2}, \dfrac{1}{3}$

3. **a)** $3x + 5$ cm, $x + 1$ cm, $x + 5$ cm   **b)** 20 cm, 10 cm, 6 cm   **4.** $(x - 1)(x + 2)(x - 3)(3x + 1)$

5. **a)** $\pm 1, \pm\dfrac{1}{2}$ **b)** $\dfrac{1}{2}$ **c)** $2 \pm \sqrt{3}$ **d)** $\dfrac{1}{2}, 2 \pm \sqrt{3}$ **6.** $-\dfrac{1}{3}, \dfrac{5}{2}, 7$

7. **a)** $\pm\dfrac{1}{2}, \pm\dfrac{1}{3}, \pm\dfrac{1}{4}, \pm\dfrac{1}{6}, \pm\dfrac{1}{12}, \pm\dfrac{2}{3}, \pm\dfrac{3}{2}, \pm\dfrac{3}{4}$ **b)** $P(x) = (2x - 1)(2x - 3)(3x + 2)$

8. $0, \dfrac{1}{2}$ **9.** B   **10.** A   **11.** A   **12.**

3	4		

Polynomial Functions and Equations Lesson #7:
Investigating the Graphs of Polynomial Functions - Part One

Review of Zeros, Roots, and x-intercepts

Fill in the blanks in the following statement regarding the function with equation $y = P(x)$.

" The _____ of the function, the _____ of the graph of the function, and

the _____ of the corresponding equation $y = 0$ are the _____ numbers."

Unique Factorization Theorem

This theorem states that every polynomial function of degree $n \geq 1$ can be written as the product of a leading coefficient, c, and n linear factors to get

$$P(x) = c(x - a_1)(x - a_2)(x - a_3)...(x - a_n)$$

This theorem implies two *important* points for polynomial functions of degree $n \geq 1$:

Point #1: Every polynomial function can be written as a product of its factors and a leading coefficient.

Point #2: Every polynomial function has the same number of factors as its degree. The factors may be real or complex, and may be repeated.

 In this lesson we will consider only polynomial functions where the leading coefficient, c, is either 1 or –1. In lesson 10, we will consider polynomial functions with a leading coefficient other than ±1.

 Class Ex. #1

The graph of $P(x) = x^3 - 2x^2 - 5x + 6$ is shown. The polynomial has integral zeros.

a) Use the graph to

    i) state the zeros of the polynomial

    ii) state the factors of the polynomial

    iii) write the polynomial in factored form

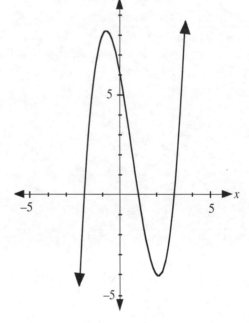

b) Use a graphing calculator to sketch $P(x)$ in expanded form and in factored form to verify the above answers.

Class Ex. #2

a) Use a graphing calculator to sketch the graph of the
   polynomial function $P(x) = -x^3 + 4x^2 + 7x - 10$.

b) Use the graph to state the x-intercepts.

c) Write the polynomial in factored form.

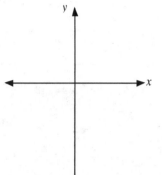

d) Circle the correct alternative:
   - The left arm of the graph is (rising / falling).
   - The right arm of the graph is (rising / falling).
   - The degree of the polynomial is (even / odd).
   - The leading coefficient of the polynomial is (positive / negative).

 Note

The investigative assignment in this lesson will develop the relationships between the
directions of the arms of the graph of a polynomial, the degree of the polynomial, and the sign
of the leading coefficient of the polynomial.

> **Complete Assignment Questions #1 - #3**

Assignment

1. In each question use a graphing calculator to:

   i)   sketch the graph of the polynomial function
   ii) state the zeros of the polynomial function
   iii) write the polynomial function in factored form.

a) $P(x) = x - 2$ **b)** $P(x) = -x + 2$ **c)** $P(x) = x^2 - 6x + 8$ **d)** $P(x) = -x^2 + 6x - 8$

i)
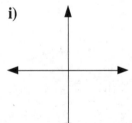

i)
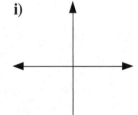

i)
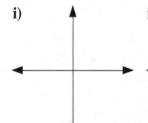

i)
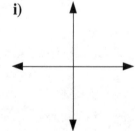

ii)   **ii)**   **ii)**   **ii)**

iii)$P(x) = (x - 2)$ **iii)**$P(x) = -(x - 2)$ **iii)** $P(x) =$ **iii)**$P(x) =$

e) $P(x) = x^3 - 7x^2 + 7x + 15$

i)

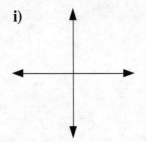

ii)

iii)

f) $P(x) = -x^3 + 7x^2 - 7x - 15$

i)

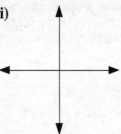

ii)

iii)

g) $P(x) = x^3 - x^2 - 12x$

i)

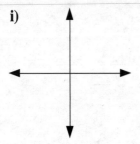

ii)

iii)

h) $P(x) = -x^3 + x^2 + 12x$

i)

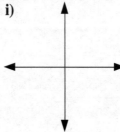

ii)

iii)

i) $P(x) = x^4 - 5x^2 + 4$

i)

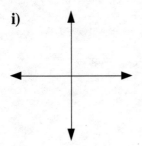

ii)

iii)

j) $P(x) = -x^4 + 5x^2 - 4$

i)

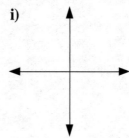

ii)

iii)

2. In each question use a graphing calculator to

    i)   sketch the graph of the polynomial function

    ii)   state the zeros of the polynomial function

    iii)   write the polynomial function in factored form

a) $P(x) = x^4 - 7x^3 + 7x^2 + 15x$

    i)

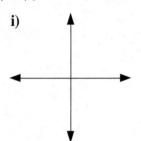

    ii)

    iii)

b) $P(x) = -x^4 + 7x^3 - 7x^2 - 15x$

    i)

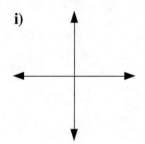

    ii)

    iii)

c) $P(x) = x^5 - 3x^4 - 5x^3 + 15x^2 + 4x - 12$

    i)

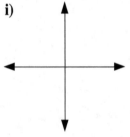

    ii)

    iii)

d) $P(x) = -x^5 + 3x^4 + 5x^3 - 15x^2 - 4x + 12$

    i)

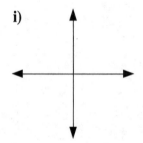

    ii)

    iii)

e) $P(x) = x^6 - 14x^4 + 49x^2 - 36$

    i)

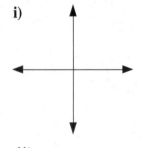

    ii)

    iii)

f) $P(x) = -x^6 + 14x^4 - 49x^2 + 36$

    i)

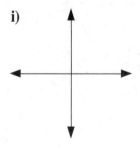

    ii)

    iii)

3. Based on your observations from questions #1 and #2, circle the correct choice in each of the following statements.

a) If the graph of a polynomial has *two rising* arms, then the

degree of the polynomial is (even, odd) and

the leading coefficient is   (positive, negative).

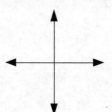

b) If the graph of a polynomial has *two falling arms*, then the

degree of the polynomial is (even, odd) and

the leading coefficient is   (positive, negative).

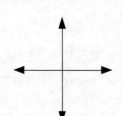

c) If the graph of a polynomial has a *right* arm *rising* **and**

the *left* arm *falling*, then the

degree of the polynomial is (even, odd) and

the leading coefficient is   (positive, negative).

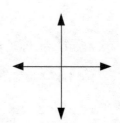

d) If the graph of a polynomial has a *right* arm *falling* **and**

the *left* arm *rising*, then the

degree of the polynomial is (even, odd) and

the leading coefficient is   (positive, negative).

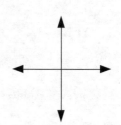

e) The **leading coefficient is positive** if the (left, right) arm

is (rising, falling).

f) The **leading coefficient is negative** if the (left, right) arm

is (rising, falling).

Answer Key

1 . a) ii) 2   **iii)** $P(x) = (x - 2)$

   b) ii) 2   **iii)** $P(x) = -(x - 2)$

   c) ii) 2, 4   **iii)** $P(x) = (x - 2)(x - 4)$

   d) ii) 2, 4   **iii)** $P(x) = -(x - 2)(x - 4)$

   e) ii) –1, 3, 5   **iii)** $P(x) = (x + 1)(x - 3)(x - 5)$

   f) ii) –1, 3, 5   **iii)** $P(x) = -(x + 1)(x - 3)(x - 5)$

   g) ii) –3, 0, 4   **iii)** $P(x) = x(x + 3)(x - 4)$

   h) ii) –3, 0, 4   **iii)** $P(x) = -x(x + 3)(x - 4)$

   i) ii) –2, –1, 1, 2   **iii)** $P(x) = (x + 2)(x + 1)(x - 1)(x - 2)$

   j) ii) –2, –1, 1, 2   **iii)** $P(x) = -(x + 2)(x + 1)(x - 1)(x - 2)$

2 . a) ii) –1, 0, 3, 5   **iii)** $P(x) = x(x + 1)(x - 3)(x - 5)$

   b) ii) –1, 0, 3, 5   **iii)** $P(x) = -x(x + 1)(x - 3)(x - 5)$

   c) ii) –2, –1, 1, 2, 3   **iii)** $P(x) = (x + 2)(x + 1)(x - 1)(x - 2)(x - 3)$

   d) ii) –2, –1, 1, 2, 3   **iii)** $P(x) = -(x + 2)(x + 1)(x - 1)(x - 2)(x - 3)$

   e) ii) –3, –2, –1, 1, 2, 3   **iii)** $P(x) = (x + 3)(x + 2)(x + 1)(x - 1)(x - 2)(x - 3)$

   f) ii) –3, –2, –1, 1, 2, 3   **iii)** $P(x) = -(x + 3)(x + 2)(x + 1)(x - 1)(x - 2)(x - 3)$

3 . a) even, positive   **b)** even, negative   **c)** odd, positive

   d) odd, negative   **e)** right, rising   **f)** right, falling

Polynomial Functions and Equations Lesson #8:
Investigating the Graphs of Polynomial Functions - Part Two

Repeated Factors

The graph of the polynomial function
$P(x) = (x + 1)(x - 3)^2$ is shown.

The polynomial has two factors, one of which
is repeated. This means that the function has
two distinct zeros, one of which is a repeated zero.

The factors are $(x - 3)$ which is repeated,
and $(x + 1)$.

The zeros of the function are therefore 3, which is
repeated, and –1.

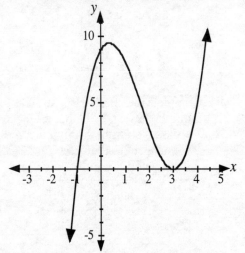

The graph of the function has two different x-intercepts, and we say that the function has **two
real distinct zeros**, –1 and 3.

- The x-intercept at –1 represents a real zero of the function.
- The x-intercept of 3 represents **two real equal zeros** of the function.

The repeated zero of 3 is said to be a zero of **multiplicity** 2.
The zero of –1 is a zero of **multiplicity** 1.

Multiplicity

The **multiplicity** of a zero corresponds to the number of times a factor is repeated
in the function.

In this lesson, we will investigate how the multiplicity of a zero affects the shape of the graph
of a polynomial function. In order to do this, we have to define the following terms.

Tangent

A polynomial graph is **tangent** to the x-axis
at a point where the graph **touches** the x-axis
and does not cross through it.

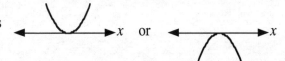

Point of Inflection

A polynomial graph has a **point of inflection**
on the x-axis if the graph **changes concavity**
at a point on the x-axis.

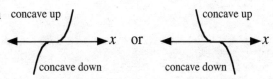

 **In this lesson we will consider only polynomials where
the leading coefficient, c, is either 1 or –1.**

Class Ex. #1

Consider the polynomial function
$$P(x) = x^6 - x^5 - 11x^4 + 13x^3 + 26x^2 - 20x - 24$$
$$= (x + 3)(x + 1)^2(x - 2)^3.$$

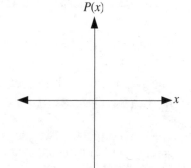

$P(x)$

a) Sketch the graph of $P(x)$ using the window
  x: $[-5, 5, 1]$ y: $[-100, 100, 20]$

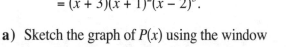

x

b) Complete the chart below to state the zeros of $P(x)$, their multiplicities, and whether each zero
  • passes straight through the x-axis
  • is tangent to the x-axis, or
  • has a point of inflection.

zero	multiplicity	description

c) Complete the following.   • The degree of $P(x)$ is _____ .
                                 • The sum of the multiplicities of the zeros of $P(x)$ is_____ .

d) Use technology to determine, to the nearest tenth, the minimum value of the function.

Class Ex. #2

A polynomial function has the equation
$$P(x) = x^4 + 2x^3 - 15x^2 - 32x - 16.$$

$P(x)$

a) Sketch the graph of $P(x)$ using the window
  x: $[-6, 6, 1]$ y: $[-150, 100, 20]$

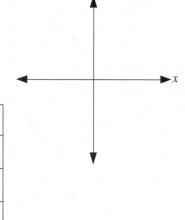

x

b) Complete the chart below.

zero	multiplicity	description

c) Complete the following.   • The degree of $P(x)$ is _____ .
                                 • The sum of the multiplicities of the zeros of $P(x)$ is_____ .

d) Write the polynomial in the form $P(x) = (x - a)(x - b)(x - c)^2$.

Note The investigative assignment in this lesson will develop the relationships between the multiplicities of the zeros of a polynomial function and its graph.

> **Complete Assignment Questions #1 - #15**

Assignment

In this assignment, choose appropriate windows which will enable you to investigate all the characteristics of the functions.

1. **a)** Graph $P(x) = x^3 - 4x^2 - 3x + 18$ and complete the table.

zero	multiplicity

   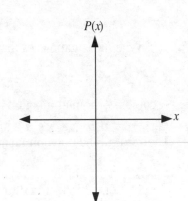

   b) Write the polynomial in the form
   $P(x) = (x - a)(x - b)^2$, where $a, b \in I$.

2. **a)** Graph $P(x) = x^4 + x^3 - 18x^2 - 52x - 40$ and complete the table.

zero	multiplicity

   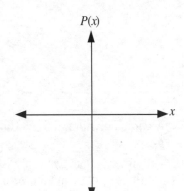

   b) Write the polynomial function in factored form.

3. **a)** Graph $P(x) = -x^3 - 6x^2 + 32$ and complete the table.

zero	multiplicity

   b) Write the polynomial in the form
   $P(x) = -(x - a)(x - b)^2$, $a, b \in I$.

4. a) Sketch the graphs of $P(x) = x^4 - 4x^3 - 2x^2 + 12x + 9$
and $Q(x) = -x^4 + 4x^3 + 2x^2 - 12x - 9$ on the grid.

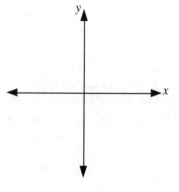

b) State the zeros, their multiplicities, and
the y-intercept of each polynomial function.

c) Write the equations of the polynomials in factored form.

$P(x) =$ $\qquad\qquad\qquad$ $Q(x) =$

5. A cubic polynomial function has the equation
$P(x) = ax^3 + bx^2 + cx + d$ with a leading coefficient of 1.
The zeros of the polynomial are $-6, 1$, and 3.

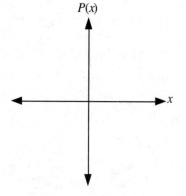

a) Sketch the graph of $P(x)$ and write the equation of the
polynomial in factored form.

b) Determine the values of a, b, c, and d in $P(x)$.

6. A cubic polynomial function has the equation
$P(x) = ax^3 + bx^2 + cx + d$ with a leading coefficient of 1.
The function has two real distinct zeros. The zero 2 has
multiplicity one, and the zero -3 has multiplicity two.

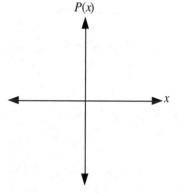

a) Sketch the graph of the function and write the equation
of the polynomial in factored form.

b) Determine the values of a, b, c, and d in $P(x)$.

c) A new function is formed by changing the signs of each of the values of a, b, c, and d.
Describe how the graph of the new function compares to the graph of $P(x)$.

7. A polynomial function has the equation
$P(x) = x^2(x - 2)(x + 3)$.

   a) Make a rough sketch without using a graphing calculator. Verify using a graphing calculator.

   b) State the zeros, their multiplicities, and the y-intercept of $P(x)$.

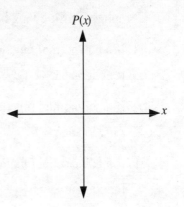

8. A polynomial function has the equation
$P(x) = -(x - 4)^2(x + 3)^2$.

   a) Make a rough sketch without using a graphing calculator. Verify using a graphing calculator.

   b) State the zeros, their multiplicities, and the y-intercept of $P(x)$.

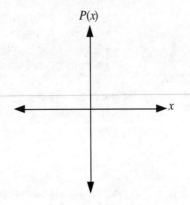

9. A polynomial function has the equation
$P(x) = (x - 1)^3(x + 3)$.

   a) Make a rough sketch without using a graphing calculator. Verify using a graphing calculator.

   b) State the zeros, their multiplicities, and the y-intercept of $P(x)$.

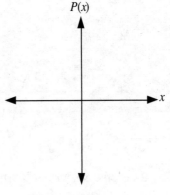

10. A polynomial function has the equation
$P(x) = (x + 2)^2(x + 5)(3 - x)$.

   a) Make a rough sketch without using a graphing calculator. Verify using a graphing calculator.

   b) State the zeros, their multiplicities, and the y-intercept of $P(x)$.

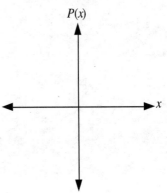

   c) State the maximum value of $P(x)$ to the nearest tenth.

11. Complete the following based on your observations from questions #1 - #10.

a) If a polynomial function has a zero of multiplicity 1 at $x = a$, then the graph of the function at $x = a$ _____ .

b) If a polynomial function has a zero of multiplicity 2 at $x = b$, then the graph of the function at $x = b$ _____ .

c) If a polynomial function has a zero of multiplicity 3 at $x = c$, then the graph of the function at $x = c$ _____ .

d) A polynomial function with a leading coefficient of 1 has three distinct zeros.
  - a zero of multiplicity 1 at $x = a$
  - a zero of multiplicity 2 at $x = b$
  - a zero of multiplicity 3 at $x = c$

If $a < b < c$, make a rough sketch of a polynomial which satisfies these conditions.

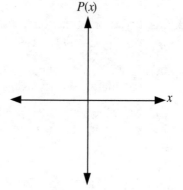

12. The graphs shown each represent a cubic polynomial function with equation $P(x) = ax^3 + bx^2 + cx + d$, where a is 1 or -1. The x-intercepts on the graphs are integers.

i)
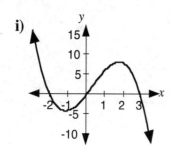

ii)
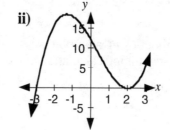

iii)
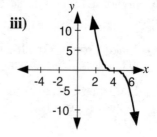

In each case, write $P(x)$ in factored form and determine the values of a, b, c, and d.

13. The graphs shown below each represent a quartic polynomial function with equation $P(x) = ax^4 + bx^3 + cx^2 + dx + e$, where a is 1 or -1. The zeros of the functions are integers.

In each case, write the equation of the polynomial function in factored form and determine the value of e.

i) ii) iii)

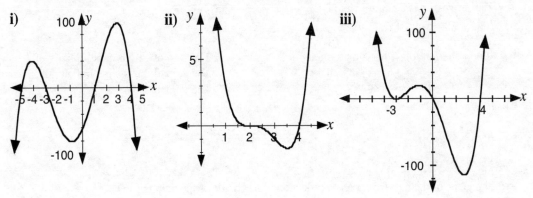

Use the following information to answer questions #14 and #15.

The partial graph of a fourth degree polynomial function $P(x)$ is shown. The leading coefficient is 1 and the x-intercepts of the graph are integers.

14. If the polynomial function is written in the form $P(x) = c(x - a)^2(x - b)(x + d)$, where $a, b, c,$ and d are all positive integers, then the respective numerical values of a, b, c, d from left to right are _____ .

(Record your answer in the numerical response box from left to right.)

15. The graph crosses the y-axis at $(0, -m)$. The value of m is _____ .

(Record your answer in the numerical response box from left to right.)

Answer Key

1. a) The zero of -2 has a multiplicity of 1.
The zero of 3 has a multiplicity of 2.
b) $P(x) = (x + 2)(x - 3)^2$

2. a) The zero of -2 has a multiplicity of 3.
The zero of 5 has a multiplicity of 1.
b) $P(x) = (x - 5)(x + 2)^3$

3. a) The zero of -4 has a multiplicity of 2.
The zero of 2 has a multiplicity of 1.
b) $P(x) = -(x - 2)(x + 4)^2$

4. b) $P(x)$: The zero of -1 has a multiplicity of 2.
The zero of 3 has a multiplicity of 2.
The y-intercept is 9.
c) $P(x) = (x +1)^2(x - 3)^2$

$Q(x)$: The zero of -1 has a multiplicity of 2.
The zero of 3 has a multiplicity of 2.
The y-intercept is -9.
$Q(x) = -(x + 1)^2(x - 3)^2$

5. a) $P(x) = (x + 6)(x - 1)(x - 3)$
b) $a = 1,\ b = 2,\ c = -21, d = 18$

6. a) $P(x) = (x - 2)(x + 3)^2$
b) $a = 1,\ b = 4,\ c = -3,\ d = -18$
c) The graph of the new function is a reflection in the x-axis of the graph of $P(x)$.

7. b) The zero of -3 has a multiplicity of 1.
The zero of 0 has a multiplicity of 2.
The zero of 2 has a multiplicity of 1.
The y-intercept is 0.

8. b) The zero of -3 has a multiplicity of 2.
The zero of 4 has a multiplicity of 2.
The y-intercept is -144.

9. b) The zero of -3 has a multiplicity of 1.
The zero of 1 has a multiplicity of 3.
The y-intercept is -3.

10.b) The zero of -5 has a multiplicity of 1.
The zero of -2 has a multiplicity of 2.
The zero of 3 has a multiplicity of 1.
The y-intercept is 60.
c) 119.8

11.a) passes straight through the x-axis
b) is tangent to the x-axis   **c)** has a point of inflection
d) answers may vary, one possible answer is

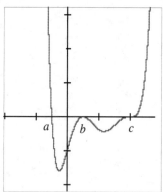

12. i) $P(x) = -x(x + 2)(x - 3)$ $a = -1,$ $b = 1,$ $c = 6,$ $d = 0$
    ii) $P(x) = (x + 3)(x - 2)^2$ $a = 1,$ $b = -1,$ $c = -8,$ $d = 12$
    iii) $P(x) = -(x - 4)^3$ $a = -1,$ $b = 12,$ $c = -48,$ $d = 64$

13.i) $P(x) = -(x + 5)(x + 3)(x - 1)(x - 4)$ $e = -60$
    ii) $P(x) = (x - 4)(x - 2)^3$ $e = 32$
    iii) $P(x) = x(x - 4)(x + 3)^2$ $e = 0$

14.

1	4	1	3

15.

1	2		

Polynomial Functions and Equations Lesson #9:
Investigating the Graphs of Polynomial Functions - Part Three

In this lesson we will investigate the graphs of polynomial functions which have zeros with multiplicities greater than three.

Investigating Odd Multiplicities

Graph the following functions on the grid showing the *x*- and *y*-intercepts.

1. $P(x) = (x - 2)^3$
2. $P(x) = (x - 2)^5$
3. $P(x) = (x - 2)^7$

What happens as the multiplicity of the zero increases through the odd numbers?

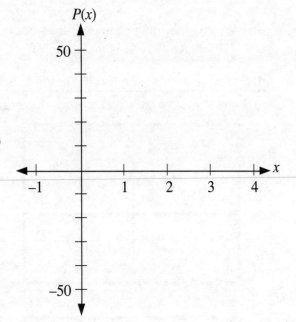

Investigating Even Multiplicities

Graph the following functions on the grid showing the *x*- and *y*-intercepts.

1. $P(x) = (x - 2)^2$
2. $P(x) = (x - 2)^4$
3. $P(x) = (x - 2)^6$

What happens as the multiplicity of the zero increases through the even numbers?

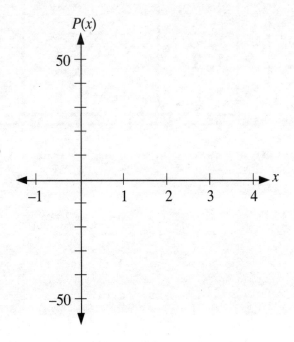

Even and Odd Multiplicities of a Zero

A real zero of **even** multiplicity (i.e. 2 or 4 or 6 or 8 or . . .) occurs where the graph of a polynomial function is <u>tangent</u> to the *x*-axis.

A real zero of **odd** multiplicity greater than 1 (i.e. 3 or 5 or 7 or . . .) occurs where the graph of a polynomial function has a <u>point of inflection</u> on the *x*-axis.

The sum of the multiplicities of the zeros of a polynomial function is equal to the degree of the polynomial function.

Use the following information to answer Class Example #1.

The graphs below are screenshots from a graphing calculator.

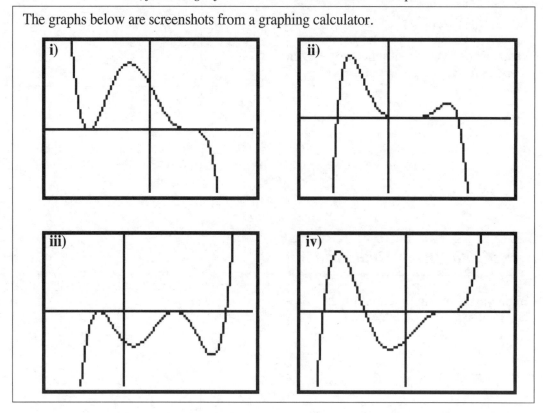

Class Ex. #1

a) In each case state the number of distinct zeros and the possible multiplicities of each zero.

b) Which graph could represent a polynomial function of degree 8?

c) In which of the graphs is the leading coefficient positive?

Class Ex. #2

Without using a graphing calculator, make a rough sketch
of the graph of

$$f(x) = -x(x - 1)^4(x - 4).$$

Verify using a graphing calculator.

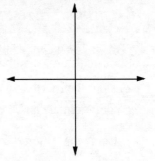

Class Ex. #3

The following graphs represent polynomial functions, $P(x)$, of lowest possible degree.
In each case,
i) state the degree of the polynomial function;
ii) for $P(x) = 0$, state the points on the graph which represent real and equal roots.

a)

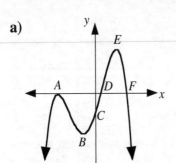

b)

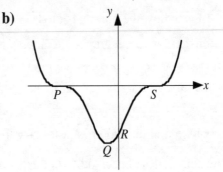

Class Ex. #4

a) On the grid, sketch a graph of a polynomial function satisfying the given conditions.

i) • positive leading coefficient
   • one real zero of multiplicity 1
   • two real zeros of multiplicity 2
   • one real zero of multiplicity 5

ii) • negative leading coefficient
   • two real zeros of multiplicity 1
   • one real zero of multiplicity 3
   • one real zero of multiplicity 4

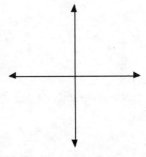

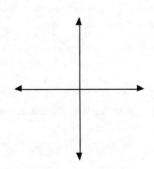

b) State the degree of each polynomial function.

Complete Assignment Questions #1 - #5, #8, #9

Extension: Investigating Non-Real Zeros

For a greater understanding of the graphs of polynomial functions, we investigate the concept of non-real zeros, and how they are represented on graphs.

Consider the fourth degree polynomial function, $P(x) = x^4 - 5x^2 + 8x - 12$.
The polynomial can be written in factored form as $P(x) = (x - 2)(x + 3)(x^2 - x + 2)$.

a) Using the factored form of $P(x)$, state two real zeros of multiplicity 1.

b) Solve the equation $x^2 - x + 2 = 0$ using the quadratic formula to show that the other two zeros are **non-real**.

c) To investigate how the non-real zeros $\dfrac{1 - \sqrt{-7}}{2}$ and $\dfrac{1 + \sqrt{-7}}{2}$
appear on a graph, use a graphing calculator to
sketch $P(x) = x^4 - 5x^2 + 8x - 12$ on the grid provided.
Use a graphing window $x:[-8, 8, 1]$ $y:[-40, 20, 10]$.

 Note • If a real polynomial function has non-real zeros, then non-real zeros always occur in pairs
which are conjugates of each other in the form $\dfrac{p \pm \sqrt{q}}{r}$, where $q < 0$.
• Non-real zeros are also known as **imaginary zeros** or **complex zeros**.

Class Ex. #5

The graphs below represent polynomial functions which have non-real zeros.

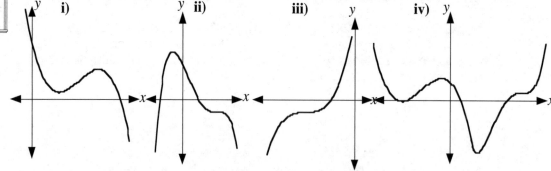

a) Indicate the region on the graph which represents non-real zeros.
b) Write a statement which describes the number, type and multiplicity of the zeros.

Complete Assignment Questions #6 and #7

Assignment

1. How does the concept **number of zeros** differ from the concept **multiplicity of zeros**?

2. Consider the graphs below.

  a) In each case state the number of distinct zeros and the possible multiplicities of each zero.

  i)

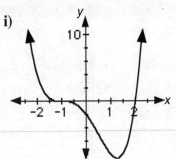

  ii)

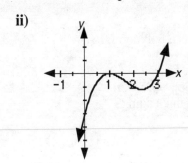

  iii)

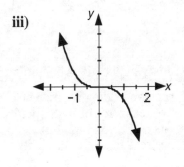

  iv)

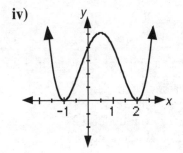

  b) Which graph(s) could represent a seventh-degree polynomial function?

  c) Which graph(s) could **not** represent a polynomial function of degree 10?

  d) In which of the graphs is the leading coefficient negative?

3. The following graphs represent functions of lowest possible degree.
State the degree in each case.

a)

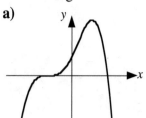

b)

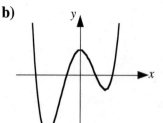

c)

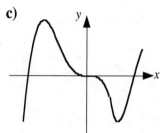

4. The graph represents a polynomial
function $P(x)$ of degree 5.

a) Write the equation of $P(x)$ in
factored form if the leading
coefficient is -1.

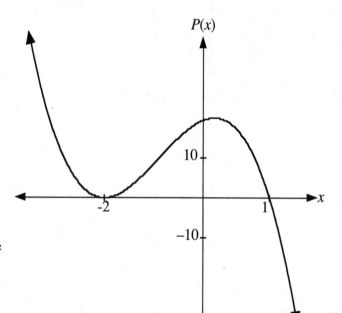

b) Determine, to the nearest whole
number, the maximum value of
$P(x)$ on the domain $-2 \le x \le 1$.

5. a) On the grid, sketch a graph of a polynomial function satisfying the given conditions.

i) • negative leading coefficient
• one real zero of multiplicity 1
• one real zero of multiplicity 2
• two real zeros of multiplicity 3

ii) • positive leading coefficient
• two real zeros of multiplicity 2
• one real zero of multiplicity 3
• one real zero of multiplicity 6

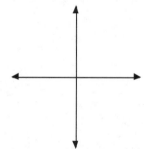

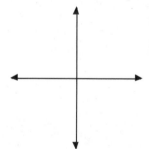

b) State the degree of each polynomial function.

6. The cubic function $f(x) = x^3 - 12x + 65$ has one real zero of multiplicity 1 and two non-real zeros.

   a) Use a graphing calculator to graph the function and make a sketch of the graph on the grid.

   b) Use synthetic division to determine the real zero of the function.

   c) Determine the two non-real zeros of the function.

7. In each case, sketch the graph of the polynomial function using a graphing calculator window of $x:[-8, 8, 1]$ and $y:[-50, 50, 10]$ and write a statement which describes the number, type, and multiplicity of the zeros.

   a) $P(x) = x^3 - 6x^2 + 6x - 5$

   b) $Q(x) = x^4 - 11x^3 + 36x^2 - 35x + 25$

   c) $R(x) = -x^5 + 13x^4 - 61x^3 + 124x^2 - 112x + 64$

Use the *following information to answer the next two questions.*

The graph of a fourth degree polynomial function of the form $P(x) = ax^4 + bx^3 + cx^2 + dx + e$ is shown.

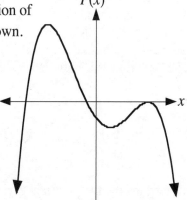

8. The values a and e must satisfy

  A. $a > 0, e < 0$ **B.** $a < 0, e > 0$ **C.** $a > 0, e > 0$ **D.** $a < 0, e < 0$

9. If $P(x) = 0$ has exactly three different solutions, then which one of the following statements about the roots of $P(x) = 0$ is true?

  A. Two roots are real, equal and negative, and two roots are real, not equal and positive.

  B. Two roots are real, equal and positive and two roots are real, not equal and negative.

  C. Two roots are real and negative, and two roots are not real.

  D. Two roots are real and positive, and two roots are not real.

Answer Key

1. - number of zeros refers to how many distinct zeros the function has
   - multiplicity refers to the number of times a zero repeats

2. **a)** **i)** two zeros, the zero –1 has a multiplicity of 3 or 5 or 7 ..., the zero 2 has a multiplicity of 1.
   ii) two zeros, the zero 1 has a multiplicity of 2 or 4 or 6 ..., the zero 3 has a multiplicity of 1.
   iii) one zero, the zero 0 has a multiplicity of 3 or 5 or 7 ... .
   iv) two zeros, both the zeros –1 and 2 have a multiplicity of 2 or 4 or 6 ...,
   b) ii), iii)   **c)** ii), iii), iv)   **d)** iii)

3. **a)** 4   **b)** 4   **c)** 5   **4.** **a)** $P(x) = -(x + 2)^4(x - 1)$ **b)** 20

5. **a)** Answers may vary → → → → → → **i)** [graph] **ii)** [graph]
   b) **i)** 9   **ii)** 13

6. **b)** –5   **c)** $\dfrac{5 - 3\sqrt{-3}}{2}$ and $\dfrac{5 + 3\sqrt{-3}}{2}$

7. **a)** One real zero of multiplicity 1, and two non-real zeros, each of multiplicity 1.
   b) One real zero of multiplicity 2, and two non-real zeros, each of multiplicity 1.
   c) One real zero of multiplicity 3, and two non-real zeros, each of multiplicity 1.

8. D   **9.** B

Polynomial Functions and Equations Lesson #10:
Polynomial Functions with a
Leading Coefficient other than ±1

In lesson 7 we introduced the Unique Factorization Theorem, which states that every polynomial function of degree $n \geq 1$ can be written as the product of a leading coefficient, c, and n linear factors to get

$$P(x) = c(x - a_1)(x - a_2)(x - a_3)...(x - a_n)$$

This theorem implies two ***important*** points for polynomial functions of degree $n \geq 1$:

Point #1: Every polynomial function can be written as a product of its factors and a leading coefficient.

Point #2: Every polynomial function has the same number of factors as its degree. The factors may be real or complex, and may be repeated.

 Note **In lessons 7 - 9 we have considered only polynomial functions where the leading coefficient, c, was either 1 or –1.**

In this lesson we will consider polynomial functions where the leading coefficient, c, can be any real number.

 Class Ex. #1
The graph of a third degree polynomial function, $P(x)$, is shown. The graph has integral x-intercepts and passes through the point $(2, -24)$.

a) Explain why the equation of the polynomial function can be written in the form
$P(x) = cx(x + 1)(x - 3)$.

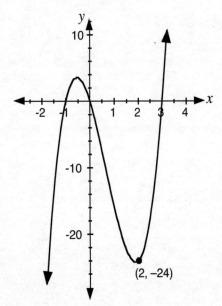

b) Use the point $(2, -24)$ to determine the value of c, and hence write the polynomial in expanded form.

Class Ex. #2

The graph represents a polynomial function of lowest possible degree. The intercepts are integers.

Determine the equation of the polynomial function in factored form.

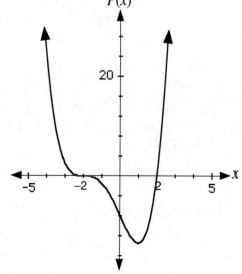

Class Ex. #3

Determine the equation, in factored form, of a fourth degree polynomial function which passes through $(1, -12)$ and is tangent to the x-axis at $(2, 0)$ and at $(-3, 0)$.

Complete Assignment Questions #1 - #5

Class Ex. #4 A fourth degree polynomial, $P(x)$, passes through the point $(1, 2)$ and has zeros $-1, 0, \frac{3}{2}$, and 2.

Determine the equation of $P(x)$ in factored form using only integral linear factors.

Class Ex. #5 A polynomial equation has the following three roots.

- -2 is a root with a multiplicity of 1
- $\frac{1}{3}$ is a root with a multiplicity of 2
- 1 is a root with a multiplicity of 3

The graph of the corresponding polynomial function has a y-intercept of $\frac{2}{3}$.

Determine the equation of the polynomial function in factored form using integral factors.

Complete Assignment Questions #6 - #14

Assignment

1. The graph of the polynomial function shown has integral intercepts.

   Determine the equation of the function in factored form.

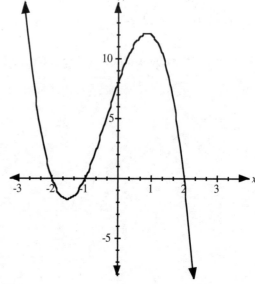

2. The graph passes through the point $(1, -6)$ and has integral *x*-intercepts.

   Determine the equation, in factored form, of the polynomial function, $P(x)$, represented by the graph.

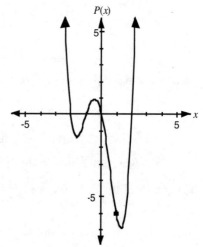

3. The graph of a third degree polynomial function is shown. The graph passes through the point $(-6, 1)$. If the polynomial function has zeros -5 and -1, determine

   a) the equation of the function in factored form;

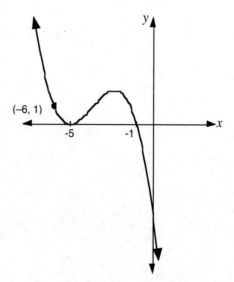

   b) the *y*-intercept of the graph.

4. Find the equation of a quartic function whose graph has a point of inflection at the origin and passes through $(4, 0)$ and $(-1, 10)$.

5. The design of a route for a cross country ski course was drawn on a Cartesian plane. The route is tangent to the x-axis at $(1, 0)$ and $(-3, 0)$. It crosses the x-axis at $(-5, 0)$ and also passes through the point $(-2, 9)$. Determine the equation of the fifth degree polynomial function that will meet these conditions.

6. The graph shown has x-intercepts of $-1, 1, 2.5,$ and 3 and a y-intercept of 60.

Determine the equation of the graph in factored form using integral factors.

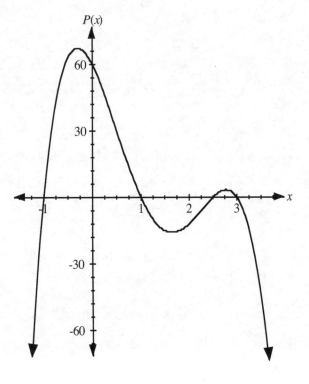

7. The graph below has x-intercepts $-\dfrac{3}{2}, 0$, and 2 and passes through the point $(1, 3)$. Determine the equation of the graph using integral factors.

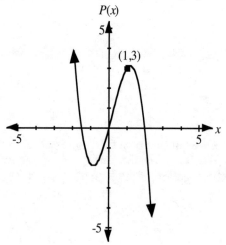

8. Determine the equation of a fifth degree polynomial function whose graph has a point of inflection at $(3, 0)$, is tangent to the x-axis at $\left(\dfrac{1}{2}, 0\right)$, and passes through $(2, 1)$.

9. If the zeros of a polynomial are $-1, \dfrac{1}{2}$ and $\dfrac{2}{3}$, then the polynomial could be

A. $12x^3 - 2x^2 + 10x - 4$
B. $6x^3 + x^2 - 5x + 2$
C. $30x^3 - 5x^2 - 25x + 10$
D. $18x^3 + 3x^2 - 15x - 6$

10. $P(x) = -3x^3 + bx^2 + cx + d$ is an integral polynomial function with zeros $2, -1$, and 4. A sketch of $y = P(x)$ is shown.

At which of the following points does the graph of $P(x)$ cross the y-axis?

A. $(0, -8)$ **B.** $(0, -15)$

C. $(0, -16)$ **D.** $(0, -24)$

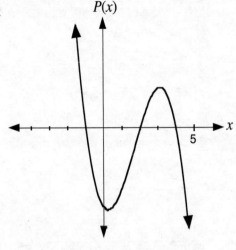

11. The graph of a fourth degree polynomial function has x-intercepts $-2, -1, 0$, and 1. If the graph passes through the point $(-3, -48)$, then the coefficient of the third degree term of $P(x)$ is

A. -4

B. -2

C. -1

D. 2

12. A third degree polynomial, $f(x)$, has three distinct zeros, $-3, -1$, and 2. If a new polynomial, $g(x)$, is found by multiplying $f(x)$ by $(x + 1)$, then which of the following statements is true?

A.   The x-intercepts of the graph of $y = g(x)$ will be $-4, -2$, and 1.

B.   The x-intercepts of the graph of $y = g(x)$ will be $-2, 0$, and 3.

C.   The y-intercept of the graph of $y = g(x)$ will be the negative of the y-intercept of the graph of $y = f(x)$.

D.   The x and y-intercepts of the graph of $y = g(x)$ are the same as the x and y intercepts of the graph of $y = f(x)$.

13. Consider a fourth degree polynomial function whose graph is tangent to the x-axis at both $(3, 0)$ and $(-4, 0)$ and passes through $(2, 9)$. The y-intercept of the graph is _____ .

(Record your answer in the numerical response box from left to right.)

14. $P(x) = ax^3 + bx^2 + cx + d, a > 0,$ is an integral polynomial function with 2 and 5 as its zeros. The graph of $y = P(x)$ is shown.

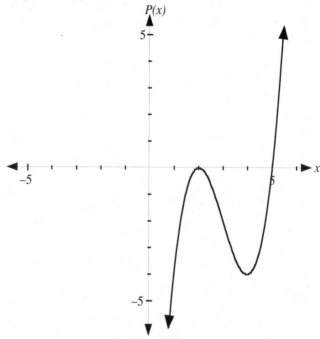

If the maximum y-intercept is at the point $(0, -m)$, then m is _____ .

(Record your answer in the numerical response box from left to right.)

Answer Key

1. $P(x) = -2(x + 2)(x + 1)(x - 2)$

2. $P(x) = x(x + 2)(x + 1)(x - 2)$

3. **a)** $P(x) = -\frac{1}{5}(x + 1)(x + 5)^2$ **b)** -5

4. $P(x) = 2x^3(x - 4)$

5. $P(x) = \frac{1}{3}(x + 5)(x - 1)^2(x + 3)^2$

6. $P(x) = -4(x + 1)(x - 1)(2x - 5)(x - 3)$

7. $P(x) = -\frac{3}{5}x(2x + 3)(x - 2)$

8. $P(x) = -\frac{1}{9}(2x - 1)^2(x - 3)^3$

9. C   10. D

11. A   12. D   13. | 3 | 6 | | | 14. | 2 | 0 | | |

Polynomial Functions and Equations Lesson #11:
Practice Test

Section A *No calculator may be used for this section of the test.*

1. Which of the following is an integral polynomial of degree 3?

   A. $3x^3 - \dfrac{1}{3}x^2 + 3$ **B.** $x + 2x^2 + 3x^3$

   C. $\dfrac{x^3 + 2x}{x}$ **D.** $3x^6 + 3x^4 + 3x$

Numerical Response

1. Consider the following partially completed synthetic division where the divisor is $x - 3$.

$$
\begin{array}{r|rrrr}
3 & -4 & 3 & -b \\
\hline
& 3 & c & a & -25
\end{array}
$$

The value of b is _____.

(Record your answer in the numerical response box from left to right.)

2. Consider two polynomial functions $f(x)$ and $g(x)$. 7 is a zero of f and when g is divided by $x - 7$, the remainder is 2. Which of the following statements must be true?

   A. $f(0) + g(7) = 9$

   B. $f(7) + g(-7) = 2$

   C. $f(7) + g(2) = 7$

   D. $f(7) + g(7) = 2$

3. The x-intercept(s) of the graph of the function $f(x) = x^3 + 3x^2 + 3x + 1$ is/are

   A. -1 only

   B. 1 only

   C. -1 and 1 only

   D. $-1, 0$ and 1

4. Which of the following best defines an integral polynomial function?

   A. an integral y-intercept   **B.** integral zeros

   C. integral coefficients   **D.** both integral zeros and integral coefficients

Use the following information to answer the next question.

The partial graph of a fourth degree polynomial function $y = P(x)$ is shown.

The graph passes through the points $(-2, 0)$, $(3, 0)$, and $(0, 54)$.

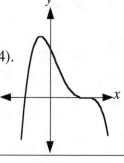

5. The equation of the polynomial function is

    A. $P(x) = (x + 2)(x - 3)^3$

    B. $P(x) = (x - 2)(x + 3)^3$

    C. $P(x) = -(x + 2)(x - 3)^3$

    D. $P(x) = -(x - 2)(x + 3)^3$

A graphing calculator may be used for the remainder of the test.

Section B   6.   When a polynomial $P(x)$ is divided by $3x - 4$, the quotient is $x^2 - x - 4$ and the remainder is -9. The polynomial $P(x)$ is

    A. $3x^3 - 7x^2 - 8x + 7$

    B. $3x^3 - 7x^2 - 8x + 25$

    C. $3x^3 - 7x^2 - 8x - 25$

    D. $x^2 - 4x - 17$

Numerical Response 2.   When the polynomial $2x^3 - 5x^2 + ax - 5$ is divided by $x - 3$, the remainder is 67. The value of a is _____ .

(Record your answer in the numerical response box from left to right.)

7. A graphing calculator screenshot of the graph of a polynomial function is shown.

    If all the *x*-intercepts are shown, then the minimum degree of the polynomial function is

    A. 4 **B.** 5

    C. 6 **D.** 7

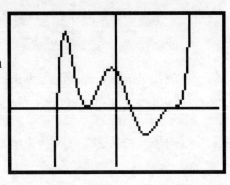

8. If $3x^4 - px^3 + x^2 + qx - 9$ is divided by $x - 2$, the remainder is -4. The equation relating p and q is

    A. $8p - 2q - 39 = 0$

    B. $8p - 2q + 39 = 0$

    C. $8p - 2q - 47 = 0$

    D. $8p - 2q + 47 = 0$

9. One factor of $6x^3 + 23x^2 - 6x - 8$ is $x + 4$. The other two factors are

    A. $2x - 1$ and $3x + 2$

    B. $2x + 1$ and $3x - 2$

    C. $6x + 1$ and $x - 2$

    D. $6x - 1$ and $x + 2$

10. If $-2, 0,$ and 4 are the only zeros of a fourth degree polynomial function, $P(x)$, which one of the following is a possible factored form of $P(x)$?

    A. $P(x) = x(x + 2)(x - 4)$

    B. $P(x) = 6x^2(x + 2)(x - 4)$

    C. $P(x) = x(x + 2)^2(x - 4)^2$

    D. $P(x) = 4x(x + 2)(x - 4)$

Use the following information to answer the next question.

The partial graph of a fourth degree polynomial function, $y = P(x)$, is shown.

The x-intercepts are integers.

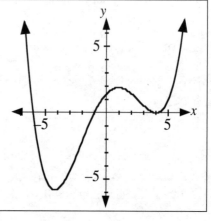

11. When $P(x)$ is divided by $x + 4$, the remainder is

   A. zero   **B.** positive
   C. negative   **D.** unable to be determined from the given information

 3. The binomial $x^2 - 3x - 4$ is a factor of the polynomial $x^3 - 6x^2 + cx + d$, where c and d are integers. The value of $c + d$ is _____ .

(Record your answer in the numerical response box from left to right.)

12. The only factors of a polynomial $P(x)$ are $(3x - 2)$, $(4x + 3)$ and $(x + 7)$.
   If the polynomial $Q(x) = -3P(x)$, then the x-intercepts of the graph of $y = Q(x)$ are

   A. $\dfrac{2}{3}$, $-\dfrac{3}{4}$ and -7

   B. $-\dfrac{2}{3}$, $\dfrac{3}{4}$ and 7

   C. 2, $-\dfrac{9}{4}$ and -21

   D. -2, $\dfrac{9}{4}$ and 21

Use the following information to answer the next three questions.

A square piece of cardboard has an area of 676 cm^2.

A box with an open top is to be constructed from the piece of cardboard by cutting out a square from each of the corners and folding up the sides.

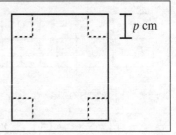

13.   If the length of each side of the four squares that are cut out is p cm, then the volume of the box is given by $V(p) =$

   A. $676 - 4p^2$

   B. $p(13 - p)^2$

   C. $2p(13 - p)^2$

   D. $4p(13 - p)^2$

14.   In the context of the question, the restrictions on the value of p are completely described by

   A. $p > 0$ **B.** $p < 13$

   C. $0 < p < 13$ **D.** $0 < p < 26$

Numerical Response 4.   The maximum volume of the box can be obtained by graphing the function $V(p)$. To the nearest cm^3, the maximum volume of the box is _____.

   (Record your answer in the numerical response box from left to right.)

Numerical Response 5.   When the polynomial $2x^3 - 5x^2 + 4x + d$ is divided by $2x + 3$, the remainder is -6. The value of d is _____.

   (Record your answer in the numerical response box from left to right.)

15. The following values are taken from the graph of a third degree polynomial function.

x	-2	-1	0	1	2
$P(x)$	0	-18	-12	0	0

The equation of the polynomial function is

A. $P(x) = (x - 1)(x + 2)(x - 2)$

B. $P(x) = -3(x - 1)(x + 2)(x - 2)$

C. $P(x) = (x + 1)(x + 2)(x - 2)$

D. $P(x) = 3(x - 1)(x + 2)(x - 2)$

16. Which of the following graphs could be the graph of the polynomial function $P(x) = c(x + a)^2(x + b)$ if $a < 0, b > 0$, and $c < 0$?

A.

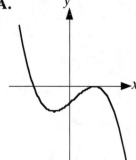

B.

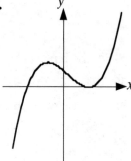

C.

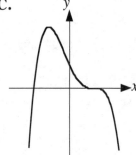

D.

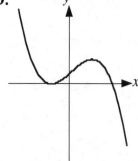

Use the following information to answer the next three questions.

The partial graphs of four polynomial functions of **degree four** are shown.
There are no *x*-intercepts other than the ones indicated on the graphs.

Graph 1

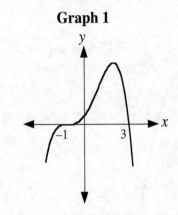

Graph 2

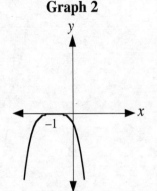

Graph 3

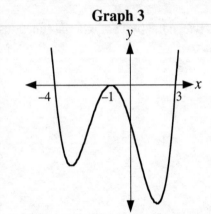

Graph 4

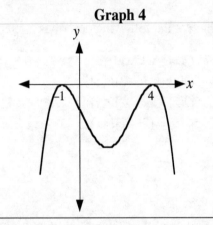

17. All the functions which have a zero of multiplicity 2 at $x = -1$, are represented in

   A. graph 1   B. graphs 2 and 3   C. graphs 3 and 4   D. graphs 2, 3, and 4

18. All the functions which have three **distinct** zeros are represented in

   A. graph 1   B. graph 3   C. graphs 1 and 3   D. graphs 3 and 4

19. If the polynomial in Graph 4 is multiplied by $(x + 4)$, a new polynomial, $f(x)$, is formed.
   Which of the following statements must be true?

   A.   The *x*-intercepts of the graph of $y = f(x)$ will be 3 and 8.
   B.   The *x*-intercepts of the graph of $y = f(x)$ will be –5 and 0.
   C.   The *y*-intercept of the graph of $y = f(x)$ will be 4 units above the *y*-intercept
        of Graph 4.
   D.   The *y*-intercept of the graph of $y = f(x)$ will be 4 times the *y*-intercept of Graph 4.

Use the following information to answer the next question.

The graphs of $y = P(x)$ and $y = Q(x)$ have x-intercepts at $-2, 0$, and 2.
The absolute values of the leading coefficients of $P(x)$ and $Q(x)$ are equal.

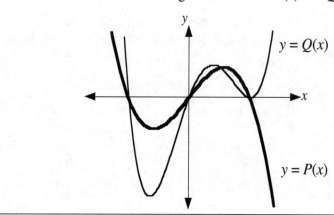

20.   Which of the following describes a relationship between the two polynomial functions?

   A. $Q(x) = 2P(x)$
   B. $Q(x) = (x + 2)P(x)$
   C. $Q(x) = (x - 2)P(x)$
   D. $Q(x) = (2 - x)P(x)$

Numerical Response   **6.**   The graph of the polynomial function $P(x) = px^3 + qx^2 + rx + s$ is tangent to the x-axis at the point $(-3, 0)$ and passes through the point $(2, 0)$.
If the graph also passes through $(-1, 24)$, then the value of s is _____.

(Record your answer in the numerical response box from left to right.)

Written Response

Use the following information to answer this question.

The illustration shown is a graphing calculator screenshot of the graph of
a polynomial function $P(x)$ with window $x:[-7, 7, 1]$ $y:[-150, 250, 25]$.
The graph is tangent to the x-axis at point A.

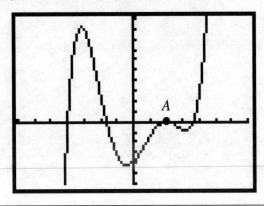

- Explain how you can use the graph to show that the degree of the polynomial cannot be an
  even number.

- The equation of the polynomial function is $P(x) = x^5 - 2x^4 - 18x^3 + 40x^2 + 40x - 96$.
  It appears from the graph that the polynomial function has two integral zeros.

  Algebraically confirm that $P(x)$ has two integral zeros.

- Determine the exact value of the other two zeros.

- Polynomials $Q(x)$ and $R(x)$ are defined by $Q(x) = -2P(x)$ and $R(x) = P(-2x)$. Determine the integral zeros of $Q(x)$ and $R(x)$.

Answer Key

Multiple Choice

1. B   **2.** D   **3.** A   **4.** C   **5.** C   **6.** A   **7.** D   **8.** C

9. B   **10.** B   **11.** C   **12.** A   **13.** D   **14.** C   **15.** B   **16.** A

17. C   **18.** B   **19.** D   **20.** D

Numerical Response

1. | 7 | 9 | | | **2.** | 2 | 1 | | | **3.** | 1 | 7 | | |

4. | 1 | 3 | 0 | 2 | **5.** | 1 | 8 | | | **6.** | 3 | 6 | | |

Written Response

1. • There are three zeros of multiplicity 1, and one zero of even multiplicity. Therefore the sum of the multiplicities is always odd, and so the degree of the polynomial is always odd and never even.

 • The integral zeros are –4 and 2.

 • The other two zeros are $1 + \sqrt{7}$ and $1 - \sqrt{7}$.

 • The integral zeros of $Q(x)$ are –4 and 2.   The integral zeros of $R(x)$ are –1 and 2.

Permutations and Combinations Lesson #1:
The Fundamental Counting Principle

Overview

In this unit, we will solve problems involving the application of the fundamental counting principle, permutations (including restrictions and repetitions) and combinations. We will also explore patterns in the expanded form of $(x + y)^n$, and solve problems using the binomial theorem.

Introduction

Joe is shopping for a car. The dealer says that he has 3 different models and that each model is available in 5 different colours.

a) Use the tree diagram to determine how may different choices Joe has.

b) Look at the number of choices there are for the model and the number of choices there are for the colour. How do you use these numbers to arrive at the answer in a)?

Model	Colour	Choice
	Blue	Model 1 in Blue
	Red	Model 1 in Red
Model 1	Purple	Model 1 in Purple
	White	Model 1 in White
	Black	Model 1 in Black
	Blue	Model 2 in Blue
	Red	Model 2 in Red
Model 2	Purple	Model 2 in Purple
	White	Model 2 in White
	Black	Model 2 in Black
	Blue	Model 3 in Blue
	Red	Model 3 in Red
Model 3	Purple	Model 3 in Purple
	White	Model 3 in White
	Black	Model 3 in Black

The Fundamental Counting Principle

Consider a task made up of several stages. If the number of choices for the first stage is a, the number of choices for the second stage is b, the number of choices for the third stage is c, etc., then the number of ways in which the task can be completed is $a \times b \times c \times \ldots$.
This is called the **fundamental counting principle**.

Class Ex. #1

A toy manufacturer makes a wooden toy in three parts:

    Part 1: the top part may be coloured red, white, blue, or pink.
    Part 2: the middle part may be orange, purple or black.
    Part 3: the bottom part may be yellow or green.

Determine how many different coloured toys can be produced using

a) a tree diagram   **b)** the fundamental counting principle

In the previous example, the toy consisted of Part 1 **and** Part 2 **and** Part 3. The total number of possible toys was found by **multiplication**.

In any example involving "**and**" the total number of arrangements will be found by **multiplying**.

Class Ex. #2 A Math 30 quiz consists of eight multiple choice questions. Each question has four choices, A, B, C, or D. How many different sets of answers are possible?

The Fundamental Counting Principle Involving Restrictions

When solving problems involving restrictions, it is important that **the restriction is dealt with first** as in the example below.

Class Ex. #3 **a)** Eric has been assigned the task of determining how many odd four digit numbers there are. He has been told that a number such as 5267 is a four digit number, whereas 0267 is classified as a three digit number.

   i)   The first step of his work is shown. Explain his reasoning for the number 5.

$$\underline{\quad}\ \underline{\quad}\ \underline{\quad}\ \underline{⑤}$$

   ii)   The second step of his work is shown. Explain his reasoning for the number 9.

$$\underline{⑨}\ \underline{\quad}\ \underline{\quad}\ \underline{⑤}$$

   iii)   Complete his work to determine how many odd four digit numbers there are.

   b) Eric has now been assigned the task of determining how many odd four digit numbers there are which have no repeating digits.

   i)   Explain why the first step in a) is still valid, but the second step is not.

   ii) Determine how many odd four digit numbers have no repeating digits.

Class Ex. #4   Car number plates in an African country consist of a letter other than I or O followed by three digits, the first of which cannot be zero, followed by any two letters which are not repeated. How many different car number plates can be produced?

Complete Assignment Questions #1 - #7

Class Ex. #5   There are two routes from Pitland to Queensville, three routes from Queensville to St. Lukes, three routes from Pitland to Rutherford, and one route from Rutherford to St. Lukes.

a) How many routes are there from Pitland to St. Lukes passing through Queensville?

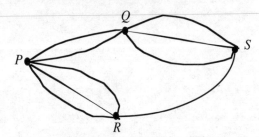

b) How many routes are there from Pitland to St. Lukes passing through Rutherford?

c) How many routes are there from Pitland to St. Lukes?

Note   In part c) we could travel from *P* to *S* via *Q* **or** from *P* to *S* via *R*. The total number of routes was found by **adding** the answer in a) to the answer in b).

In any example involving "**or**" the total number of arrangements will be found by **adding**.

Class Ex. #6   The telephone numbers allocated to subscribers in a rural area consist of one of the following:
* the digits 345 followed by any three further digits, *or*,
* the digit 2 followed by one of the digits 1 to 5 followed by any three further digits.

How many different telephone numbers are possible?

Class Ex. #7

Consider Class Ex. #3 in which Eric was asked to determine how many odd four digit numbers there are.

As an extension to his assignment, Eric has been asked to determine

i) how many **even** four digit numbers there are, and,

ii) how many **even** four digit numbers have <u>no repeated</u> digits.

a) Determine the answer to i).

b) Eric started his answer to ii), as shown below, but he was not sure how to fill in the first space in his work. Explain why he needs to consider two separate cases to solve the problem.

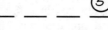

c) Determine the answer to ii).

Class Ex. #8

Consider the number of distinguishable four letter arrangements that can be formed from the word **ENGLISH**. (Note: There is an implication that each of the letters in the word ENGLISH only occurs once and cannot be repeated).

Determine the number of distinguishable four letter arrangements that can be formed from the word **ENGLISH**, if

a) any letter can be in any position

b) the first letter must be **E**

c) the first and last letters must be vowels

d) the "word" must contain **G**

Complete Assignment Questions #8 - #18

Assignment

1. A football team has the following kit :   jersey: red or black
                                                     pants: white, red, or black
                                                     socks: red or white

    The team plays in a different uniform each week until it has to repeat a previous uniform.

    Determine how many weeks the team can play before repeating a previous uniform
    by using

    a) a tree diagram   **b)** the fundamental counting principle

2. How many ways are there of arranging 6 different books side by side on a shelf?

3. With the new renovations completed at Prestwick High School, there will be seven
    entrances. In how many different ways can a student coming for Math tutorials

    a) enter and exit through any entrance?

    b) enter the school and exit through a different entrance?

    c) enter and exit through the same entrance?

4. The score at the end of the second period of a hockey game is: Flames 6   Oilers 3.

    Jarome was attempting to determine how many different possibilities there are
    for the score at the end of the first period. He used the fundamental counting principle
    and multiplied 6 by 3 to get an answer of 18. Explain the error in his reasoning.

5. If each of the students in a class of 30 students is capable of winning any of the class
    prizes, how many ways are there of awarding

    a) a first prize, a second prize, and a third prize in Mathematics?

    b) a Mathematics prize, a Chemistry prize, and a Physics prize?

6. Three digit numbers are formed using only the digits 2, 3, 5, 6, 7, and 9.

   a) If repetitions are not permitted, how many 3-digit numbers can be formed?

   b) How many of these are

     i) less than 400?   **ii)** even?   **iii)** odd?   **iv)** multiples of 5?

7. A vehicle license plate consists of 3 letters followed by 3 digits. How many different license plates are possible if:

   a) there are no restrictions on the letters or digits used?

   b) no letters may be repeated?

   c) the first digit cannot be zero and no digits can be repeated?

8. How many ways are there of getting from A to C in each diagram, passing through each point at most once?

   Answer to Diagram 1

   Answer to Diagram 2

   Answer to Diagram 3

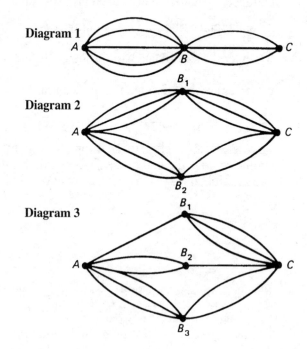

9. Determine the number of four letter "words" that can be formed from the letters of the word **PRODUCE** if

  a) each letter can only be used once

  b) each letter can only be used once and the "word" must

  i) contain only consonants   **ii)** begin and end with a consonant

  iii) begin with a vowel   **iv)** contain the letter **P**

  v) begin with **D** and end with a vowel

10. a) How many different three-digit numerals can be formed from the digits 1, 5, and 8 if the digits cannot be repeated?

  b) How many different three-digit numerals can be formed using the digits 1, 3, 5, 7, and 9 if the digits may be repeated?

  c) How many four-digit numerals can be formed from the digits 0, 2, and 3 if the digits may be repeated?   (Note: 0223 is classified as the 3-digit numeral 223).

  d) How many different non-zero numerals are possible using some or all of the numerals 0, 1, 2, and 3 if the digits cannot be repeated?

11. Mr. and Mrs. McDonald want a family picture taken with their children, Hamish, Flora and James. In how many different ways can all five line up in a straight line for the picture if

  a) there are no restrictions?

  b) the parents must be at either end of the line?

  c) baby James must be in the middle?

  d) the children alternate with the adults?

12. a) How many odd six digit numbers have no repeating digits?

b) How many even six digit numerals have no repeating digits?

Use the following information to answer the next question.

The word **PRODUCT** has been spelled using letter tiles. An illustration is shown.

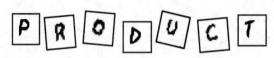

13. Using only these tiles, determine the number of four letter arrangements if the arrangement

a) has any letter in any position

b) begins with **PR**

c) has two vowels in the middle

d) has two consonants in the middle

14. Dania had two pennies, four nickels, two quarters, and five dollar coins in her purse. She correctly determined that there are 269 different sums of money she could make using one or more of the coins. Explain her reasoning.

15. Ocean-going ships have use coloured flags hung vertically for signalling. By changing the order of the coloured flags, the ships can send out different signals.

If ships carry six different coloured flags, one flag of each colour, how many different signals are possible if

a) all six flags are used?

b) four flags are used?

c) at least two flags are used?

16. How many even 5-digit whole numbers are there? Note that 31248 is acceptable, but 01248 is not.

    A.   13 776

    B.   15 120

    C.   45 000

    D.   50 000

17. The final of a 100-metre race contains 8 competitors. The number of possible ways in which the gold, silver, and bronze medals can be awarded is

    A.   21

    B.   24

    C.   336

    D.   512

Numerical Response

18. Sandra is taking an examination which consists of two parts, A and B, with the following instructions.

    - Part A consists of three questions and the student must do two.
    - Part B consists of four questions and the student must do two.
    - Part A must be completed before starting Part B.
    - At the end of the exam the student has to list the order in which she attempted the questions.

The number of different possible orders is _____ .

(Record your answer in the numerical response box from left to right.)

Answer Key

1. 12   **2.** 720   **3. a)** 49   **b)** 42   **c)** 7

4. He should have multiplied 7 by 4 to get 28.   **5. a)** 24360   **b)** 27000

6. a) 120   **b) i)** 40   **ii)** 40   **iii)** 80   **iv)** 20

7. a) 17 576 000   **b)** 15 600 000   **c)** 11 389 248

8. Diagram 1 → 15   **Diagram 2** → 15   **Diagram 3** → 11

9. a) 840   **b) i)** 24   **ii)** 240   **iii)** 360   **iv)** 480   **v)** 60

10. a) 6   **b)** 125   **c)** 54   **d)** 48

11. a) 120   **b)** 12   **c)** 24   **d)** 12

12. a) 67 200   **b)** 68 880

13. a) 840   **b)** 20   **c)** 40   **d)** 400

14. There are not enough pennies to make a nickel, not enough nickels to make a quarter, and not enough quarters to make a dollar, so each grouping of coins will result in a different sum of money. She has three choices for the number of pennies (0, 1, or 2), five choices for the number of nickels, three choices for the number of quarters, and six choices for the number of dollar coins. Using the fundamental counting principle, this results in 3·5·3·6 = 270 choices. One of these arrangements consists of no coins, which does not meet the condition of the question, therefore the total number of different sums of money is 270 − 1 = 269.

15. a) 720   **b)** 360   **c)** 1950   **16.** C   **17.** C   **18.** | 7 | 2 | | |

Permutations and Combinations Lesson #2:
Factorial Notation and Permutations

Investigating Factorial Notation

Consider how many ways there are of arranging 6 different books side by side on a shelf. Using the fundamental counting principle, we calculate the product $6 \times 5 \times 4 \times 3 \times 2 \times 1$.

In mathematics this product can be written in a simplified form called **factorial notation**.

$6 \times 5 \times 4 \times 3 \times 2 \times 1$ is denoted by 6! ("6 factorial" or "factorial 6").

a) Without using a calculator, determine the value of:

   i) 4!   **ii)** 3! × 2!

Notice that 6! can be written in a variety of ways.

$$6! = 6 \times 5 \times 4 \times 3 \times 2 \times 1$$

$$6! = 6 \times 5 \times 4 \times 3 \times 2!$$

$$6! = 6 \times 5 \times 4 \times 3!$$

$$6! = 6 \times 5 \times 4!$$

$$6! = 6 \times 5!$$

The table above can be used to help us simplify quotients such as $\dfrac{6!}{4!}$.

$$\frac{6!}{4!} = \frac{6 \times 5 \times 4!}{4!} = 6 \times 5 = 30.$$

b) Express 5! as a product in four different ways.

   5! = _____   5! = _____   5! = _____   5! = _____

c) Complete the following: **i)** 12! = ___ × 11!   **ii)** 8! = _____ × 6!

d) Express as a quotient of factorials.

   i) $6 \times 5 \times 4 = \dfrac{!}{!}$ **ii)** $15 \times 14 \times 13 \times 12 =$

e) Without using a calculator, simplify

   i) $\dfrac{10!}{7!}$ **ii)** $\dfrac{8!}{5!3!}$

Factorial Notation

In general $n! = n(n-1)(n-2)(n-3) \dots (3)(2)(1)$, where $n \in N$.

• Note that, in the above definition of $n!$, n has to be a **natural number**.

• 0! is defined to be equal to 1, and the reasoning for this will be given later in this lesson.

$n!$ can be written as a product in many different ways.

For example $n! = n(n-1)!$
$n! = n(n-1)(n-2)!$
$n! = n(n-1)(n-2)(n-3)!$, etc.

Class Ex. #1   Complete the following.

a) $n! = \underline{\quad\quad} \times (n-1)!$ **b)** $(n+2)! = \underline{\qquad\qquad\qquad} n!$

c) $(n-4)(n-5)(n-6) \dots (3)(2)(1) = \underline{\quad\quad}!$

Class Ex. #2   Simplify the following expressions. Leave the answer in product form where appropriate.

a) $\dfrac{(n+2)!}{n!}$ **b)** $\dfrac{(n-2)!}{(n-1)!}$ **c)** $\dfrac{n!}{n(n-1)}$

Class Ex. #3   Algebraically solve the equation $\dfrac{n!}{(n-2)!} = 42$.

Factorial Notation on a Calculator

Many calculators have a factorial key which can be used to simplify calculations.

a) Use the factorial key on a calculator to evaluate the following.

$6! =$ _____ $9! =$ _____

b) To simplify a quantity like $\dfrac{10!}{7!3!}$ on a calculator we can evaluate numerator and denominator separately and then divide, or enter it in one calculation using brackets.

i) Complete the work below.

$$\dfrac{10!}{7!3!} = \dfrac{3\ 628\ 800}{30\ 240} = \qquad \text{or} \qquad \dfrac{10!}{(7!3!)} =$$

ii) To verify without using a calculator, complete the work below

$$\dfrac{10!}{7!3!} = \dfrac{10 \times 9 \times 8 \times 7!}{7! \times 6} =$$

Class Ex. #4

Calculate the value of: **a)** $\dfrac{43!}{40!}$ **b)** $\dfrac{37!}{33!\ 4!}$

Complete Assignment Questions #1 - #6

Permutations

An internet site's access code consists of three digits. Knowing the three digits is not enough to access the site. The digits have to be entered in the correct order. The ***order*** of the ***arrangement*** of the digits is important.

John cannot remember the access code, except that it contains the digits 3, 5 and 7.

- List all the arrangements of these three digits that John could use to determine the access code.

There are six possible arrangements to consider and only one of them will access the site. This type of arrangement, where the order is important, is called a **permutation**.

A **permutation** is an **arrangement** of a set of elements in which the **order of the elements is important**.

> ## *Permutations of "n" Different Elements Taken "n" at a Time*

a) List all the arrangements of the letters of the word **CAT**.

b) Write the number of permutations in factorial notation.

This is an example of the following general rule:

> **The number of permutations of "n" different elements taken all at a time is $n!$**

Determine the number of permutations of the letters of each word.

a) REGINA   **b) KELOWNA**

> ## *Permutations of "n" Different Elements Taken "r" at a Time* $(r \leq n)$

a) Use the fundamental counting principle to determine how many three letter arrangements can be made from the letters of the word **GRAPHITE.**

In the example above we have found the number of permutations of 8 (n) elements taken 3 (r) at a time. This is denoted by $_8P_3$.

$$_8P_3 = 8 \times 7 \times 6 = \frac{8 \times 7 \times 6 \times 5!}{5!} = \frac{8!}{(8-3)!}$$

This is an example of the following general rule:

> **The number of permutations of "n" different elements taken "r" at a time is**
>
> $$_nP_r = \frac{n!}{(n-r)!}$$

b) Use the $_nP_r$ key on a calculator to evaluate $_8P_3$. Verify using factorials.

Defining 0!

If we replace r by n in the previous formula we get the number of permutations of n elements taken n at a time. This we know is $n!$.

$$_nP_n = n! = \frac{n!}{(n-n)!} = \frac{n!}{0!}$$ For this to be equal to $n!$ the value of $0!$ must be 1.

0! is defined to have a value of 1.

Class Ex. #6

In a region, vehicle license plates consist of 2 different letters followed by 4 different digits. If the letters I, O, Y, and Z are not used, determine how many different license plates are possible by

a) the fundamental counting principle   **b)** permutations

Class Ex. #7

Algebraically solve the equation $_{n-1}P_2 = 90$.

Note

In many cases involving simple permutations, the fundamental counting principle can be used in place of the permutation formulas.

Complete Assignment Questions #7 - #15

Assignment

1. Without using a calculator, determine the value of

a) $5!$ **b)** $\dfrac{10!}{8!}$ **c)** $\dfrac{99!}{100!}$

2. Express as single factorials.

   a) $6 \times 5 \times 4 \times 3 \times 2 \times 1$ **b)** $9 \times 8 \times 7 \times 6!$ **c)** $(n + 2)(n + 1)n(n - 1) \; ... \times 3 \times 2 \times 1$

3. Express as a quotient of factorials.

   a) $9 \times 8 \times 7 \times 6$ **b)** $20 \times 19 \times 18$ **c)** $(n + 2)(n + 1)n$

4. Use a calculator to determine the exact value of the following:

   a) $10!$ **b)** $\dfrac{8!}{4!}$ **c)** $\dfrac{15!}{10! \, 5!}$ **d)** $\left(\dfrac{25!}{21!}\right)\left(\dfrac{7!}{11!}\right)$

5. Simplify the following expressions. Leave the answer in product form where appropriate.

   a) $\dfrac{n!}{n}$ **b)** $\dfrac{(n - 3)!}{(n - 2)!}$ **c)** $\dfrac{(n + 1)!}{(n - 1)!}$ **d)** $\dfrac{(3n)!}{(3n - 2)!}$

6. Solve the equation.

   a) $\dfrac{(n + 1)!}{n!} = 6$ **b)** $(n + 1)! = 6(n - 1)!$

   c) $\dfrac{(n + 2)!}{n!} = 12$ **d)** $\dfrac{(n + 1)!}{(n - 2)!} = 20(n - 1)$

7. Determine the number of arrangements that can be made using all of the letters in the word

a) DOG **b)** DUCK **c)** SANDWICH **d)** CANMORE

8. Consider the number of five-digit numbers that can be made from the digits $2, 3, 4, 7,$ and 9 if no digit can be repeated. Express your answer using

a) factorial notation **b)** $_nP_r$ notation **c)** the fundamental counting principle

9. a) Use the formula for $_nP_r$ to show that $_7P_0 = 1$.

b) Explain why n must be greater than or equal to r in the notation $_nP_r$.

10. In each case determine the number of arrangements of the given letters by
  i) using the fundamental counting principle **ii)** writing in $_nP_r$ form and evaluating

a) two letters from the word **GOLDEN** **b)** three letters from the word **CHAPTERS**

c) four letters from the word **WEALTH** **d)** one letter from the word **VALUE**

11. Solve each equation, where n is an integer.

a) $\dfrac{n!}{84} = {}_{n-2}P_{n-4}$

b) $_nP_4 = 8({}_{n-1}P_3)$

12. How many numbers (up to a maximum of four digit numbers) can be made from the digits 2, 3, 4, and 5 if no digit can be repeated?

 13. In a ten-team basketball league, each team plays every other team twice, once at home and once away. The number of games that are scheduled is

    A.   45   **B.**   90

    C.   100   **D.**   180

14. The value of $_nP_2$ is

    A. $\dfrac{n}{n-2}$ **B.** $\dfrac{n!}{2!}$

    C. $\dfrac{n}{2}$ **D.** $n(n-1)$

15. In a competition on the back of a cereal packet, seven desirable qualities for a kitchen (eg. spaciousness, versatility, etc.) must be put in order of importance. The number of different entries that must be completed in order to ensure a winning order is _____ .

(Record your answer in the numerical response box from left to right.)

Answer Key

1. a) 120   **b)** 90   **c)** $\dfrac{1}{100}$ **2. a)** 6!   **b)** 9!   **c)** $(n+2)!$

3. a) $\dfrac{9!}{5!}$ **b)** $\dfrac{20!}{17!}$ **c)** $\dfrac{(n+2)!}{(n-1)!}$ **4. a)** 3 628 800   **b)** 1680   **c)** 3003   **d)** $\dfrac{115}{3}$

5. a) $(n-1)!$ **b)** $\dfrac{1}{n-2}$ **c)** $n(n+1)$ **d)** $3n(3n-1)$

6. a) $n=5$ **b)** $n=2$ **c)** $n=2$ **d)** $n=4$

7. a) 6   **b)** 24   **c)** 40 320   **d)** 5040

8. a) 5!   **b)** $_5P_3$ **c)** $5 \times 4 \times 3 \times 2 \times 1 = 120$

9. a) $_7P_0 = \dfrac{7!}{(7-0)!} = \dfrac{7!}{7!} = 1$

   b) You cannot arrange more elements than the number of elements there are to begin with.

10. a) $_6P_2 = 30$ **b)** $_8P_3 = 336$ **c)** $_6P_4 = 360$ **d)** $_5P_1 = 5$

11. a) $n=7$ **b)** $n=8$ **12.** 64   **13.** B   **14.** D   **15.** | 5 | 0 | 4 | 0 |

Permutations and Combinations Lesson #3:
Permutations with Restrictions; Permutations with Repetitions

Permutations with Restrictions

In many problems, restrictions are placed on the order in which objects are arranged.
In this type of situation, deal with the restrictions first. Many of the problems in this lesson can be solved using the fundamental counting principle.

Class Ex. #1 In how many ways can all of the letters of the word **ORANGES** be arranged if:

a) there are no further restrictions? **b)** the first letter must be an **N**?

c) the vowels must be together in the order **O**, **A**, and **E**?

Class Ex. #2 In how many of the arrangements of the letters of the word **BRAINS** are the vowels together?

Class Ex. #3 Find the number of permutations of the letters in the word **KITCHEN** if:

a) the letters **K**, **C**, and **N** must be together but not necessarily in that order **b)** the vowels must not be together

Class Ex. #4 In how many ways can 3 girls and 4 boys be arranged in a row if no two people of the same gender can sit together?

Class Ex. #5 Six actors and eight actresses are available for a play with four male roles and three female roles. How many different cast lists are possible?

Complete Assignment Questions #1 - #5

Permutations With Repetitions

In the previous section, the objects in each set were all different. But what happens when there are letters which repeat within the same word?

- To examine this scenario, consider the following four letter permutations of a word without repetitive letters, ROSE. Notice there are $_4P_4$, or 24 different arrangements.

ROSE	REOS	OSRE	SROE	SERO	EORS
ROES	RESO	OSER	SREO	SEOR	EOSR
RSOE	ORSE	OERS	SORE	EROS	ESRO
RSEO	ORES	OESR	SOER	ERSO	ESOR

- Now, if we change the E in ROSE to a S, we get ROSS, a word with two letters which are repeating. If we change all the E's in the above list to S's, we will get all the arrangements for ROSS as shown in the list below.

ROSS	RSOS	OSRS	SROS	SSRO	SORS
ROSS	RSSO	OSSR	SRSO	SSOR	SOSR
RSOS	ORSS	OSRS	SORS	SROS	SSRO
RSSO	ORSS	OSSR	SOSR	SRSO	SSOR

Notice that the 24 original arrangements now become 12 different arrangements: 12 matching pairs of 2 four-letter arrangements. Arrangements like ROSE and ROES from the first list both become ROSS in the second list and count as only one arrangement.

There are $\dfrac{1}{2}$ or $\dfrac{1}{2!}$ as many permutations of ROSS as there are of ROSE.

Hence, the number of permutations of ROSS is $\dfrac{4!}{2!}$, or 12.

- If we change the O and E in ROSE to S, we get RSSS, a "word" with three repeating letters, with the arrangements shown below.

RSSS	RSSS	SSRS	SRSS	SSRS	SSRS
RSSS	RSSS	SSSR	SRSS	SSSR	SSSR
RSSS	SRSS	SSRS	SSRS	SRSS	SSRS
RSSS	SRSS	SSSR	SSSR	SRSS	SSSR

Notice the 24 original arrangements now become 4 different arrangements - 4 matching sets of 6 four-letter arrangements. Arrangements like ROSE, ROES, RSOE, RSEO, REOS, and RESO from the first list all become one arrangement of RSSS.

There are $\dfrac{1}{6}$ or $\dfrac{1}{3!}$ as many permutations of RSSS as there are of ROSE.

Hence, the number of permutations of RSSS is $\dfrac{4!}{3!}$, or 4.

There is a pattern in the above lists. If a letter appears twice in a word, we divide the total number of arrangements by 2!. If a letter appears three times in a word we divide the total number of arrangements by 3!.

The following formula gives the number of permutations when there are **repetitions.**

> The number of permutations of *n* objects, where *a* are the same of one type, *b* are the same of another type, and *c* are the same of yet another type, can be represented by the expression below.
>
> $$\frac{n!}{a!\,b!\,c!}$$

Class Ex. #6

Find the number of permutations of the letters of the word:

a) VANCOUVER   **b) MATHEMATICAL**

Class Ex. #7

Brett bought a carton containing 10 mini boxes of cereal. There are 3 boxes of Corn Flakes, 2 boxes of Rice Krispies, 1 box of Coco Pops, 1 box of Shreddies, and the remainder are Raisin Bran. Over a ten day period, Brett plans to eat the contents of one box of cereal each morning.

How many different orders are possible if on the first morning he has Raisin Bran?

Class Ex. #8

Paul and Katherine are considering the following problem.

"Find the number of routes from *A* to *B* if routes must always move closer to *B*".

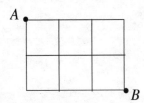

Paul arrived at the correct answer by tracing 10 routes on the grid.

Katherine developed a quicker method. She realized that travel from *A* to *B*, involves moving three units east, and two units south, and that the answer to the problem is the number of ways in which this can be done (i.e. EEESS in any order).

Solve the problem using Katherine's approach.

> **Complete Assignment Questions #6 - #12**

Assignment

1. How many arrangements could be made of the word
   a) **FATHER** if **F** is first?   b) **UNCLE** if **C** is first and **L** is last?

   c) **DAUGHTER** if **UG** is last?   d) **MOTHER** if the vowels are first and last?

2. How many arrangements of the following words can be made if all the vowels must be kept together?
   a) **FATHER**   b) **DAUGHTER**   c) **EQUATION**

3. Determine the number of different arrangements of the six letters in the word **ANSWER**
   a) without restrictions   b) that begin with an **S**

   c) that begin with a vowel and end with a consonant

   d) that have the three letters **A, N,** and **S** adjacent and in the order **ANS**

   e) that have the three letters **A, N,** and **S** adjacent but not necessarily in that order

4. Ann, Brian, Colin, Diane, and Eric go to watch a movie and sit in 5 adjacent seats.
In how many ways can this be done if

a) Brian sits next to Diane? **b)** Ann refuses to sit next to Eric?

5. In how many ways can four adults and five children be arranged in a single line

a) without restriction? **b)** if children and adults are alternated?

c) if the adults are all together and
the children are all together?

d) if the adults are all together?

6. How many different arrangements can be made using all of the letters of each word?

a) COCHRANE **b) WINNIPEG** **c) OSOYOOS**

7. The bakery is four blocks south and five blocks
west of the supermarket. The bakery driver, bored
with travelling the same route, decides to use a
different route for each delivery.

Assuming that he always travels closer to the
supermarket, how many deliveries are possible
before he has to repeat a route?

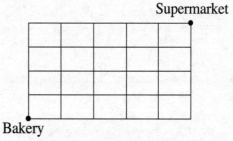

Supermarket

Bakery

8. A race at the Olympics has 8 runners. In how many orders can their countries finish if

a) there are 2 Canadian, 1 Russian, 1 German, 1 South African, and 3 American runners?

b) there are 1 Canadian, 2 British, 2 Ethiopian, 1 Algerian, and 2 Kenyan runners?

9. Naval signals are made by arranging coloured flags in a vertical line and the flags are then read from top to bottom. How many signals using six flags can be made if you have

    a) 3 red, 1 green, and 2 blue flags?

    b) 2 red, 2 green, and 2 blue flags?

    c) unlimited supplies of red, green, and blue flags?

Multiple Choice **10.** The number of different arrangements can be made using all the letters of the word **SASKATOON** is

    A. 720   **B.** 45 360

    C. 362 880   **D.** 725 760

11. The number of pathways from X to Y if paths must always move closer to Y is

    A. $\dfrac{6!}{3!\,3!} + \dfrac{4!}{2!\,2!}$ **B.** $\dfrac{6!}{3!\,3!} \times \dfrac{4!}{2!\,2!}$

    C. $\dfrac{8!}{4!\,4!} + \dfrac{6!}{3!\,3!}$ **D.** $\dfrac{8!}{4!\,4!} \times \dfrac{6!}{3!\,3!}$

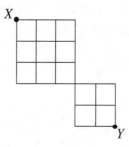

Numerical Response **12.** The number of different ways that seven basketball players can be seated on a bench so that two specified players are always sitting side by side is _____ .

    (Record your answer in the numerical response box from left to right.)

Answer Key

1. **a)** 120   **b)** 6   **c)** 720   **d)** 48   2. **a)** 240   **b)** 4320   **c)** 2880
3. **a)** 720   **b)** 120   **c)** 192   **d)** `24   **e)** 144
4. **a)** 48   **b)** 72   5. **a)** 362 880   **b)** 2880   **c)** 5760   **d)** 17 280
6. **a)** 20 160   **b)** 10 080   **c)** 105   7. 126   8. **a)** 3360   **b)** 5040
9. **a)** 60   **b)** 90   **c)** $3^6 = 729$ **10.** B   **11.** B   **12.**

1	4	4	0

Permutations and Combinations Lesson #4:
Combinations - Part One

Combinations

Part 1: As part of the Grade 12 English course, students are required to read the following three books in a three month period:

"The Grapes of Wrath", "The Wars", "The Bean Trees".

a) Due to previous late returns, Steve is only allowed to sign out one English book from the school library per month.
List all the different orders in which Steve could sign out the three books.

b) Tariq is allowed to sign out all three books at the same time.
How many different ways can he sign out all three books at the same time?

Part a) is an example of a permutation where the order is important.
Part b) is an example of a combination where the order is NOT important.

A **selection** of a set of elements in which the **order of the selection is NOT important** is called a **combination**.

Part 2: Suppose that the students in Part 1 were required to read only two of the books.

a) Complete the table to show the number of ways in which Steve and Tariq could do this:

Steve (Permutations)	Tariq (Combinations)
The Grapes of Wrath, The Wars	
The Grapes of Wrath, The Bean Trees	The Grapes of Wrath, The Wars
The Wars, The Grapes of Wrath	

b) Complete the following statement:
  • The number of combinations is equal to the number of permutations divided by _____ or _____ factorial.

  • A **permutation** is an **arrangement** of elements in which the order of the arrangement is taken into account.
  • A **combination** is a **selection** of elements in which the order of selection is not taken into account.

Part 3: Five students, Al, Byron, Colin, Dave and Eric take part in a cross country race to represent their school.

a) Suppose the winner of the race wins $50, the runner-up wins $25, and third place runner wins $10.

The table below shows all possible ways in which the three prizes could be awarded to the five participants in the race.

"A" stands for Al, "B" for Byron, "C" for Colin, "D" for Dave, "E" for Eric.

ABC	ABD	ABE	ACD	ACE	ADE	BCD	BCE	BDE	CDE
ACB	ADB	AEB	ADC	AEC	AED	BDC	BEC	BED	CED
BAC	BAD	BAE	CAD	CAE	DAE	CBD	CBE	DBE	DCE
BCA	BDA	BEA	CDA	CEA	DEA	CDB	CEB	DEB	DEC
CAB	DAB	EAB	DAC	EAC	EAD	DBC	EBC	EBD	ECD
CBA	DBA	EBA	DCA	ECA	EDA	DCB	ECB	EDB	EDC

• Is this an example of permutations or combinations?

• How many ways are there to award the three prizes?

b) For participating in the cross-country race, the school has been awarded three places at a running clinic. The school coach decides to select the 3 lucky students from the ones who took part in the cross country race.

• Use the table from a) (which has been duplicated below) to circle the different ways the three students can be chosen.

ABC	ABD	ABE	ACD	ACE	ADE	BCD	BCE	BDE	CDE
ACB	ADB	AEB	ADC	AEC	AED	BDC	BEC	BED	CED
BAC	BAD	BAE	CAD	CAE	DAE	CBD	CBE	DBE	DCE
BCA	BDA	BEA	CDA	CEA	DEA	CDB	CEB	DEB	DEC
CAB	DAB	EAB	DAC	EAC	EAD	DBC	EBC	EBD	ECD
CBA	DBA	EBA	DCA	ECA	EDA	DCB	ECB	EDB	EDC

• Is this an example of permutations or combinations?

• How many ways are there to select the three students?

c) Complete the following statement:

• The number of combinations is equal to the number of permutations divided by _____ or _____ factorial.

Combinations of "n" different elements taken "r" at a time   (r ≤ n)

The examples on the previous pages reflect the following general rule:

$$_nC_r = \frac{_nP_r}{r!} = \frac{n!}{(n-r)!\, r!}$$

> **The number of combinations of "n" elements taken "r" at a time is**
>
> $$_nC_r = \frac{n!}{(n-r)!\, r!}$$

- The $_nC_r$ key on a calculator can be used to evaluate combinations.

- In some texts $_nC_r$ is written as $\binom{n}{r}$.

Class Ex. #1

Three students from a class of ten are to be chosen to go on a school trip.

a) In how many ways can they be selected?
   Write the answer in factorial notation and evaluate.

b) Confirm the answer in a) using the $_nC_r$ key on a calculator.

Class Ex. #2

To win the LOTTO 649 a person must correctly select six numbers between 1 to 49.
Jasper selected the six numbers from the birth dates of his family, 3 7 9 11 20 29.
How many different selections of numbers could he have made?

Class Ex. #3

The Athletic Council decides to form a sub-committee of seven council members to look at how funds raised should be spent on sports activities in the school. There are a total of 15 athletic council members, 9 males and 6 females. The sub-committee must consist of exactly 3 females.

a) Determine the number of ways of selecting

   i) the females   **ii)** the males   **iii)** the sub-committee

b) In how many ways can the sub-committee be selected if Bruce, the football coach, must be included?

Class Ex. #4

A standard deck of 52 cards has the following characteristics:
- 4 suits (spades, clubs, diamonds, and hearts).
- Each suit has 13 cards.
- Two suits are black (spades and clubs).
- Two suits are red (diamonds and hearts).
- Face cards are considered to be Jacks, Queens, and Kings.

Poker is a card game played from a deck of 52 cards.

a) How many different five card poker hands are possible?

b) In how many of the hands in a) will there be:

    i) all diamonds?   **ii)** 4 black cards and 1 red card?   **iii)** 3 kings and 2 queens?

    iv) 3 kings?   **v)** four aces?   **vi)** 5 cards of the same suit? (called a "flush")

Complete Assignment Questions #1 - #12

Assignment

1. Pete's Perfect Pizza Company has 9 choices of topping available.

    a) How many different 2-topping pizzas can be made?

    b) How many different 3-topping pizzas can be made?

2. A theatre company consisting of 6 players is to be chosen from 15 actors. How many selections are possible if the company must include Mrs. Jones?

3. How many different rectangles can be formed by eight horizontal lines and three vertical lines?

4. Edinburgh High School has a twelve-member student council. A four member sub-committee is to be selected to organize dances.

    a) How many different sub-committees are possible?

    b) How many four member sub-committees are possible if the council president and vice-president must be members?

5. A basketball coach has five guards and seven forwards on his basketball team.

    a) In how many different ways can he select a starting team of two guards and three forwards?

    b) How many different starting teams are there if the star player, who plays guard, must be included?

6. Twelve face cards are removed from a deck of fifty-two cards. From the face cards, three card hands are dealt. Determine the number of distinct three card hands that are possible which include

    a) no restrictions

    b) 3 kings

    c) 1 Queen and 2 kings

    d) exactly 1 Jack

7. Consider a standard deck of 52 cards. Determine the number of distinct six card hands that are possible which include

    a) no restrictions

    b) only clubs

    c) 2 clubs and 4 diamonds

    d) no sevens

    e) 4 tens

    f) exactly 1 Jack and 4 Queens

8. Explain the meaning of $\begin{pmatrix} 10 \\ 2 \end{pmatrix}$. Why does $\begin{pmatrix} 2 \\ 10 \end{pmatrix}$ not make sense?

9. Develop a problem where $_9C_4$ would be applicable as a solution.

10. There are 16 students in a class. The number of ways in which four students can be chosen to complete a survey is

    A. 4!   **B.** $\dfrac{16!}{4!}$

    C. $\dfrac{16!}{12!\,4!}$ **D.** $\dfrac{16!}{12!}$

11. There are three girls and six boys on Leven High School softball team. Each of the students is capable of playing any fielding position on the team. There are nine fielding positions: a pitcher, a catcher, four infielders (first base, second base, third base, shortstop), and three outfielders (left field, centre field, right field).

    For a particular game, Leven High School is in the field first. If the pitcher must be a girl and the catcher must be a boy, how many different positional line-ups are possible at the start of the game?

    A. $_3C_1 \times {_6C_1} \times 7!$
    B. $_3C_1 \times {_6C_1} \times 9!$
    C. $_3C_1 \times {_6C_1} \times {_7C_4} \times {_3C_3}$
    D. $_3C_1 \times {_6C_1}$

12. Sarah is one of a group of eight people from which a committee of four people must be formed. The number of different committees possible if Sarah must sit on the committee is _____ .

    (Record your answer in the numerical response box from left to right.)

Answer Key
1. **a)** 36   **b)** 84   **2.** 2002   **3.** 84   **4.** **a)** 495   **b)** 45
5. **a)** 350   **b)** 140   **6.** **a)** 220   **b)** 4   **c)** 24   **d)** 112
7. **a)** 20 358 520   **b)** 1716   **c)** 55 770   **d)** 12 271 512   **e)** 1128   **f)** 176
8.   The number of ways of selecting 2 items from 10 where the order of selection is not important. You cannot select 10 items from 2.
9.   Answers may vary.   **10.** C   **11.** A   **12.** 3   5

Permutations and Combinations Lesson #5:
Combinations - Part Two

> **Combinations Problems with "at least", "at most", etc.**

Class Ex. #1

The Student Council decides to form a sub-committee of five council members to look at how funds raised should be spent on the students of the school. There are a total of 11 student council members, 5 males and 6 females.
How many different ways can the sub-committee consist of

a) exactly three females?   **b)** at least three females?

c) at least one female?

Class Ex. #2

Consider a standard deck of 52 cards. How many different five card hands can be formed containing

a) at least 1 red card?   **b)** at most 2 kings?

c) exactly two pairs?

> **Complete Assignment Questions #1 - #5**

Combinations Which are Equivalent

Class Ex. #3 Fran and Bernie have identical collections of vintage toy vehicles.
- Fran selects 2 toys from the 10 shown for display in her cabinet. Since the order of display does not matter to her, she calculates that this can be done in $_{10}C_2$, or 45, ways.

- Bernie selects 8 toys from the 10 shown for display in his cabinet. Since the order of display does not matter to him, he calculates that this can be done in $_{10}C_8$, or 45, ways.

a) Explain in words why $_{10}C_2 = {_{10}C_8}$.

b) Use factorial notation to show that $_{10}C_2 = {_{10}C_8}$.

c) Give another two examples of equivalent combinations.

The above examples are representations of the general rule

$$_nC_r = {_nC_{n-r}}. \qquad \text{or} \qquad \binom{n}{r} = \binom{n}{n-r}$$

d) Algebraically show that $_nC_r = {_nC_{n-r}}$.

Solving for "n" in Combination Problems

Class Ex. #4 During a Pee Wee hockey tryout, all the players met on the ice after the last practice and shook hands with each other. Algebraically determine the number of players who attended the tryouts if there were 300 handshakes in all.

Polygons and Diagonals

Consider circles with five points marked on the circumference.

a) How many triangles can be formed using these five points? Write the answer in combination notation.

b) How many lines can be drawn connecting two points on the circle? Write the answer in combination notation.

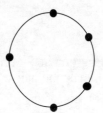

c) Sketch a regular pentagon.

i) How many lines can be drawn connecting two points on the pentagon, including the sides of the pentagon?

ii) How many of these lines are diagonals of the pentagon?

iii) Express the answer to ii) in terms of combinations.

d) How many diagonals are there in a regular octagon?

e) How many diagonals are there in a regular n-sided polygon?

The number of diagonals in a regular n-sided polygon is

$$_nC_2 - n \quad \text{or} \quad \binom{n}{2} - n$$

Class Ex. #5

A polygon has 65 diagonals. Algebraically determine how many sides it has.

Complete Assignment Questions #6 - #15

Assignment

1. The Athletic Council decides to form a sub-committee of 6 council members to look at a new sports program. There are a total of 15 Athletic Council members, 6 females and 9 males. How many different ways can the sub-committee consist of at most one male?

2. A group of 4 journalists is to be chosen to cover a murder trial. There are 5 male and 7 female journalists available. How many possible groups can be formed

    a) consisting of 2 men and 2 women?   b) consisting of at least one woman?

3. Consider a standard deck of 52 cards. How many different four card hands have
    a) at least one black card?   b) at least 2 kings?

    c) two pairs?   d) at most 2 clubs?

4. City Council decides to form a sub-committee of five aldermen to investigate transportation concerns. There are 4 males and 7 females. How many different ways can the sub-committee be formed consisting of at least one female member?

5. An all-night showing at a movie theatre is to consist of five movies. There are fourteen different movies available, ten disaster movies and four horror movies. How many possible schedules include:

a) at least one horror movie?   **b)** at least four disaster movies?

c) both "Airport Disaster" and "Halloween Horror"?

6. Use "guess and check" on a calculator to determine the solution(s) to the following equations.

a) $\begin{pmatrix} n \\ 2 \end{pmatrix} = 105$ **b)** $_nC_3 = 84$ **c)** $_{11}C_n = 330$

7. Algebraically determine the solution to the equation $_nC_7 = {}_{n+1}C_8$.

8. Determine the number of diagonals in

a) a regular hexagon   **b)** a regular decagon

9. Show that the number of diagonals in a regular p-sided polygon is $\dfrac{p(p-3)}{2}$.

10. There are eight visible points on the circle below. How many triangles can be made using these eight points?

Multiple Choice

11. After everyone had shaken hands once with everyone else in a room, there was a total of 66 handshakes. How many people were in the room?

    A.   11

    B.   12

    C.   33

    D.   67

12. There are 20 different ways of selecting three students from a class of students. Which of the following equations can be used to determine the number, n, of students in the class?

    A. $n^3 - 3n^2 - 2n - 20 = 0$

    B. $n^3 - 3n^2 - 2n - 120 = 0$

    C. $n^3 - 3n^2 + 2n - 20 = 0$

    D. $n^3 - 3n^2 + 2n - 120 = 0$

Numerical Response

13. The number of ways that a selection of 7 students can be chosen from a class of 28 is the same as the number of ways that n students can be chosen from the same class. The value of n is _____ .

(Record your answer in the numerical response box from left to right.)

14. Collinear points are points which share the same straight line. The number of triangles which can be formed from 10 points if no three of the points are collinear is _____ .

(Record your answer in the numerical response box from left to right.)

15. There are 170 diagonals in a polygon. The number of sides of the polygon is _____ .

(Record your answer in the numerical response box from left to right.)

Answer Key

1. 55

2. a) 210   b) 490   c) 2808   d) 258 856

3. a) 255 775   b) 6961

4. 462   5. a) 1750   b) 1092   c) 220

6. a) 15   b) 9   c) 4 or 7   7. 7

8. a) 9   b) 35   10. 56   11. B   12. D

13. | 2 | 1 | | | 14. | 1 | 2 | 0 | | 15. | 2 | 0 | | |

Permutations and Combinations Lesson #6:
Problem Solving with Permutations and Combinations

Review

Recall the following formulas from earlier lessons.

- Fundamental counting principle, number of ways = $a \times b \times c \times$ ...

- Factorial notation, $n! = n(n-1)(n-2)(n-3) \dots (3)(2)(1)$, where $n \in N$, and $0! = 1$

- Number of permutations of r from n, $\quad {}_nP_r = \dfrac{n!}{(n-r)!}$

- Permutations with repetitions, number of ways $= \dfrac{n!}{a! \, b! \, c!}$

- Number of combinations of r from n, $\quad {}_nC_r = \begin{pmatrix} n \\ r \end{pmatrix} = \dfrac{n!}{(n-r)! \, r!}$

Note In problem solving, it is essential to determine whether order is important or not.

Class Ex. #1

How many arrangements of the word **POPPIES** can be made under each of
the following conditions?

a) without restrictions

b) if each arrangement begins with a **P**

c) if the first two letters are **P**

d) if all the **P**'s are to be together

e) if the first letter is **P** and the next one is not **P**

Class Ex. #2

A class consists of 5 girls and 7 boys. A committee is to be formed consisting of 2 girls and 3 boys. Determine the number of ways a teacher can choose the committee if

a) there are no further restrictions

b) Johnny, the Principal's son, has to be on the committee

c) the twins, Peter and Paul, cannot both be on the committee

Use the following information to answer the next class example.

David, Steven, and Helen were trying to answer the following homework question.

" The students in a school band have practiced 5 popular and 6 classical music compositions. For the school concert they will choose a program consisting of 3 popular and 2 classical music compositions. If the order of the compositions matters, determine the number of different programs which can be presented."

The students' answers are shown below.

David: $_{11}P_5$ Steven: $_5P_3 \times _6P_2$ Helen: $_5C_3 \times _6C_2$

Each student was convinced their answer was correct, and asked their teacher to check their work. The teacher asked the students to write their answers on the board and asked the class to discuss the merits of each answer.

Class Ex. #3

a) If possible, discuss the merits of each answer with other students and indicate errors in any of David's, Steven's, or Helen's reasoning.

b) The teacher indicated that all three students had given an incorrect answer. Determine the correct solution to the problem.

| Complete Assignment Questions #1 - #20 |

Assignment

1. A basketball squad of 11 players is to be chosen from 17 available players.
   In how many ways can this be done if:

   a) Colin and Darryl must be selected?   **b)** Jeff and Brent cannot both be selected?

2. Fifteen rugby players line up for a team picture, with seven players in the front row and eight players in the back row. Expressing your answer in factorial notation, determine the number of arrangements of the fifteen players

   a) without restrictions   **b)** if the captain is in the middle of the front row

3. Determine the number of arrangements of the letters of the word **TATTOO** which
   a) begin with a **T**   **b)** begin with two **T**'s

   c) begin with three **T**'s   **d)** begin with exactly two **T**'s

4.   Ten students have been elected to serve on students' council.

    a) In how many ways can 4 of these students be chosen to represent the school as ambassadors at the provincial education conference?

    b) In how many ways can a president, vice-president, secretary, and treasurer be chosen from the ten students?

    c) Six of the ten students elected to students' council are girls. In how many different orders can four of the students line up for a photograph if there must be an equal number of boys and girls in the photograph?

5.   A town has 6 streets running from north to south and 4 avenues running from west to east. A man wishes to drive from the extreme south-west intersection to the extreme north-east intersection, moving either north or east along one of the streets or avenues.

Tania used the expression $\dfrac{10!}{6!4!}$ to determine the number of different ways to drive from the extreme south-west intersection to the extreme north-east intersection.
Draw a diagram to illustrate the situation and explain why Tania was incorrect in her reasoning.

6.   How many arrangements are there of the letters of the word **MONOTONOUS** under each condition?

    a) without restrictions

    b) if each arrangement begins with a **T**

    c) if each arrangement begins with an **O**

    d) if the four **O**'s are to be together

7. The number of ways that an executive committee consisting of prime minister, deputy prime minister, treasurer, and secretary can be chosen from 16 student council members is

A. $4!$

B. $\dfrac{16!}{4!}$

C. $\dfrac{16!}{12!\,4!}$

D. $\dfrac{16!}{12!}$

Use the following information to answer the next question.

A sports store has jerseys representing the seven Canadian NHL teams and the eight Canadian CFL teams. Five of these jerseys have to be chosen for display in a store window. The store owner decides to choose three NHL and two CFL jerseys. These jerseys will be arranged in a row in the store window.

8. The number of displays that can be made by choosing the jerseys and then arranging them in the window is

A. 4900

B. 11 760

C. 117 600

D. 1 411 200

9. A researcher has collected data on families with 3 children, families with 4 children, and families with 5 children. Each family is given a code, reflecting the number, gender, and birth order of the children. For example, the code MMMF is given to a family with 4 children where the first 3 children born are boys and the youngest child is a girl. How many different codes are required in this study?

A. 32

B. 56

C. 150

D. 4096

10. The number of arrangements of the letters of the word **PARALLEL** in which all the **L**'s are together at the end of the arrangement is

A. 60

B. 120

C. 180

D. 360

Use the following information to answer the next question.

A student enrolled in a General Studies program at a particular university must take four courses in the first semester.

The student must take English, either Mathematics or Psychology, and either two courses from Group A or two courses from Group B below.

Group A	Group B
French	Biology
Spanish	Chemistry
German	Computing
History	Geology
Geography	

11. The number of four-course programs available to the student is

    A. $_2C_1 \times (_5C_2 \times _4C_2)$

    B. $_2C_1 \times (_5C_2 + _4C_2)$

    C. $_2P_1 \times (_5P_2 \times _4P_2)$

    D. $_2P_1 \times (_5P_2 + _4P_2)$

12. The area codes in a country all contain three digits from the digits 1 to 9. Which of the following restrictions will result in the most area codes?

    A. The digits are all different.

    B. The middle digit must be odd.

    C. The digit 7 cannot be used.

    D. All the digits are even, or all the digits are odd.

13. If $_nP_r = 11\,880$ and $_nC_r = 495$, then the value of n is

    A. 4

    B. 12

    C. 24

    D. unable to be determined from the given information

Use the following information to answer the next two questions.

On the floor of her study, a student has
5 different English books, 2 different
Science books, and 2 different
Mathematics books.

14. The number of ways in which three of these books can be arranged on a bookshelf is

    A. $_5P_1 \times {_2P_1} \times {_2P_1}$

    B. $_9P_3$

    C. $_9C_3$

    D. $3!$

15. The number of ways of arranging two English books, two Science books, and a
    Mathematics book on a bookshelf is _____ .

    (Record your answer in the numerical response box from left to right.)

16. The number of arrangements of the letters of the word **STUDENT** in which
    the two **T**'s are not adjacent is _____ .

    (Record your answer in the numerical response box from left to right.)

17. 35 different quadrilaterals can be formed by connecting points on the circumference
    of a circle. The number of points on the circle is _____ .

    (Record your answer in the numerical response box from left to right.)

18. A basketball team consists of some guards and six forwards. If there are 420 ways to select two guards and three forwards to the starting line-up, then the number of guards on the team is _____.

(Record your answer in the numerical response box from left to right.)

19. Customer service representatives at a men's designer store must wear company attire. They have a choice of three different shirts, four different ties, and two different pairs of pants. The number of different outfits that a customer service representative could create using these items is _____ .

(Record your answer in the numerical response box from left to right.)

20. A coach must choose the 5 starters for a basketball team from 6 males and 5 females. If there must be at least two of each gender in the starting line-up, the number of different groups of players that can be chosen is _____ .

(Record your answer in the numerical response box from left to right.)

Answer Key

1. a) 5005   **b)** 7371   **2. a)** 15!   **b)** 14!
3. a) 30   **b)** 12   **c)** 3   **d)** 9   **4. a)** 210   **b)** 5040   **c)** 2160

5. He has to drive 5 blocks east and 3 blocks north in any order. So the answer is $\dfrac{8!}{5!3!} = 56$.

6. a) 75 600   **b)** 7560   **c)** 30 240   **d)** 2520
7. D   **8.** C   **9.** B   **10.** A   **11.** B   **12.** C   **13.** B   **14.** B

15.	2	4	0	0		16.	1	8	0	0		17.	7			
18.	7					19.	2	4				20.	3	5	0

Permutations and Combinations Lesson #7:
Pascal's Triangle

Investigating the Expansion of $(x + y)^n$

In this section we investigate patterns in the expanded form of $(x + y)^n$, for $n \leq 4$, $n \in N$.

a) Write the following in simplest form.

    i) $(x + y)^0 =$ **ii)** $(x + y)^1 =$

b) Expand $(x + y)^2$, $(x + y)^3$, and $(x + y)^4$.

c) Complete the following using your answers above.

$(x + y)^0 = 1$

$(x + y)^1 = x +$

$(x + y)^2 = x^2 +$

$(x + y)^3 = x^3 +$

$(x + y)^4 = x^4 +$

d) State the number of terms in the expansion of

    i) $(x + y)^2$ **ii)** $(x + y)^3$ **iii)** $(x + y)^4$ **iv)** $(x + y)^{20}$

e) State the sum of the exponents in each term in the expansion of

    i) $(x + y)^2$ **ii)** $(x + y)^3$ **iii)** $(x + y)^4$ **iv)** $(x + y)^{20}$

f) Complete the following arrays which show the <u>coefficients</u> of the terms in each of the expansions.

                Array   Triangular Array

$(x + y)^0 \Rightarrow$ ___

$(x + y)^1 \Rightarrow$ ___ ___

$(x + y)^2 \Rightarrow$ <u>1</u>   <u>2</u>   <u>1</u>   <u>1</u>   <u>2</u>   <u>1</u>

$(x + y)^3 \Rightarrow$ ___ ___ ___ ___

$(x + y)^4 \Rightarrow$ ___ ___ ___ ___ ___

g) Explore the patterns in the triangular array
and complete the next row in the triangle.

Properties of the Expansion of $(x + y)^n$

The expansion of $(x + y)^n$, where $0 \le n \le 5$, is shown below.

$$(x + y)^0 = 1$$
$$(x + y)^1 = x + y$$
$$(x + y)^2 = x^2 + 2xy + y^2$$
$$(x + y)^3 = x^3 + 3x^2y + 3xy^2 + y^3$$
$$(x + y)^4 = x^4 + 4x^3y + 6x^2y^2 + 4xy^3 + y^4$$
$$(x + y)^5 = x^5 + 5x^4y + 10x^3y^2 + 10x^2y^3 + 5xy^4 + y^5$$

Use the above expansions to complete the following:

1. There are _____ terms.
2. The sum of the exponents of x and y in each term is _____ .
3. The exponents of x _____ term by term from n to 0.
4. The exponents of y _____ term by term from 0 to n.
5. The coefficients in each expansion form a _____ arrangement.

Investigating Pascal's Triangle

The coefficients in the above expansion can be put in a triangular array known as Pascal's Triangle (named after Blaise Pascal, who developed applications of the triangle in the seventeenth century).

a) Use the patterns to complete the next three rows of Pascal's Triangle.

$$
\begin{array}{c}
1 \\
1 \quad 1 \\
1 \quad 2 \quad 1 \\
1 \quad 3 \quad 3 \quad 1 \\
1 \quad 4 \quad 6 \quad 4 \quad 1 \\
1 \quad 5 \quad 10 \quad 10 \quad 5 \quad 1
\end{array}
$$

b) Complete the following expansions:

$(x + y)^6 = x^6 +$

$(x + y)^7 =$

c) Which row of Pascal's Triangle is equivalent to the coefficients of the terms in the expansion of   **i)** $(x + y)^6$?   **ii)** $(x + y)^7$?   **iii)** $(x + y)^{12}$?   **iv)** $(x + y)^n$?

Pascal's Triangle and Combinations

Pascal's Triangle is actually an array of combinations. The reasoning behind this will be developed in the next lesson on the Binomial Theorem.

Row Number	Pascal's Triangle	Pascal's Triangle in Combination Form
1	1	$_0C_0$
2	1 1	$_1C_0$ $_1C_1$
3	1 2 1	$_2C_0$ $_2C_1$ $_2C_2$
4	1 3 3 1	$_3C_0$ $_3C_1$ $_3C_2$ $_3C_3$
5	1 4 6 4 1	$_4C_0$ $_4C_1$ $_4C_2$ $_4C_3$ $_4C_4$
6	1 5 10 10 5 1	$_5C_0$ $_5C_1$ $_5C_2$ $_5C_3$ $_5C_4$ $_5C_5$
7	1 6 15 20 15 6 1	$_6C_0$ $_6C_1$ $_6C_2$ $_6C_3$ $_6C_4$ $_6C_5$ $_6C_6$

a) State the first three terms of the eighth row of Pascal's Triangle in numerical form and in combination form.

b) State the last three terms of the eighth row of Pascal's Triangle in numerical form and in combination form.

c) Use Pascal's Triangle to write the following as a single combination.

  i) $_4C_2 + {_4C_3}$ **ii)** $_6C_0 + {_6C_1}$ **iii)** $_nC_r + {_nC_{r+1}}$

Investigating Three Sums Equal to 2^n

Part 1: • Complete the table for the sum of the numbers in each of the first six rows of Pascal's Triangle.

• Complete the following statement.

The sum of the numbers in the $(n+1)^{\text{th}}$ row of Pascal's Triangle is _____.

Part 2: • Look at row 5 in Pascal's Triangle in combination form. The sum of the numbers in this row can be written as $_4C_0 + {_4C_1} + {_4C_2} + {_4C_3} + {_4C_4}$.

Refer to Part 1 and express this sum as a power of 2.
$_4C_0 + {_4C_1} + {_4C_2} + {_4C_3} + {_4C_4} =$ _____ .

Row Number	Sum of the Numbers in the Row	Sum as a Power of 2
1		
2		
3		
4		
5		
6		
n		
$n+1$		

• Look at row 7 and complete the following.
$_6C_0 + {_6C_1} + {_6C_2} + {_6C_3} + {_6C_4} + {_6C_5} + {_6C_6} =$ _____ .

• Complete the following statement.
$_nC_0 + {_nC_1} + {_nC_2} + {_nC_3} + \ldots + {_nC_{n-1}} + {_nC_n} =$ _____ .

Part 3: • Consider the expansion of $(x + y)^n$, where $0 \le n \le 5$.

$$(x + y)^0 = 1$$
$$(x + y)^1 = x + y$$
$$(x + y)^2 = x^2 + 2xy + y^2$$
$$(x + y)^3 = x^3 + 3x^2y + 3xy^2 + y^3$$
$$(x + y)^4 = x^4 + 4x^3y + 6x^2y^2 + 4xy^3 + y^4$$
$$(x + y)^5 = x^5 + 5x^4y + 10x^3y^2 + 10x^2y^3 + 5xy^4 + y^5$$

n	Sum of Coefficients	Sum as a Power of 2
1		
2		
3		
4		
5		
n		

Complete the table for the sum of the coefficients in each of the first five expansions of $(x + y)^n$.

• Complete the following statement.

The sum of the coefficients in the expansion of $(x + y)^n$ is _____ .

Three Sums Equal to 2^n

The following statements summarize the previous investigative work.

- The sum of the numbers in the $(n + 1)^{\text{th}}$ row of Pascal's Triangle is 2^n.

- $_nC_0 + {}_nC_1 + {}_nC_2 + {}_nC_3 + ... + {}_nC_{n-1} + {}_nC_n = 2^n$.

- The sum of the coefficients in the expansion of $(x + y)^n$ is 2^n.

Class Ex. #1

a) Determine the sum of the numbers in the tenth row of Pascal's Triangle.

b) Determine the sum of the coefficients in the expansion of $(m + n)^{12}$.

c) Determine the value of the following.

    i) $_{15}C_0 + {}_{15}C_1 + {}_{15}C_2 + ... + {}_{15}C_{15}$ **ii)** $_6C_0 + {}_6C_1 + {}_6C_2 + ... + {}_6C_5$

Complete Assignment Questions #1 - #8

Exploring Routes using Pascal's Triangle

Recall the following problem from Lesson #3:

Paul and Katherine are considering the following problem.

   "Find the number of routes from A to B if paths must always move closer to B".

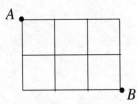

Katherine's method was to use permutations with repetitions to get $\dfrac{5!}{3!2!} = 10$ routes.

This answer can be determined by a different method which involves Pascal's Triangle.

Complete the following to develop the method. The diagram has been rotated.

a) There is one route from A to C. This number has been placed on the second diagram.
    Determine the number of routes from A to the points D, E, F, G, H, I and write the
    answers in the corresponding positions on the second diagram.

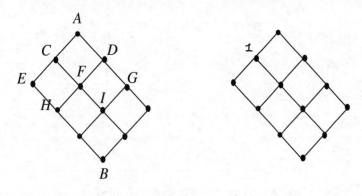

b) How do the following answers relate?

   i) *F* compared to *C* and *D*   **ii)** *H* compared to *E* and *F*   **iii)** *I* compared to *F* and *G*

c) Use the relationship in b) to complete the second diagram and compare your answer
    with Katherine's answer.

Pascal's Triangle and Routes

The exploration on the previous page can be used to illustrate how Pascal's Triangle may be used to determine the number of routes in a diagram. Notice that the numbers on the diagram on the previous page are part of Pascal's Triangle as shown in the overlays below.

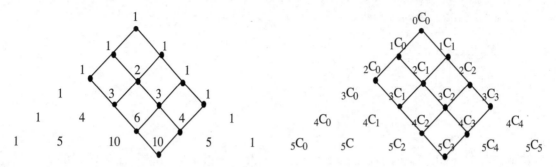

 Note As shown in the second diagram, the answer 10 is equivalent to $_5C_3$ which can be written in factorial notation as $\dfrac{5!}{2!3!}$. This is the same as the formula for permutations with repetitions.

 Class Ex. #2

A supervisor of the city bus department is determining how many routes there are from the bus station to the concert hall.

Determine the number of routes possible if the bus must always move closer to the concert hall.

a) using Pascal's Triangle

b) using permutations with repetitions

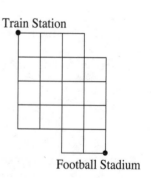

 Class Ex. #3

A taxi company is trying to find the quickest route during rush hour traffic from the train station to the football stadium.

a) Use Pascal's Triangle to determine the number of different routes that must be considered if at each intersection the taxi must always move closer to the football stadium.

b) Explain why the permutations with repetitions formula $\dfrac{9!}{4!5!}$ cannot be used to determine the answer to this problem.

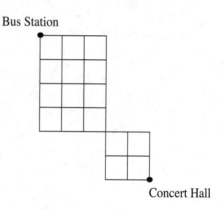

Complete Assignment Questions #9 - #15

Assignment

1. Draw the first six rows of Pascal's Triangle
  a) in numerical form   **b)** in combination form

2. Consider the expansion of $(x + y)^5$.
  a) How many terms are in the expansion of $(x + y)^5$?

  b) What is the sum of the coefficients in each term of the expansion of $(x + y)^5$?

  c) In numerical form and in combination form, state the coefficient of
    i) the first term   **ii)** the second term   **iii)** the last term

  d) Which term of the expansion contains   **i)** x^4?   **ii)** y^4?

3. Consider the expansion of $(x + y)^n$.
  a) How many terms are in the expansion of $x + y)^n$?

  b) What is the sum of the coefficients in each term of the expansion of $(x + y)^n$?

  c) In numerical form and in combination form, state the coefficient of
    i) the first term   **ii)** the last term

  d) In combination form, state the coefficient of
    i) the second term   **ii)** the third term   **iii)** the second-last term

4. Determine the first three terms in the ninth row of Pascal's Triangle.

5. Determine the last three terms in the sixteenth row of Pascal's Triangle.

6. Determine the value of n if the expansion of

a) $(x + y)^n$ has 14 terms

b) $(x + y)^{4n - 3}$ has 26 terms

7. a) Determine the sum of the terms in the ninth row of Pascal's Triangle.

b) Determine the sum of the coefficients in the expansion of $(a + b)^9$.

c) Determine the sum $_9C_0 + _9C_1 + _9C_2 + ... + _9C_9$.

8. Determine the following sums :

a) $_{10}C_1 + _{10}C_2 + _{10}C_3 + ... + _{10}C_{10}$

b) $_7C_6 + _7C_5 + _7C_4 + ... + _7C_1$

9. If routes must always move closer to B, determine the number of routes from A to B

i) using Pascal's Triangle   **ii)** using permutations with repetitions

a)

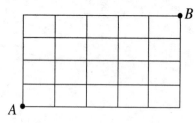

b)

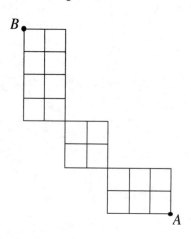

10. Determine the number of pathways from A to B if paths must always move closer to B.

a)

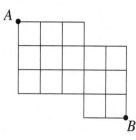

b)

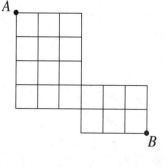

c)

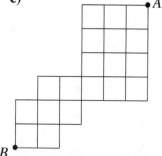

Use the following information to answer the next question.

Part of Pascal's Triangle is shown.

$$
\begin{array}{ccccccccc}
 & & & & 1 & & & & \\
 & & & 1 & & 1 & & & \\
 & & 1 & & 2 & & 1 & & \\
 & \_ & \_ & a & \_ & b & \_ & \_ & \_ \\
 \_ & \_ & & c & & d & & \_ & \_ \\
 \_ & \_ & e & & f & & g & \_ & \_
\end{array}
$$

Four statements are made about the entries in the triangle.

Statement 1: $b = {}_4C_2$ **Statement 2:** $e = g$

Statement 3: $a + b = d$ **Statement 4:** $f = \dfrac{6!}{3!3!}$

Multiple Choice **11.** How many of the four statements above are true?

   A. 1   **B.** 2

   C. 3   **D.** 4

Use the following information to answer the next question.

Students about to enter high school were given the following survey to complete.

Place a checkmark (√) in the box beside any of the following extra-curricular activities that interest you. You may place a checkmark (√) in as many boxes as you like, or you may leave all boxes blank.

    ☐ Volleyball   ☐ Basketball   ☐ Track and Field

    ☐ Football   ☐ Concert Band ☐ Speech and Debate

    ☐ Art Club   ☐ Yearbook   ☐ Photography

12. The number of different possible combinations that can be selected is

   A. 45

   B. 256

   C. 512

   D. 362 880

13. If $(x + y)^4 = ax^4 + bx^3y + cx^2y^2 + dxy^3 + ey^4$, then the value of $a + b + c + d + e$ is

    A.   5

    B.   8

    C.   16

    D.   32

Use the following information to answer the next question.

A student makes the following three statements:

Statement 1:   The sum of the numbers in the kth row of Pascal's Triangle is 2^{k-1}.

Statement 2:   The sum of the coefficients in the expansion of $(x + y)^k$ is 2^k.

Statement 3: $_kC_0 + {_kC_1} + {_kC_2} + {_kC_3} + \dots + {_kC_{k-1}} + {_kC_k} = 2^k$.

14. Which of the student's statements are true?

    A.   Statement 1 and Statement 2 only.   **B.**   Statement 1 and Statement 3 only.

    C.   Statement 2 and Statement 3 only.   **D.**   All three statements.

 15. If $(x + y)^{2n+3}$ has 18 terms, then the value of n is _____ .

    (Record your answer in the numerical response box from left to right.)

    ☐☐☐☐

Answer Key

1. Refer to the diagrams in the lesson.
2. **a)** 6   **b)** 5   **c) i)** $1, {_5C_0}$ **ii)** $5, {_5C_1}$ **iii)** $1, {_5C_5}$ **d) i)** Term 2   **ii)** Term 5
3. **a)** $n+1$ **b)** n **c) i)** $1, {_nC_0}$ **ii)** $1, {_nC_n}$ **d) i)** $_nC_1$ **ii)** $_nC_2$ **iii)** $_nC_{n-1}$
4. $1, 8, 28$ 5. $105, 15, 1$ 6. **a)** 13   **b)** 7   7. **a)** 256   **b)** 512   **c)** 512
8. **a)** 1023   **b)** 126   9. **a)** 126   **b)** 900   10. **a)** 106   **b)** 260   **c)** 495
11. D   12. C   13. C   14. D   15. | 7 | | | |

Permutations and Combinations Lesson #8:
The Binomial Theorem

Review

In the last lesson, we investigated the expansion of $(x + y)^n$, where $0 \leq n \leq 5$, and developed Pascal's Triangle in numerical form and in combination form.

$$(x + y)^0 = 1$$
$$(x + y)^1 = x + y$$
$$(x + y)^2 = x^2 + 2xy + y^2$$
$$(x + y)^3 = x^3 + 3x^2y + 3xy^2 + y^3$$
$$(x + y)^4 = x^4 + 4x^3y + 6x^2y^2 + 4xy^3 + y^4$$
$$(x + y)^5 = x^5 + 5x^4y + 10x^3y^2 + 10x^2y^3 + 5xy^4 + y^5$$

Row Number	Pascal's Triangle	Pascal's Triangle in Combination Form
1	1	$_0C_0$
2	1 1	$_1C_0$ $_1C_1$
3	1 2 1	$_2C_0$ $_2C_1$ $_2C_2$
4	1 3 3 1	$_3C_0$ $_3C_1$ $_3C_2$ $_3C_3$
5	1 4 6 4 1	$_4C_0$ $_4C_1$ $_4C_2$ $_4C_3$ $_4C_4$
6	1 5 10 10 5 1	$_5C_0$ $_5C_1$ $_5C_2$ $_5C_3$ $_5C_4$ $_5C_5$
7	1 6 15 20 15 6 1	$_6C_0$ $_6C_1$ $_6C_2$ $_6C_3$ $_6C_4$ $_6C_5$ $_6C_6$

Exploring the Binomial Theorem

Referring to the combination array and Pascal's Triangle above, it is not just a coincidence that the combination symbols represent the numbers in Pascal's Triangle.

To investigate this consider the expansion of $(x + y)^6$.

$$(x + y)^6 = (x + y)(x + y)(x + y)(x + y)(x + y)(x + y)$$
$$= x^6 + 6x^5y + 15x^4y^2 + 20x^3y^3 + 15x^2y^4 + 6xy^5 + y^6$$

Notice that each term in the expansion is a *combination* of x's and y's.

Consider how the third term (i.e. $15x^4y^2$) is formed. It is formed by choosing a y from any two of the six factors in the expansion of $(x + y)^6$ and an x from the remaining four factors. The two y's can be chosen in $_6C_2$ (or 15) ways.

The four x's can then be chosen in $_4C_4$ (or 1) way. This leads to the term $_6C_2x^4y^2$.

• Write the coefficients <u>in terms of combinations</u> for the expansion below.

$$(x + y)^6 = (x + y)(x + y)(x + y)(x + y)(x + y)(x + y)$$
$$= x^6 + 6x^5y + 15x^4y^2 + 20x^3y^3 + 15x^2y^4 + 6xy^5 + y^6$$
$$= + {}_6C_2x^4y^2$$

The expansion of the binomial $(x + y)^6$ using combinations given on the previous page can be extended for any exponent that is a natural number. This leads to the following general formula for binomial expansions known as the Binomial Theorem.

Binomial Theorem

$$(x + y)^n = {}_nC_0x^n + {}_nC_1x^{n-1}y + {}_nC_2x^{n-2}y^2 + \ldots + {}_nC_kx^{n-k}y^k + \ldots + {}_nC_ny^n, \text{ where } n \in I, n \geq 0.$$

General Term of the Expansion of $(x + y)^n$

The term ${}_nC_kx^{n-k}y^k$ is called the **general term** of the expansion of $(x + y)^n$.
Note that the general term in the expansion is term $(k + 1)$ and not term k.

$$\boxed{t_{k+1} = {}_nC_kx^{n-k}y^k}$$

Class Ex. #1

Determine **a)** the fifth term of $(x + y)^8$ **b)** the middle term of $(a + b)^{10}$

Class Ex. #2

Use the binomial theorem to write the expansion of $(x + y)^7$.

The Binomial Theorem Applied to More Complex Binomials

Class Ex. #3

Susan was determining the fourth term of $(2x - 5)^6$. Part of her work is shown below.
Complete her work to show that the fourth term is $-20\,000x^3$.

$$x \rightarrow 2x \qquad\qquad t_{k+1} = {}_nC_kx^{n-k}y^k$$

$$y \rightarrow -5 \qquad\qquad t_4 = t_{3+1} = {}_6C_3(2x)^{6-3}(-5)^3$$

$$k \rightarrow 3$$

$$n \rightarrow 6$$

Class Ex. #4   Determine the fifth term of $(3x - 2y)^7$.

Complete Assignment Questions #1 - #4

Applying the Binomial Theorem Where k is Unknown

Class Ex. #5   Aldon has been asked to solve the following problem.

" One term in the expansion of $(x^2 + a)^8$ is $114\,688\,x^4$.
Determine the numerical value of a, if $a > 0$."

Aldon does not know how to proceed because he does not know which term he is looking for.
His friend Griffin explains how to determine the value of k by showing him the following
work.

$x \rightarrow x^2$ $\qquad$ $t_{k+1} = {}_nC_k x^{n-k} y^k$

$y \rightarrow a$

$k \rightarrow k$ $\qquad$ $t_{k+1} = {}_8C_k (x^2)^{8-k}(a)^k$

$n \rightarrow 8$ $\qquad$ $t_{k+1} = {}_8C_k x^{16-2k} a^k$

a) Since the term we are looking for contains x^4, determine the value of k that satisfies this
condition.

b) Use this value of k to simplify t_{k+1}.

c) Equate t_{k+1} with $114\,688\,x^4$ and solve for a.

Determine the numerical coefficient of the term containing a^7 in the expansion of $(3 - a)^{10}$.

Determine the constant term (i.e. the term independent of x) in the expansion of $\left(2x - \dfrac{1}{x^2}\right)^{15}$.

Complete Assignment Questions #5 - #13

Assignment

1. Determine **a)** the third term of $(x + y)^{15}$ **b)** the middle term of $(p + q)^{12}$

2. Use the binomial theorem to write the expansion of $(x + y)^8$.

3. Find the indicated term of each expansion.

a) the fifth term of $(a - b)^5$ **b)** the second term of $(x - 2)^6$

c) the third term of $(3x + 2y)^9$ **d)** the fourth term of $(a^2 - 2a)^7$

e) the middle term of $\left(2 - \dfrac{x}{2} \right)^6$

4. Expand and write in the simplest form:

a) $(2x + y)^3$

b) $\left(x - \dfrac{1}{x}\right)^4$

5. Find the indicated term of each expansion.

a) the term in x^3 in $(1 - 2x)^{12}$

b) the term in $x^4 y^3$ in $(3x - y)^7$

6. a) One term in the expansion of $(x + a)^8$ is $448x^6$. Determine the value of a, $a > 0$.

b) One term in the expansion of $(x + b)^{11}$ is $-4455x^8$. Determine the value of b.

7. Find the indicated term of each expansion.

   a) the constant term in the expansion of $\left(x^2 - \dfrac{1}{x}\right)^6$

   b) the term independent of x in $\left(2x + \dfrac{1}{x^3}\right)^8$

8. In the expansion of $(x - 3)^8$, the numerical coefficient of the third degree term is

   A.   −13 608

   B.   5670

   C.   −1512

   D.   252

9. If the first term in the expansion of $(3x + 2y)^n$ is $243x^5$, then the coefficient of the second term is

   A.   30

   B.   162

   C.   240

   D.   810

Numerical
Response **10.** If $(2x + 3)^{3n+4}$ has 38 terms, then the value of n is _____ .

(Record your answer in the numerical response box from left to right.)

11. The term in x^{11} in the expansion of $\left(x^2 + \dfrac{1}{x}\right)^{10}$ has a numerical coefficient of _____ .

(Record your answer in the numerical response box from left to right.)

12. In the expansion of $(3x + 2y)^6$, the numerical coefficient of the term containing x^4y^2 is _____ .

(Record your answer in the numerical response box from left to right.)

13. A term of the binomial expansion $(cx + y)^6$, where c is a positive integer, is $42xy^5$. The value of c is _____ .

(Record your answer in the numerical response box from left to right.)

Answer Key

1. **a)** $105x^{13}y^2$ **b)** $924p^6q^6$

2. $x^8 + 8x^7y + 28x^6y^2 + 56x^5y^3 + 70x^4y^4 + 56x^3y^5 + 28x^2y^6 + 8xy^7 + y^8$

3. **a)** $5ab^4$ **b)** $-12x^5$ **c)** $314\,928\,x^7y^2$ **d)** $-280a^{11}$ **e)** $-20x^3$

4. **a)** $8x^3 + 12x^2y + 6xy^2 + y^3$ **b)** $x^4 - 4x^2 + 6 - \dfrac{4}{x^2} + \dfrac{1}{x^4}$ **5.** **a)** $-1760x^3$ **b)** $-2835x^4y^3$

6. **a)** 4   **b)** -3 **7.** **a)** 15   **b)** 1792   **8.** A   **9.** D   **10.**

1	1		

11.

1	2	0	

12.

4	8	6	0

13.

7			

Permutations and Combinations Lesson #9:
Practice Test

1. How many routes are there from A to B if each route must always move closer to B?

    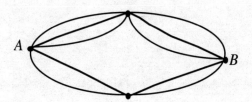

    A. 10

    B. 13

    C. 24

    D. 36

2. How many arrangements of all of the letters in the word **NOISE** are possible if the vowels, **E, I**, and **O**, must be together but not necessarily in that order?

    A. 6

    B. 12

    C. 18

    D. 36

3. A committee consists of eleven elected members. From this committee, a President, a Treasurer, and a Secretary have to be chosen. In how many ways can this be done?

    A. $_{11}P_3$ B. $_{11}C_3$ C. 11^3 D. $\dfrac{11!}{3!}$

4. Six children and five adults are to be seated in a row so that none of the children sits beside another child. The number of different ways in which this can be done is

    A. $11!$ B. $6! \times 5!$

    C. $_{11}C_6 \times _5C_5$ D. $_6C_6 \times _5C_5$

 1. A car dealership has 5 **different** models of car in the showroom. The 5 cars are to be displayed in a straight line. Three of the cars are blue, one is black and one is green.

The number of ways in which all of the cars can be displayed in the showroom if *no two blue cars* can be next to one another is _____.

(Record your answer in the numerical response box from left to right.)

5. An alternative form of the expression $\dfrac{(n+2)!}{n(n-1)!}$ is

   A. $(n+2)(n+1)$

   B. $\dfrac{(n+2)(n+1)}{(n-1)}$

   C. $\dfrac{(n+2)(n+1)}{n}$

   D. $\dfrac{(n+2)(n+1)}{(n-1)!}$

Section B   *A graphing calculator may be used for the remainder of the test.*

6. The number of different 6-letter permutations of all of the letters in the word **BANANA** is

   A. 60   B. 120

   C. 144   D. 720

7. The schedule in a soccer league consists of each team playing every other team twice. If there are six teams in the league, the total number of games on the schedule is

   A. 60   B. 36

   C. 30   D. 15

8. A committee of 6 students is to be selected from 5 boys and 6 girls. How many different committees are possible if there must be an equal number of boys and girls on the committee?

   A. $_{11}C_6$ B. $_5C_3 \times {}_6C_3$

   C. $_{11}C_3 \times {}_6C_3$ D. $_5C_1 \times {}_6C_1$

Numerical Response 2. A computer access code consists of three **different** digits followed by one of the letters A, B, C, or D.
If the first digit in the access code cannot be zero, then the number of different access codes possible is _____.

(Record your answer in the numerical response box from left to right.)

[| | |]

Use the following information to answer the next question.

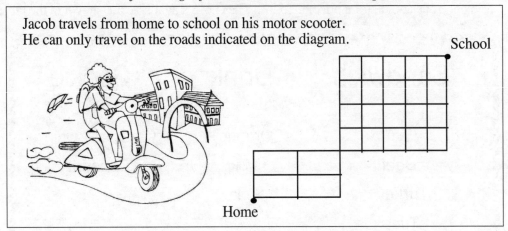

Jacob travels from home to school on his motor scooter.
He can only travel on the roads indicated on the diagram.

School

Home

9. The number of different routes he can take without backtracking is

A. 132

B. 756

C. 1716

D. 9240

10. The sum of the coefficients in the expansion of $(a + b)^5$ is

A. 64

B. 32

C. 16

D. 6

11. Al's Pizza is to expand its operation by opening 4 new stores in Calgary, 1 new store in Red Deer, and 3 new stores in Edmonton.

If there are 6 possible locations in Calgary, 4 possible locations in Red Deer, and 4 possible locations in Edmonton, then the number of ways in which the 8 different locations can be chosen is

A. 12

B. 165

C. 240

D. 34560

Numerical
Response **3.** The "special" menu at a fast food restaurant allows you to choose one sandwich, one drink and one cookie for a price of $5.99. The choices available are shown in the table.

Sandwich	Drink	Cookie
Ham	Orange	Chocolate Chip
Beef	Milk	Coconut
Turkey	Cola	
Tuna		
Chicken Salad		

The number of different ways that a student can choose a meal from the special menu, consisting of one sandwich, one drink, and one cookie, is _____.

(Record your answer in the numerical response box from left to right.)

12. Part of Pascal's Triangle is shown.

$$\begin{array}{ccccccc}
 & & & 1 & & & \\
 & & 1 & & 1 & & \\
 & 1 & & 2 & & 1 & \\
\_ & & \_ & & \_ & & \_ \\
\_ & a & & b & & \_ & \_ \\
\_ & & c & & d & & \_ \quad \_ \quad \_
\end{array}$$

Which entry in the triangle is equivalent to $_5C_2$?

A. a **B.** b **C.** c **D.** d

13. A 5-card hand is dealt from a standard deck of 52 playing cards. The number of different hands containing 4 diamonds and 1 spade is

A. 9 295

B. 18 590

C. 223 080

D. 1 115 400

4. If $\dfrac{n!}{(n-2)!} = 240$, the value of n is _____ .

(Record your answer in the numerical response box from left to right.)

14. Rajinder and six of his friends are in a line-up to buy tickets for a movie.
The number of ways in which they can line up if Rajinder is first in the line is

    A. 20   **B.** 120

    C. 720   **D.** 5040

15. If all of the letters in the word **FLAGPOLE** are used, then the number of different
8-letter arrangements that can be made ending with 3 vowels is

    A. 4320

    B. 720

    C. 360

    D. 120

5. One of the terms in the expansion of $(2x + 3)^5$ can be written in the form cx^2.
The value of c is _____ .

(Record your answer in the numerical response box from left to right.)

16. Ten students in a leadership class at Memorial High School are going to do some volunteer work. Five of the students will volunteer at the Food Bank, two of the students will volunteer at the Central Hospital and the remaining three students will volunteer at Memorial Elementary School.

The number of ways in which the ten students can be assigned to these three locations is

    A.   417

    B.   2520

    C.   845 020

    D.   1 360 800

17. The number of 7-letter arrangements of all of the letters of the word **SAILING** in which all the vowels are together is

    A.   72

    B.   144

    C.   360

    D.   720

18. In the expansion of $(3a - 2b)^7$ the coefficient of the term containing a^2b^5 is

    A.   −6048

    B.   6048

    C.   −126

    D.   126

19. A Graduation Committee of 6 students is to be selected from the 4 males and 6 females on the Student Council.
How many Graduation Committees are possible if the President of the Student Council, who is female, must be on the committee?

    A.   84

    B.   126

    C.   210

    D.   252

20. Mr. and Mrs. LaMarre want a family photograph taken with their four children. In how many ways can the family stand in a straight line if the parents must occupy the two middle positions in the line?

A. 4 **B.** 24

C. 48 **D.** 120

Use the following information to answer the next question.

Pizza Palace uses the following advert to promote its pizzas.

Pizza Palace

1024 Different Pizzas Available

$10.99 to $18.99. Tel. (123) 456-7890

Customers can choose from 1024 different 14-inch pizzas. Each pizza contains cheese and you can have a plain cheese pizza or add any number of the available toppings.

6. The number of different toppings available to a customer is _____ .

(Record your answer in the numerical response box from left to right.)

_____

Written Response

1. The Riverview High School Games Club meets once a week to play a variety of card and board games. The club currently has 14 male and 16 female members.

• Four members of the club are selected to play the card game "euchre".
  How many ways can those four players be selected from the 30 members of the club?

• The game of "euchre" only uses 24 cards from a standard deck. All cards are removed, except the 9's, 10's, jacks, queens, kings, and aces, which are used for the game.
  How many five card hands of "euchre" can be dealt that have exactly 2 red cards?

> ## Written Response

2. Phil is a golf professional at a local private golf course. He owns many golf clubs, and will choose the clubs he uses to play a particular round of golf based on weather conditions, course conditions, and course length. His clubs are categorized by drivers, fairway woods, irons, wedges, and putters. The chart below shows the golf clubs Phil currently owns.

Drivers (3)	Fairway Woods (4)	Irons (8)	Wedges (4)	Putters (3)
11° loft	3 wood	2 iron	60° lob wedge	Blade putter
10° loft	5 wood	3 iron	56° sand wedge	Mallet putter
8.5° loft	7 wood	4 iron	52° gap wedge	2-ball putter
	9 wood	5 iron	48° pitching wedge	
		6 iron		
		7 iron		
		8 iron		
		9 iron		

- Phil is giving a golf lesson today, and he will take one driver, one iron, and one wedge to the driving range. In how many ways can he select the three clubs he will use for the lesson?

- One of the official rules of golf states,

  "The player must start a stipulated round with not more than 14 clubs."

  Before each round, Phil must choose the 14 clubs he will use for that round.
  For tomorrow's round, Phil will choose 1 driver, 3 fairway woods, 6 irons, 3 wedges and his mallet putter. In how many ways can Phil choose the 14 golf clubs he will use in tomorrow's round?

Answer Key

Multiple Choice

1. B	2. D	3. A	4. B	5. A	6. A	7. C	8. B
9. B	10. B	11. C	12. D	13. A	14. C	15. C	16. B
17. C	18. A	19. B	20. C				

Numerical Response

1. | 1 | 2 | | |

2. | 2 | 5 | 9 | 2 |

3. | 3 | 0 | | |

4. | 1 | 6 | | |

5. | 1 | 0 | 8 | 0 |

6. | 1 | 0 | | |

Written Response

1. • 27 405
   • 14 520

2. • 96
   • 1344

Analyzing Radical and Rational Functions Lesson #1: Radical Functions - Part One

Overview

In this unit, we will graph and analyze radical functions and determine solutions to equations involving a single radical. We will also graph and analyze rational functions and determine solutions to rational equations.

Radical Function

A radical function is a function which contains a radical.
The simplest radical function is $y = \sqrt{x}$. In this lesson we will analyze the graph of $y = \sqrt{x}$, and transformations of this graph of the form $y - k = a\sqrt{b(x - h)}$.

Analyzing the Function $y = \sqrt{x}$

a) To sketch the graph of the function $y = \sqrt{x}$, complete the table of values below and plot the points obtained on the grid. Join the points with a smooth curve.

x	-4	-1	0	1	4	9	16
y							

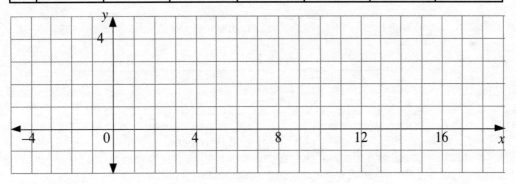

b) Explain why the domain of the function $y = \sqrt{x}$ is not the set of real numbers.

c) State the domain of the function $y = \sqrt{x}$.

d) State the range of the function $y = \sqrt{x}$.

Transforming $y = \sqrt{x}$ to $y - k = a\sqrt{b(x - h)}$

The table below summarizes the connection between transformations, replacements for x or y, and resulting equations established in the transformation unit.

Transformation	Replacement for x or y	Equation
Vertical Translation	$y \rightarrow y - k$	$y - k = f(x)$ or $y = f(x) + k$
Horizontal Translation	$x \rightarrow x - h$	$y = f(x - h)$
Reflection in the x-axis	$y \rightarrow -y$	$-y = f(x)$ or $y = -f(x)$
Reflection in the y-axis	$x \rightarrow -x$	$y = f(-x)$
Reflection in the line $y = x$	$x \rightarrow y,\ y \rightarrow x$	$x = f(y)$ or $y = f^{-1}(x)$
Vertical Stretch about the x-axis	$y \rightarrow \dfrac{1}{a}y$	$\dfrac{1}{a}y = f(x)$ or $y = af(x)$
Horizontal Stretch about the y-axis	$x \rightarrow bx$	$y = f(bx)$

To "build" the equation $y - k = a\sqrt{b(x - h)}$ from $y = \sqrt{x}$, transformations should be done in the order

1. Stretches   2. Reflections   3. Translations

Class Ex. #1

In each case

i) describe the series of transformations required to transform the graph of $y = \sqrt{x}$ to the graph of the given function

ii) make a rough sketch of the graph on the grid provided

iii) state the domain and range of the function

iv) verify using the features of a graphing calculator

a) $y - 4 = \sqrt{x + 2}$

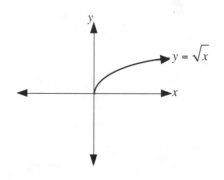

b) $2y = \sqrt{-x}$

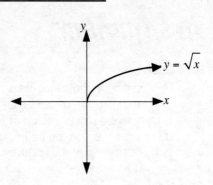

c) $y + 5 = -\sqrt{x}$

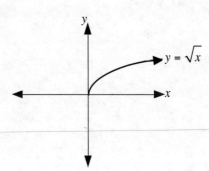

d) $y = 3\sqrt{2x - 1}$

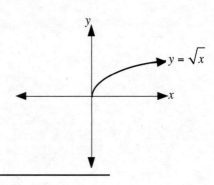

Class Ex. #2

Determine the domain and range of the function $y = a\sqrt{bx}$ if

a) $a > 0, b > 0$ **b)** $a < 0, b > 0$

c) $a > 0, b < 0$ **d)** $a < 0, b < 0$

Complete Assignment Questions #1 - #5

Assignment

1. In each case,
    i) describe the transformation(s) required to transform the graph of $y = \sqrt{x}$ to the graph of the given function
    ii) make a rough sketch of the graph on the grid provided
    iii) state the domain and range of the function
    iv) verify using the features of a graphing calculator

a) $y = -\sqrt{x}$

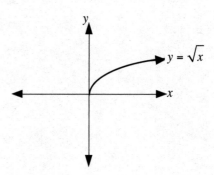

b) $y = \sqrt{-x}$

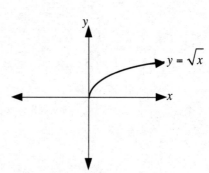

c) $x = \sqrt{y}$

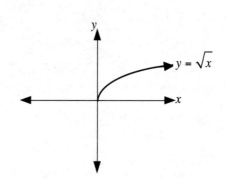

d) $y + 2 = \sqrt{x + 1}$

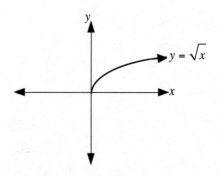

2. In each case,

    i)   describe the series of transformations required to transform the graph of $y = \sqrt{x}$ to
          the graph of the given function

    ii) make a rough sketch of the graph on the grid provided

    iii) state the domain and range of the function

    iv) verify using the features of a graphing calculator

a) $y = \dfrac{1}{2}\sqrt{\dfrac{1}{2}x}$

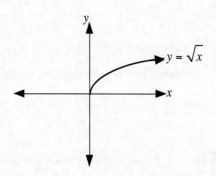

b) $2y = -\sqrt{3x}$

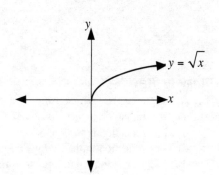

c) $\dfrac{1}{3}y = \sqrt{x-1} - 1$

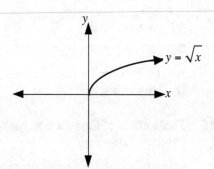

d) $3y + 3 = \sqrt{-2x + 8}$

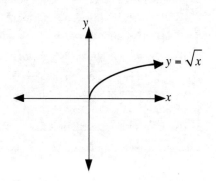

3. Determine, using interval notation, the domain and range of the function $y - k = a\sqrt{b(x - h)}$ if

a) $a > 0, b > 0$

b) $a > 0, b < 0$

c) $a < 0, b > 0$

d) $a < 0, b < 0$

4. The domain and range of the function $y = -\sqrt{-x}$ are, respectively, all real numbers such that

    A. $x \geq 0, y \geq 0$
    B. $x \geq 0, y \leq 0$
    C. $x \leq 0, y \geq 0$
    D. $x \leq 0, y \leq 0$

5. The domain of the function $y = \sqrt{4x - 3} + 2$ is $[k, \infty)$. The value of k, to the nearest hundredth, is _____ .

(Record your answer in the numerical response box from left to right.)

Answer Key

1. All graphs can be verified using a graphing calculator.
    a) i) reflection in the x-axis   **iii)** $\{x \mid x \geq 0, x \in R\}$, $\{y \mid y \leq 0, y \in R\}$
    b) i) reflection in the y-axis   **iii)** $\{x \mid x \leq 0, x \in R\}$, $\{y \mid y \geq 0, y \in R\}$
    c) i) reflection in the line $y = x$ **iii)** $\{x \mid x \geq 0, x \in R\}$, $\{y \mid y \geq 0, y \in R\}$
    d) i) translation 1 unit left and 2 units down   **iii)** $\{x \mid x \geq -1, x \in R\}$, $\{y \mid y \geq -2, y \in R\}$

2. All graphs can be verified using a graphing calculator.
    a) i) vertical stretch by a factor of $\frac{1}{2}$ about the x-axis, horiz. stretch by a factor of 2 about the y-axis
        iii) $\{x \mid x \geq 0, x \in R\}$, $\{y \mid y \geq 0, y \in R\}$
    b) i) vertical stretch by a factor of $\frac{1}{2}$ about the x-axis, horiz. stretch by a factor of $\frac{1}{3}$ about the y-axis,
        then a reflection in the x-axis   **iii)** $\{x \mid x \geq 0, x \in R\}$, $\{y \mid y \leq 0, y \in R\}$
    c) i) vertical stretch by a factor of 3 about the x-axis, then a translation 1 unit right and
        3 units down   **iii)** $\{x \mid x \geq 1, x \in R\}$, $\{y \mid y \geq -3, y \in R\}$
    d) i) vertical stretch by a factor of $\frac{1}{3}$ about the x-axis, horiz. stretch by a factor of $\frac{1}{2}$ about the y-axis,
        then a reflection in the y-axis, then a translation 4 units right and 1 unit down
        ii) $\{x \mid x \leq 4, x \in R\}$, $\{y \mid y \geq -1, y \in R\}$

3. a) Domain: $[h, \infty)$ Range: $[k, \infty)$ **b)** Domain: $(-\infty, h]$ Range $[k, \infty)$
   c) Domain: $[h, \infty)$ Range: $(-\infty, k]$ **d)** Domain: $(-\infty, h]$ Range $(-\infty, k]$

4. D   **5.** $\boxed{0 \mid . \mid 7 \mid 5}$

Analyzing Radical and Rational Functions Lesson #2:
Radical Functions - Part Two

Investigating the Graph of $y = \sqrt{f(x)}$

---

1. In each case, the graphing calculator screenshot of the partial graph of a function, $y = f(x)$, is shown. The window x:$[-2, 2, 1]$ y:$[-2, 2, 1]$ has been used.

  a) Determine $y = \sqrt{f(x)}$. Then use the same window to graph $y = \sqrt{f(x)}$ and sketch the graph on the grid.

  b) State the domain and range of $y = f(x)$ and $y = \sqrt{f(x)}$.

  i) $y = f(x) = x^2$
     $y = \sqrt{f(x)} = \sqrt{x^2}$

  ii) $y = f(x) = x^3$
     $y = \sqrt{f(x)} =$

  iii) $y = f(x) = x + 1$
     $y = \sqrt{f(x)} =$

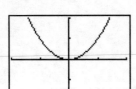 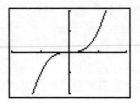 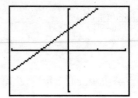

Domain of $y = f(x)$

Range of $y = f(x)$

Domain of $y = \sqrt{f(x)}$

Range of $y = \sqrt{f(x)}$

  iv) $y = f(x) = |x|$
     $y = \sqrt{f(x)} =$

  v) $y = f(x) = \log x$
     $y = \sqrt{f(x)} =$

  vi) $y = f(x) = -x^2 - 1$
     $y = \sqrt{f(x)} =$

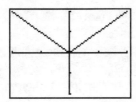 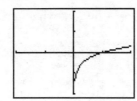 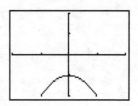

Domain of $y = f(x)$

Range of $y = f(x)$

Domain of $y = \sqrt{f(x)}$

Range of $y = \sqrt{f(x)}$

2. Repeat the work in 1. on the previous page for the functions below using the window $x:[-8, 8, 1]$ $y:[-10, 10, 1]$.

vii)

$y = f(x) = x^2 + 4$

$y = \sqrt{f(x)} =$

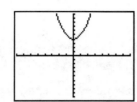

viii)

$y = f(x) = x^2 - 4$

$y = \sqrt{f(x)} =$

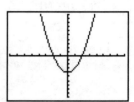

Domain of $y = f(x)$

Range of $y = f(x)$

Domain of $y = \sqrt{f(x)}$

Range of $y = \sqrt{f(x)}$

3. Answer the following questions based on your observations in 1. and 2.

   a) In which of these examples are the domains of $y = f(x)$ and $y = \sqrt{f(x)}$ the same?

   b) What do these graphs in a) have in common that the other graphs do not?

   c) From the options in the curly brackets, circle the correct alternative in each of the statements below.

    • The graph of $y = \sqrt{f(x)}$ does not exist when $\{\, x < 0 \ / \ f(x) < 0 \,\}$.

    • If $f(x) = 0$, the graph of $y = \sqrt{f(x)}$ lies $\{$ above / on / below $\}$ the graph of $y = f(x)$.

    • If $0 < f(x) < 1$, the graph of $y = \sqrt{f(x)}$ lies $\{$ above / on / below $\}$ the graph of $y = f(x)$.

    • If $f(x) = 1$, the graph of $y = \sqrt{f(x)}$ lies $\{$ above / on / below $\}$ the graph of $y = f(x)$.

    • If $f(x) > 1$, the graph of $y = \sqrt{f(x)}$ lies $\{$ above / on / below $\}$ the graph of $y = f(x)$.

4. We shall look in more detail at graphs that contain **oblique straight line segments** such as graphs iii) and iv) from the beginning of this lesson.

The graphs of $y = f(x)$ and $y = \sqrt{f(x)}$ from these examples are shown below.

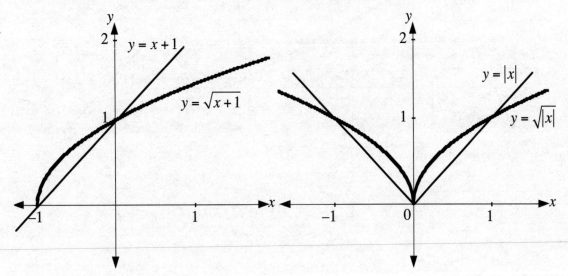

Notice that in both cases the graph of $y = \sqrt{f(x)}$ is curved similar to the shape of an opened umbrella. In mathematics, a graph which is curved like any part of an upturned U shape such as ⌒ or ⌐ or ⌒ or ⌐⌒ is called concave down.

If any part of a graph of $f(x)$ contains an **oblique straight line segment**, then the corresponding part on the graph of $y = \sqrt{f(x)}$ will be concave down. This can be investigated using a graphing calculator.

The concept of concavity will be studied in much greater detail in Calculus courses.

> ## *Graphing $y = \sqrt{f(x)}$ from the Graph of $y = f(x)$*

Consider the following points when sketching the graph of $y = \sqrt{f(x)}$ from the graph of $y = f(x)$.

- When $f(x) < 0$, the graph of $y = \sqrt{f(x)}$ does not exist.

- When $f(x) = 0$, $\sqrt{f(x)} = 0$, and when $f(x) = 1$, $\sqrt{f(x)} = 1$ leading to invariant points.

- When $0 < f(x) < 1$, the graph of $y = \sqrt{f(x)}$ lies above the graph of $y = f(x)$.

- When $f(x) > 1$, the graph of $y = \sqrt{f(x)}$ lies below the graph of $y = f(x)$.

- The values of $\sqrt{f(x)}$ are the square roots of the values of $f(x)$. If possible, choose values of $f(x)$ which have simple square roots.

- If the graph of $y = f(x)$ has intervals containing oblique straight line segments, the graph of $y = \sqrt{f(x)}$ will be concave down ⌒ or ⌐ on those intervals.

Class Ex. #1 The graph of a function $y = f(x)$ is shown.

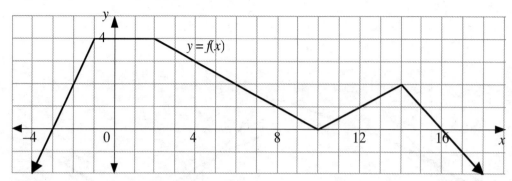

a) Sketch the graph of $y = \sqrt{f(x)}$ on the grid.

b) State the domain of

   i) $y = f(x)$ ii) $y = \sqrt{f(x)}$

c) State the range of

   i) $y = f(x)$ ii) $y = \sqrt{f(x)}$

Class Ex. #2 In each case the graph of $g(x)$ is shown.
If $h(x) = \sqrt{g(x)}$, determine the domain and range of $h(x)$ without sketching the graph of $h(x)$.

a)

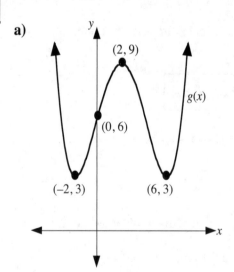

b)

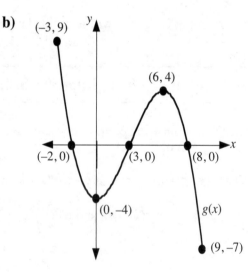

Complete Assignment Questions #1 - #12

Assignment

1. The graph of a function $y = f(x)$ is shown.

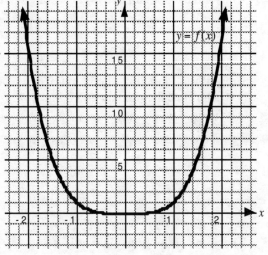

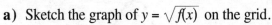

 a) Sketch the graph of $y = \sqrt{f(x)}$ on the grid.

 b) State the domain of

  i) $y = f(x)$

  ii) $y = \sqrt{f(x)}$

 c) State the range of

  i) $y = f(x)$

  ii) $y = \sqrt{f(x)}$

2. a) The graph of a function $y = f(x)$ is shown. Sketch the graph of $y = \sqrt{f(x)}$ on the grid.

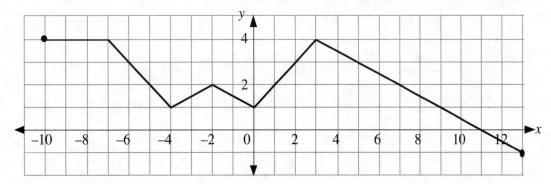

 b) State the domain of

  i) $y = f(x)$ 　　　　　　　　　　**ii)** $y = \sqrt{f(x)}$

 c) State the range of

  i) $y = f(x)$ 　　　　　　　　　　**ii)** $y = \sqrt{f(x)}$

3. Given that $y = f(x)$ is a continuous function,

 a) explain how you can determine the domain of $y = \sqrt{f(x)}$ from the graph of $y = f(x)$

 b) explain how you can determine the range of $y = \sqrt{f(x)}$ from the graph of $y = f(x)$.

4. The graph of a function $y = f(x)$ is shown.

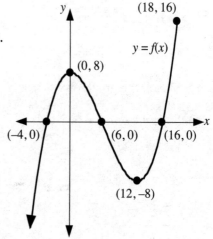

a) State the domain and range of the function $y = f(x)$.

b) Without sketching the graph of $y = \sqrt{f(x)}$,
determine the domain and range of the
function $y = \sqrt{f(x)}$.

5. The zeros of the function g are –8 and –3. The graph of $y = g(x)$ is shown below.
Determine the domain and range of the function $y = \sqrt{g(x)}$.

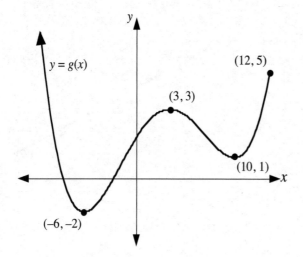

6. The points $A\left(-12, \dfrac{9}{4}\right)$, $B(-9, 1)$, $C(-4, 3)$, and $D\left(-2, \dfrac{1}{4}\right)$ lie on the graph of $y = f(x)$ as
shown. Determine the domain and range of the function $y = \sqrt{f(x)}$.

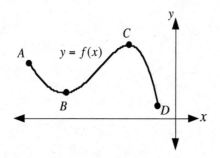

7. Olivia was investigating how the graph of $y = \sqrt{f(x)}$ is connected to the graph of $y = f(x)$.
   She chose the example $y = f(x) = -x^2$. When she graphed $y = \sqrt{f(x)}$, she deduced from the
   empty screen on her graphing calculator that this graph does not exist for any values of x.
   Explain why Olivia's deduction is incorrect.

Use the following information to answer the next two questions.

> $y = f(x)$ is a continous function with domain $[-4,16]$
> and range $[-4,16]$.

8. The domain of the function $y = \sqrt{f(x)}$ is

   A. $[-4, 16]$
   B. $[0, 16]$
   C. $[0, 4]$
   D.   unable to be determined from the given information

9. The range of the function $y = \sqrt{f(x)}$ is

   A. $[-4, 16]$
   B. $[0, 16]$
   C. $[0, 4]$
   D. $[-2, 4]$

10. The range of the function $y = \sqrt{g(x)}$ is $[2, \infty)$. Which one of the following statements
    regarding the function g **must** be true?

    A.   The maximum value of g is 4.
    B.   The function g has no zeros.
    C.   The graph of $y = g(x)$ has no y-intercept.
    D.   The domain of g is $(-\infty, \infty)$.

11. f is a continuous function with zeros $-3, 2$, and 4. The domain of $y = \sqrt{f(x)}$ is the set of
    real numbers such that $x \leq -3$ or $2 \leq x \leq 4$. Which of the following values is negative?

    A. $f(-4)$
    B. $f(-3)$
    C. $f(-2)$
    D. $f(3)$

Numerical Response **12.** The domain of $y = \sqrt{f(x)}$ is $x \in R$ and the range is $a \le y \le b$ where $y \in R$. If the minimum and maximum values of $y = f(x)$ are 12 and 36 respectively, then the product ab can be written in the form $k\sqrt{3}$, $k \in N$. The value of k is _____ .

(Record your answer in the numerical response box from left to right.)

Answer Key

1. a)

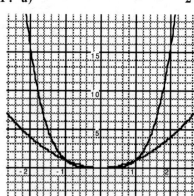

2. a)

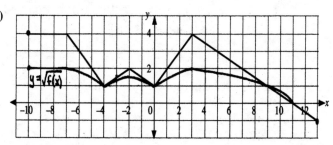

b)i) $\{x \mid -10 \le x \le 13, x \in R\}$ **ii)** $\{x \mid -10 \le x \le 11, x \in R\}$
c)i) $\{y \mid -1 \le y \le 4, y \in R\}$ **ii)** $\{y \mid 0 \le y \le 2, y \in R\}$

b)i) $\{x \mid x \in R\}$ **ii)** $\{x \mid x \in R\}$
c)i) $\{y \mid y \ge 0, y \in R\}$ **ii)** $\{y \mid y \ge 0, y \in R\}$

3. a) The domain of $y = \sqrt{f(x)}$ is the same as that part of the domain of $y = f(x)$ for which $f(x) \ge 0$. If $f(x)$ is completely below the x-axis, then $y = \sqrt{f(x)}$ does not exist, and there is no domain.

b) If $f(x)$ has an x-intercept, the range of $y = \sqrt{f(x)}$ is from zero to the square root of the maximum value of f (which could be infinite).

If $f(x)$ is completely above the x-axis, the range of $y = \sqrt{f(x)}$ is from the square root of the minimum value of f to the square root of the maximum value of f (which could be infinite).

If $f(x)$ is completely below the x-axis, then $y = \sqrt{f(x)}$ does not exist, and there is no range.

4. a) Domain $\{x \mid x \le 18, x \in R\}$ Range $\{y \mid y \le 16, y \in R\}$
b) Domain $\{x \mid -4 \le x \le 6 \text{ or } 16 \le x \le 18, x \in R\}$, Range $\{y \mid 0 \le y \le 4, y \in R\}$

5. Domain $\{x \mid x \le -8 \text{ or } -3 \le x \le 12, x \in R\}$, Range $\{y \mid y \ge 0, y \in R\}$

6. Domain $\{x \mid -12 \le x \le -2, x \in R\}$ Range $\{y \mid \frac{1}{2} \le y \le \sqrt{3}, y \in R\}$

7. The graph of $y = -x^2$ is a parabola with a maximum point at $(0, 0)$. The graph of $y = \sqrt{-x^2}$ will not exist when $-x^2$ is less than zero, but will exist when $x = 0$. The point $(0, 0)$ is therefore the only point on the graph of $y = \sqrt{f(x)}$. It cannot be seen on the calculator screen because it is hidden by the axes. By turning the axes off on the calculator, the point $(0, 0)$ can be seen.

8. D **9.** C **10.** B **11.** C **12.** | 1 | 2 | | |

Analyzing Radical and Rational Functions Lesson #3:
Rational Functions - Asymptotes

Rational Functions

A rational function is a function which takes the form $f(x) = \dfrac{n(x)}{d(x)}$ where $n(x)$ and $d(x)$ are polynomial functions and $d(x) \neq 0$. The degree of $d(x)$ needs to be greater than zero or the function $f(x)$ is simply a polynomial function.

Examples of rational functions are $\quad f(x) = \dfrac{x+2}{x-1}, \quad g(x) = \dfrac{1}{x^2-9}, \quad h(x) = \dfrac{x^2-4}{x+2}$.

Discontinuities

Since rational functions are expressed as fractions, the denominator cannot equal zero.

If the denominator of a rational function can be made equal to zero for a particular value of the independent variable, then this value of the variable is called a **non-permissible value** of the function.
In the examples above, the non-permissible values are $1, \pm 3$, and -2, respectively.

Note that not all rational functions have non-permissible values for the independent variable, e.g. $f(x) = \dfrac{1}{x^2+1}$.

If a rational function has non-permissible values, then the graph of the rational function will not be a **continuous** curve. There must be some kind of **discontinuity** in the graph.

In this course we will learn about two types of discontinuity:

   i) **Infinite Discontinuity** (leading to a **vertical asymptote** on the graph)

   ii) **Point Discontinuity** (leading to a **hole** on the graph)

In this lesson, we will examine the behaviour of the graphs of rational functions which have infinite discontinuities.

In the next lesson, we will examine the behaviour of the graphs of rational functions which have point discontinuities.

Graphing a Rational Function using a Table of Values

Consider the rational function $f(x) = \dfrac{1}{x-1}$.

a) Since division by zero is not defined, the non-permissible value of the function is _____ .

b) Complete the table of values below. Plot the points on the grid, but do not connect the points at this time.

x	−5	−2	−1	0	1	2	3	4	5
$f(x)$									

c) To investigate the behaviour of the rational function near the non-permissible value, we include values of the independent variable close to the non-permissible value.

Complete the table below, plot the points on the grid, and join the points with a smooth curve.

x	0.5	0.9	0.99	1	1.01	1.1	1.5
$f(x)$							

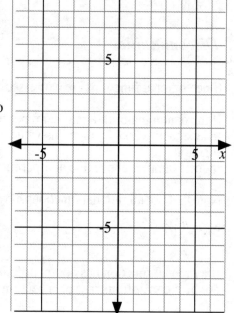

d) Verify the graph using a graphing calculator.

e) Describe what happens to the value of the function as x gets more and more positive, i.e. as $x \to \infty$ (read "as x approaches infinity").

f) Describe what happens to the value of the function as x gets more and more negative i.e. as $x \to -\infty$.

g) From the options in the curly brackets, circle the correct alternative in each of the statements below.

- As x gets closer and closer to the non-permissible value of 1, from the left, the value of the function approaches $\{ \infty / -\infty \}$.

- As x gets closer and closer to the non-permissible value of 1, from the right, the value of the function approaches $\{ \infty / -\infty \}$.

Asymptotes

A line that a curve approaches more and more closely is called an **asymptote**.

With reference to the exploration on the previous page.

- As x gets closer and closer to 1, the graph of $f(x)$ gets closer and closer to the line with equation $x = 1$ but will never reach the line $x = 1$.

  The graph has an infinite discontinuity at $x = 1$ and the line $x = 1$ is called a **vertical asymptote** of the graph of $f(x)$.

  This occurs because 1 is a zero of the denominator of the rational function.

- As $|x|$ increases in value (i.e. as $x \to \pm\infty$), the graph of $f(x)$ gets closer and closer to the x-axis (the line with equation $y = 0$) but will never reach the x-axis.

  The line $y = 0$ is a **horizontal asymptote** of the graph of $f(x)$.

  Note that a horizontal asymptote is not representative of an infinite discontinuity.

- Vertical and horizontal asymptotes are often represented on graphs with dashed lines, but these dashed lines do not form part of the graph.

Investigating Asymptotes on the Graphs of Rational Functions

Part 1

Consider the function $f(x) = \dfrac{3}{x}$.

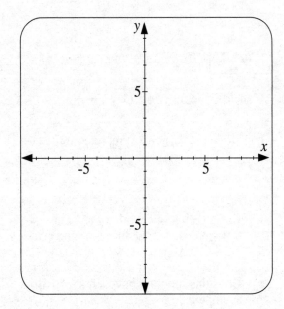

a) State the domain of the function.

b) Use a graphing calculator to graph the function, but <u>do not sketch</u> on the grid.

c) Write the equation of the vertical asymptote using the information from a) and b).

d) Show the vertical asymptote on the grid with a dashed line.

e) Complete the graph on the grid.

f) State the equation of the horizontal asymptote.

g) State the range of the function.

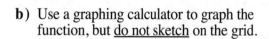

Part 2

Consider the function $f(x) = \dfrac{2x}{x + 1}$.

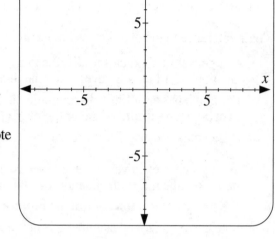

a) State the domain of the function.

b) Use a graphing calculator to graph the
   function, but <u>do not sketch</u> on the grid.

c) Write the equation of the vertical asymptote
   using the information
   from a) and b).

d) Show the vertical asymptote on the grid
   with a dashed line.

e) Estimate the equation of the horizontal asymptote. Verify the equation by using the
   `table` feature of the calculator with very large values of x, eg. 100, 1000, 10000, etc.

f) Complete the graph on the grid using a dashed line for the horizontal asymptote.

g) State the range of the function.

Part 3

Consider the function $f(x) = \dfrac{x^2}{x - 2}$.

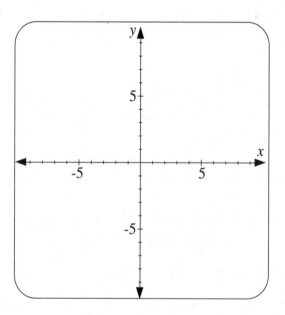

a) Draw the vertical asymptote on the grid
   and state its equation.

b) Use a graphing calculator to graph the
   function, sketch the graph on the grid.

c) Does this function have a horizontal
   asymptote?

d) Use the features of the calculator to
   determine the domain and range of
   the function.

In the previous investigation the horizontal asymptote falls into one of three categories based on the equation of the function and the degrees of the numerator and denominator:

i) The graph has a horizontal asymptote with equation $y = 0$ (as in Part 1).

ii) The graph has a horizontal asymptote with equation $y = k$, where $k \neq 0$ (as in Part 2).

iii) The graph has no horizontal asymptote (as in Part 3).

We will investigate how the degrees of the numerator and denominator *a*ffect the equation of the horizontal asymptote in the first three assignment questions.

The graphing calculator has limitations when graphing some rational functions. The suggestions below may help to give a clearer representation of the graph of the function.

• If the calculator is in <u>connected mode</u>, a line will connect two parts of the graph. This line is an approximation of the vertical asymptote. The horizontal asymptote line does not appear.

• If the calculator is set in <u>dot mode</u>, neither the vertical asymptote nor the horizontal asymptote appears.

• Using zoom decimal (ZDecimal), or a multiple of the zoom decimal window, may produce a clearer representation of the graph.

The asymptotes are **not** part of the graph of the function, and are shown with dashed lines in order to give greater understanding of the behaviour of the function.

Assignment Questions #1 - #3 must be completed before moving on to the next section in this lesson.

Complete Assignment Questions #1 - #3

Algebraically Determining the Equations of Asymptotes

Investigations Part 1 to Part 3 and Assignment Questions #1 - #3 are examples of the following rules which can be used to algebraically determine the equations of vertical and horizontal asymptotes of rational functions.

These rules apply for rational functions of the form $f(x) = \dfrac{n(x)}{d(x)}$ **provided that** $n(x)$ **and** $d(x)$ **have no factors in common**. Situations where the numerator and denominator have a factor in common will be dealt with under **point discontinuity** in the next lesson.

Vertical Asymptotes

Algebraically we can find the equations of vertical asymptotes of rational functions by finding the zeros of the denominator because the graph is undefined at those value(s). The equation(s) will be $x = $ *the zero value(s)* of the denominator.

Horizontal Asymptotes

The graph of $f(x)$ has a horizontal asymptote under the following conditions:

- If the degree of $n(x)$ is <u>less than</u> the degree of $d(x)$, then the line $y = 0$ is a horizontal asymptote. See Investigation Part 1 where $f(x) = \dfrac{3}{x}$.

- If the degree of $n(x)$ is <u>equal to</u> the degree of $d(x)$, then the line $y = \dfrac{a}{b}$ is a horizontal asymptote, where a is the leading coefficient of $n(x)$ and b is the leading coefficient of $d(x)$. See Investigation Part 2 where $f(x) = \dfrac{2x}{x + 1}$.

- If the degree of $n(x)$ is <u>greater than</u> the degree of $d(x)$, then the graph has <u>no</u> horizontal asymptote. See Investigation Part 3 where $f(x) = \dfrac{x^2}{x - 2}$.

Class Ex. #1

Algebraically determine the equations of the asymptotes of the graph of the function $f(x) = \dfrac{x^2 + x - 6}{2x^2 - x - 3}$. Verify using a graphing calculator.

Complete Assignment Questions #4 - #9

Assignment

1. In the following examples use a graphing calculator to sketch the graph of the function and determine the

    i)   equation(s) of the vertical asymptote(s)   **ii)**   equation of the horizontal asymptote

    iii) domain and range of the function   **iv)** x and y-intercepts of the graph

a) $f(x) = \dfrac{5}{x-4}$

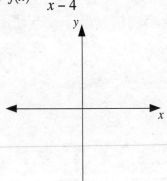

b) $f(x) = \dfrac{4x+5}{x+2}$

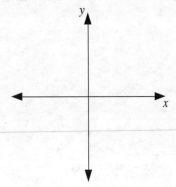

c) $f(x) = \dfrac{x^2+9}{2x-3}$

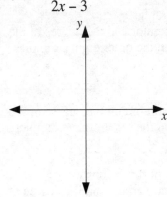

d) $f(x) = \dfrac{x^3+1}{x^2}$

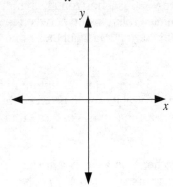

2. In each of the following examples use a graphing calculator to sketch the graph of the function and state the equations of any horizontal and vertical asymptotes on the graph.

a) $y = \dfrac{-4}{2x + 3}$ b) $y = \dfrac{-4x}{2x + 3}$ c) $y = \dfrac{-4x^2}{2x + 3}$

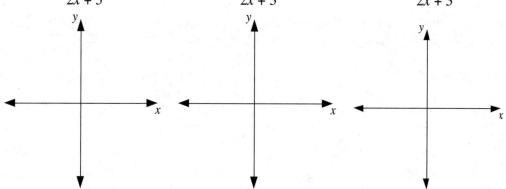

d) $y = \dfrac{x^2 + 4x + 4}{x^2 + 3x - 10}$ e) $y = \dfrac{6x}{x^2 + x - 12}$

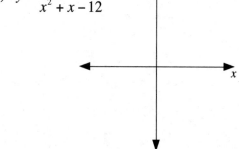

3. Consider the twelve graphs and equations of rational functions in the Investigation and in Assignment Questions #1 and #2.

a) The line $y = 0$ is a horizontal asymptote in four of the graphs .
   Determine a relationship between the degree of the numerator and the degree of the denominator that exists in these four examples and not in the other eight examples.

b) There is no horizontal asymptote in four of the graphs .
   Determine a relationship between the degree of the numerator and the degree of the denominator that exists in these four examples and not in the other eight examples.

c) A line other than $y = 0$ is a horizontal asymptote in four of the graphs .
   i) Determine a relationship between the degree of the numerator and the degree of the denominator that exists in these four examples and not in the other eight examples.

   ii) Suggest a rule that will determine the value of k if the horizontal asymptote has equation $y = k$.

4. Algebraically determine the equations of the asymptotes of the graph of each of the following functions.

a) $f(x) = \dfrac{2}{x + 3}$

b) $f(x) = \dfrac{x^2 + 5x + 6}{x + 6}$

c) $f(x) = \dfrac{4x}{1 - 4x}$

d) $f(x) = \dfrac{x}{x^2 - 4}$

5. Students were asked to sketch a graph of a function with one x-intercept and a horizontal asymptote at the x-axis.

Tricia claimed that this could not be done as a graph cannot cross an asymptote.

Mandy claimed it is possible for a graph to cross the x-axis, but still get closer and closer to the x-axis as $x \to \pm\infty$.

Investigate the students' claims by sketching the graph of $y = \dfrac{x + 4}{x^2 + 4}$ on the grid provided.

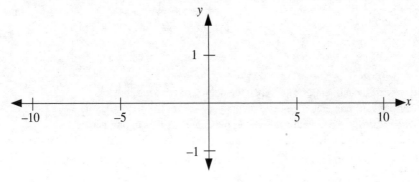

6. The horizontal asymptote of the graph of the function $g(x) = \dfrac{-7x + 2}{3x + 2}$ is

A. $y = 0$ **B.** $y = -\dfrac{7}{3}$ **C.** $y = -\dfrac{3}{7}$ **D.** $x = -\dfrac{2}{3}$

7. Consider the rational function $f(x) = -\dfrac{ax + 5}{7x - b}$, where a and b are natural numbers. The vertical asymptote and the horizontal asymptote of the graph of $f(x)$, respectively, are

A. $x = b, y = a$ **B.** $x = \dfrac{7}{b}, y = -\dfrac{5}{a}$ **C.** $x = \dfrac{b}{7}, y = \dfrac{a}{7}$ **D.** $x = \dfrac{b}{7}, y = -\dfrac{a}{7}$

8. The graph of the function $f(x) = \dfrac{3x - 8}{x - 8}$ has a vertical asymptote with equation $x = p$ and a horizontal asymptote with equation $y = q$. The value of pq is _____ .

(Record your answer in the numerical response box from left to right.)

9. The graph of the function $g(x) = \dfrac{5x}{10x^2 - 27x + 5}$ has asymptotes with equations $x = a, x = b,$ and $y = c$. To the nearest tenth, the value of $a + b + c$ is _____ .

(Record your answer in the numerical response box from left to right.)

Answer Key

1. a)	b)	c)	d)
i) $x = 4$	$x = -2$	$x = \dfrac{3}{2}$	$x = 0$
ii) $y = 0$	$y = 4$	none	none

iii) $\{x \mid x \ne 4, x \in R\}$ $\{x \mid x \ne -2, x \in R\}$ $\left\{x \mid x \ne \dfrac{3}{2}, x \in R\right\}$ $\{x \mid x \ne 0, x \in R\}$

$\{y \mid y \ne 0, y \in R\}$ $\{y \mid y \ne 4, y \in R\}$ $\{y \mid y \le -1.85$ or $y \ge 4.85, y \in R\}$ $\{y \mid y \in R\}$

iv) x-intercept = none x-intercept = $-\dfrac{5}{4}$ x-intercept = none x-intercept = -1

y-intercept = $-\dfrac{5}{4}$ y-intercept = $\dfrac{5}{2}$ y-intercept = -3 y-intercept = none

2. a) $y = 0, x = -\dfrac{3}{2}$ **b)** $y = -2, x = -\dfrac{3}{2}$ **c)** none, $x = -\dfrac{3}{2}$
  d) $y = 1, x = -5, x = 2$ **e)** $y = 0, x = -4, x = 3$

3. a) The degree of the numerator is less than the degree of the denominator.
  b) The degree of the numerator is greater than the degree of the denominator.
  c) i) The degree of the numerator is equal to the degree of the denominator.
    ii) k = the leading coefficient of the numerator divided by the leading coefficient of the denominator.

4. a) $y = 0, x = -3$ **b)** $x = -6$ **c)** $y = -1, x = \dfrac{1}{4}$ **d)** $y = 0, x = -2, x = 2$

5. Mandy is correct   **6.** B   **7.** D   **8.** | 2 | 4 | | | **9.** | 2 | . | 7 | |

Analyzing Radical and Rational Functions Lesson #4:
Rational Functions - Points of Discontinuity

Review

Recall the following from the previous lesson.

If the denominator of a rational function can be made equal to zero for a particular value of the independent variable, then this value of the variable is called a **non-permissible value**.

If a rational function has non-permissible values, then the graph of the rational function will not be a **continuous** curve. There must be some kind of **discontinuity** in the graph.

Investigating Points of Discontinuity

Part 1: Consider the function $f(x) = \dfrac{x^2 - 4x + 2}{x - 3}$ and $g(x) = \dfrac{x^2 - 4x + 3}{x - 3}$.

a) State the non-permissible value of each function.

b) Use a graphing calculator to graph $y = f(x)$ and sketch the graph on Grid 1.

c) State the equation of the asymptote of the graph of f.

d) A student assumed that the graph of $y = g(x)$ would be similar to the graph of $y = f(x)$ with a vertical asymptote with equation $x = 3$. To investigate the student's assumption, graph $y = g(x)$ using a graphing calculator, and answer the following questions.

- What shape does the graph of $y = g(x)$ appear to take?

- Does the graph of $y = g(x)$ have a vertical asymptote?

- Explain why the graph of $y = g(x)$ must have a discontinuity.

e) The discontinuity on the graph can be seen by using the use zoom decimal window feature of the graphing calculator (press $\boxed{\text{ZOOM}}$ $\boxed{4}$).

Graph $y = g(x)$ on Grid 2 using an open circle to represent the "hole", or discontinuity, of the graph. The "hole" in the graph is referred to as a **point of discontinuity**.

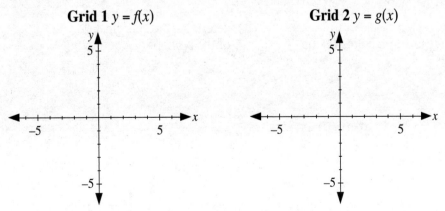

Grid 1 $y = f(x)$ **Grid 2** $y = g(x)$

Part 2: Consider the functions $A(x) = x + 2$ and $B(x) = \dfrac{x^2 + 3x + 2}{x + 1}$.

a) State the domain of each function.

b) Use a graphing calculator to graph each function using zoom decimal.
   Show each graph on a separate grid.

$A(x) = x + 2$

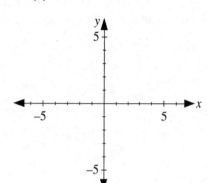

$B(x) = \dfrac{x^2 + 3x + 2}{x + 1}$

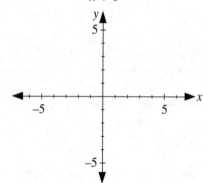

c) Explain the difference between the two graphs.

d) Factor the numerator of $B(x)$ to show that $B(x)$ is identical to $A(x)$ except for a domain restriction.

e) Determine the coordinates of the points of discontinuity by replacing the non-permissible value into the equation of the line.

Part 3: Consider the function $g(x) = \dfrac{x^2 - 4x + 3}{x - 3}$ from Part 1.
   Use the methods in Part 2 d) and e) to

a) express $g(x)$ in linear form, including the domain restriction

b) determine the coordinates of the point of discontinuity

> ### *Point of Discontinuity*

If the numerator and denominator of a rational function have a factor in common, then the graph of the rational function has a "hole" in it.

The point where the break in the graph occurs is called a **point of discontinuity** and the function is said to have **point discontinuity**.

The point of discontinuity is represented on a graph by an **open circle**.

The coordinates of the point of discontinuity can be determined algebraically by using the following procedure:

1. Factor the rational expression.
2. Simplify the rational expression by cancelling the common factors.
3. Substitute the non-permissible value of x into the simplified form.

- When graphing a function with a point of discontinuity, the "hole" in the graph will usually NOT be seen unless the calculator is set to zoom decimal (`ZDecimal`), or a multiple of the zoom decimal window.
- If there are multiple points of discontinuity, the calculator may not show them all (especially in a multiple of the zoom decimal window).
  An algebraic verification is necessary to confirm the accuracy of the calculator graph.

Class Ex. #1

Consider the rational function $f(x) = \dfrac{x^3 - 7x + 6}{x - 1}$.

a) Write the numerator of the function as a product of three binomial factors, and hence express $f(x)$ in simplest form.

b) Determine the coordinates of the point of discontinuity of the graph of the function.

c) State the zeros of the function.

d) Use a graphing calculator to graph $y = f(x)$ and sketch the graph on the grid.

The graph of the rational function $f(x) = \dfrac{2x^3 + x^2 - 16x - 15}{2x^2 + 7x + 5}$ is a straight line with two

points of discontinuity.

a) Algebraically determine the equation of the straight line.

b) Determine the coordinates of the points of discontinuity.

c) Make a rough sketch of the graph using the answers in parts a) and b) and compare it with a calculator graph.

Complete Assignment Questions #1 - #12

Assignment

1. Consider the function $f(x) = \dfrac{x^2 + 2x - 8}{x - 2}$.

   a) Algebraically determine the point of discontinuity and sketch the graph of the function $f(x)$.

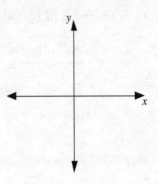

   b) State the domain and range of f.

2. Consider the function $g(x) = \dfrac{15 - 2x - x^2}{x + 5}$.

   a) Algebraically determine the point of discontinuity and sketch the graph of the function $g(x)$.

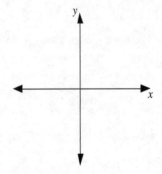

   b) State the domain and range of g.

3. Consider the function $f(x) = \dfrac{3x^2 - 10x + 3}{3x - 1}$.

   a) Sketch the graph of the function $f(x)$ and determine the point of discontinuity.

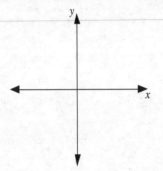

   b) State the domain and range of f.

4. Algebraically determine the point(s) of discontinuity

of the graph of $g(x) = \dfrac{-3x^3 + 17x^2 - 28x + 12}{3x^2 - 11x + 6}$.

Determine the domain and range of the function and sketch the graph on the grid.

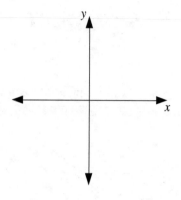

5. Algebraically determine the point(s) of discontinuity and the domain and range for the

function $f(x) = \dfrac{2x^3 - 5x^2 - 9x + 18}{2x - 3}$. Sketch the graph on the grid.

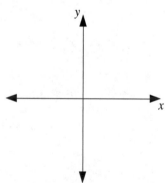

6. The range of the function $f(x) = \dfrac{2x^2 + 7x + 3}{x + 3}$ is

    A. $\{y \mid y \neq -3, y \in R\}$

    B. $\{y \mid y \neq -4, y \in R\}$

    C. $\{y \mid y \neq -5, y \in R\}$

    D. $\{y \mid y \in R\}$

7. The equation of a rational function can be written in the form $y = x - p, x \neq -3$.
The graph of the rational function has a point of discontinuity at $(-3, 10)$.
The value of p is

    A. 13   **B.** 7

    C. −7   **D.** −13

Use the following information to answer the next three questions.

Leo was given a function in the form $f(x) = \dfrac{ax^3 + bx^2 + cx + d}{2x + 5}$. He was told that
the numerator could be expressed in the factored form $(2x + 5)(x^2 - p)$, and that
the graph of the function had a point of discontinuity at $\left(q, \dfrac{9}{4} \right)$.

---

8. The value of q is

    A. $\dfrac{2}{5}$ **B.** $\dfrac{5}{2}$ **C.** $-\dfrac{2}{5}$ **D.** $-\dfrac{5}{2}$

9. The value of p is

    A. 4   **B.** −4

    C. $\dfrac{17}{2}$ **D.** $-\dfrac{17}{2}$

10. The value of $a + b + c + d$ is

    A. 7

    B. −21

    C. 23

    D. none of the above

11. The graph of $y = \dfrac{x^2 + bx + c}{x - d}$ is a straight line with a point of discontinuity $(2, 5)$.

The value of c is

    A.   –6

    B.   –3

    C.   3

    D.   6

Numerical Response 12. The function $f(x) = \dfrac{x^2 - 4x - k}{x + 3}$ has a point of discontinuity. The value of k is _____ .

(Record your answer in the numerical response box from left to right.)

Answer Key

See graphs below for questions 1a), 2a), 3a), 4, and 5.

1. a) $(2, 6)$ **b)** Domain: $\{x \mid x \neq 2, x \in R\}$ Range: $\{y \mid y \neq 6, y \in R\}$

2. a) $(-5, 8)$ **b)** Domain: $\{x \mid x \neq -5, x \in R\}$ Range: $\{y \mid y \neq 8, y \in R\}$

3. a) $\left(\frac{1}{3}, -\frac{8}{3}\right)$ **b)** Domain: $\left\{x \mid x \neq \frac{1}{3}, x \in R\right\}$ Range: $\left\{y \mid y \neq -\frac{8}{3}, y \in R\right\}$

4. Points of Discontinuity $\left(\frac{2}{3}, \frac{4}{3}\right)$, $(3, -1)$. Domain: $\left\{x \mid x \neq \frac{2}{3}, 3, x \in R\right\}$ Range: $\left\{y \mid y \neq -1, \frac{4}{3}\ y \in R\right\}$

5. Point of Discontinuity $\left(\frac{3}{2}, -\frac{21}{4}\right)$.   Domain: $\left\{x \mid x \neq \frac{3}{2}, x \in R\right\}$ Range: $\left\{y \mid y \geq -\frac{25}{4}, y \neq -\frac{21}{4}\ y \in R\right\}$

6. C   **7.** D   **8.** D   **9.** A   **10.** B   **11.** A   **12.** | 2 | 1 | | |

1a) $f(x) = \dfrac{x^2 + 2x - 8}{x - 2}$ **2a)** $g(x) = \dfrac{15 - 2x - x^2}{x - 2}$ **3a)** $f(x) = \dfrac{3x^2 - 10x + 3}{3x - 1}$

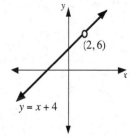

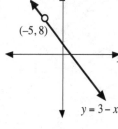

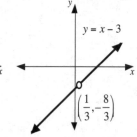

4. $g(x) = \dfrac{-3x^3 + 17x^2 - 28x + 12}{3x^2 - 11x + 6}$ **5.** $f(x) = \dfrac{2x^3 - 5x^2 - 9x + 18}{2x - 3}$

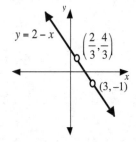

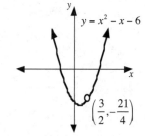

Analyzing Radical and Rational Functions Lesson #5:
Graphs of Rational Functions

If a rational function has a denominator which can be made equal to zero, then the graph of the rational functions will have a vertical asymptote, or a point of discontinuity corresponding to each zero of the denominator.

Asymptotes

Consider $f(x) = \dfrac{n(x)}{d(x)}$ where $n(x)$ and $d(x)$ have <u>no factors in common</u>.

Vertcial Asymptotes

Algebraically we can find the equations of vertical asymptotes of rational functions by finding the zeros of the denominator because the graph is undefined at those value(s). The equation(s) will be $x = $ *the zero value(s)*.

Horizontal Asymptotes

The graph of $f(x)$ has a horizontal asymptote under the following conditions:

- If the degree of $n(x)$ is <u>less than</u> the degree of $d(x)$, then the line $y = 0$ is a horizontal asymptote.

- If the degree of $n(x)$ is <u>equal to</u> the degree of $d(x)$, then the line $y = \dfrac{a}{b}$ is a horizontal asymptote, where a is the leading coefficient of $n(x)$ and b is the leading coefficient of $d(x)$.

- If the degree of $n(x)$ is <u>greater than</u> the degree of $d(x)$, then the graph has <u>no</u> horizontal asymptote.

Points of Discontinuity

Consider $f(x) = \dfrac{n(x)}{d(x)}$ where $n(x)$ and $d(x)$ <u>have a factor in common</u>.

The point where the break in the graph occurs is called a **point of discontinuity** and is represented on a graph by an **open circle**.

The coordinates of the point of discontinuity can be determined algebraically by using the following procedure:

1. Factor the rational expression.
2. Simplify the rational expression by cancelling the common factors.
3. Substitute the non-permissible value of x into the simplified form.

Investigating Graphs of Rational Functions with No Discontinuities

If the denominator of a rational function has no zeros, there will be no discontinuities on the graph of the function.

Part 1: Consider the function $f(x) = \dfrac{1}{x^2 + 1}$.

Answer questions a) to f) before graphing the function.

a) Does the function have any non-permissible values?

b) State the domain of the function.

c) The maximum value of the function will occur when the denominator has its lowest value. Determine the maximum value of the function.

d) Explain why the value of $f(x)$ can never be negative.

e) Does the function have any zeros?

f) Use the answers above to suggest a possible range for the function.

g) Use a graphing calculator to graph $y = f(x) = \dfrac{1}{x^2 + 1}$
using window $x{:}[-7, 7, 1], y{:}[-1, 2, 1]$.

Sketch the graph on the grid.

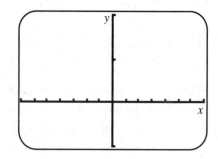

h) Does the graph of the function have

    i) a vertical asymptote? **ii)** a point of discontinuity? **iii)** a horizontal asymptote?

Part 2: Graphing calculator screenshots of four rational functions are shown using a window of $x{:}[-3, 3, 1]$, $y{:}[-2, 2, 1]$.

i) $f(x) = \dfrac{1}{x^2 + 1}$

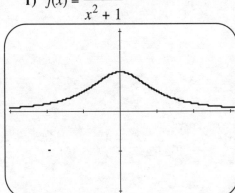

ii) $g(x) = \dfrac{x}{x^2 + 1}$

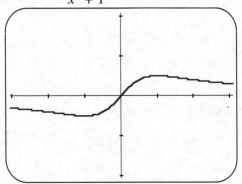

iii) $h(x) = \dfrac{x^2}{x^2 + 1}$

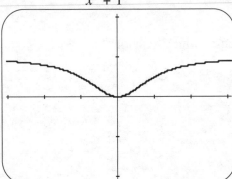

iv) $k(x) = \dfrac{x^3}{x^2 + 1}$

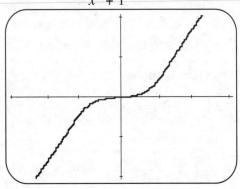

a) State the equation of the horizontal asymptote (if any) of each graph.

i) $f(x) = \dfrac{1}{x^2 + 1}$ **ii)** $g(x) = \dfrac{x}{x^2 + 1}$ **iii)** $h(x) = \dfrac{x^2}{x^2 + 1}$ **iv)** $k(x) = \dfrac{x^3}{x^2 + 1}$

b) Do the equations in a) agree with the rules for horizontal asymptotes in the review at the beginning of the lesson?

c) Explain why, as $x \to \infty$, the graph of $g(x) = \dfrac{x}{x^2 + 1}$ approaches the asymptote $y = 0$ from above, but, as $x \to -\infty$, the graph approaches the asymptote $y = 0$ from below.

d) Explain why the graph of $h(x) = \dfrac{x^2}{x^2 + 1}$ has no points in quadrants three and four.

Note that whether or not the graph of a rational function has horizontal asymptotes is **not** related to whether or not the function has discontinuities.

Class Ex. #1 Consider the following functions.

$$a(x) = \frac{x-4}{x+4} \qquad b(x) = \frac{x^2-4}{x^2+4} \qquad c(x) = \frac{x+4}{x^2-4} \qquad d(x) = \frac{x+2}{x^2-4} \qquad e(x) = \frac{x^2+4}{x+4}$$

$$f(x) = \frac{x^2+4}{x^2-4} \qquad g(x) = \frac{-x-4}{-x^2-4} \qquad h(x) = \frac{-x^2-4}{-x^2+4} \qquad i(x) = \frac{x^2-4}{x+2} \qquad j(x) = \frac{x^3-4x^2}{x^2-2x}$$

Without sketching the graph of the function, determine which functions have

   a) no discontinuities

   b) no vertical asymptote

   c) no horizontal asymptote

   d) the *x*-axis as a horizontal asymptote

   e) a horizontal asymptote with equation $y = 1$

   f) point(s) of discontinuity

Class Ex. #2 Algebraically determine the equations of any asymptotes and the coordinates of any point(s) of discontinuity on the graph of the function $f(x) = \dfrac{(2x-1)(x-5)}{x^2-2x-15}$.
State the domain and range of *f*.

Complete Assignment Questions #1 - #5

Assignment

1. For each of the graphs of the following rational functions, algebraically determine the equation of any asymptotes and the coordinates of any points of discontinuity.

a) $f(x) = \dfrac{2(x + 1)}{x^2 + 1}$

b) $g(x) = -\dfrac{4x^3}{x^3 + 1}$

c) $h(x) = \dfrac{3 - x^4}{3x^4 + 6}$

d) $k(x) = \dfrac{x + 4}{x^2 + 5x + 4}$

e) $f(x) = \dfrac{2(3x - 1)(x + 4)}{3x^2 + 4x + 1}$

f) $f(x) = \dfrac{2(3x - 1)(x + 4)}{3x^2 + 10x - 8}$

2. Consider the functions $f(x) = x^2 - 9$ and $g(x) = 9x - x^3$.

  a) Express $f(x)$ and $g(x)$ in factored form.

  b) Express the function $\left(\dfrac{f}{g}\right)(x)$ in simplest form.

  c) Algebraically determine the equation of any asymptotes and the coordinates of any points of discontinuity on the graph of $y = \left(\dfrac{f}{g}\right)(x)$.

  d) Sketch a graph of $y = \left(\dfrac{f}{g}\right)(x)$ on the grid illustrating the features in c).

  e) Determine the domain and range of the function $\left(\dfrac{f}{g}\right)(x)$.

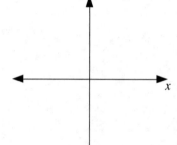

3. Consider the functions $f(x) = \dfrac{3}{x+2}$ and $g(x) = x - 2$.

  a) Show that $(g \circ f)(x) = \dfrac{-2x - 1}{x + 2}$.

  b) Determine the equations of the asymptotes of the graph of $y = (g \circ f)(x)$.

  c) State the domain and range of the function $(g \circ f)(x)$.

4. The equations of seven rational functions and the graphs of these functions are shown. If $a, b,$ and c are distinct natural numbers, match the set of rational functions to their graphs and explain the reasoning.

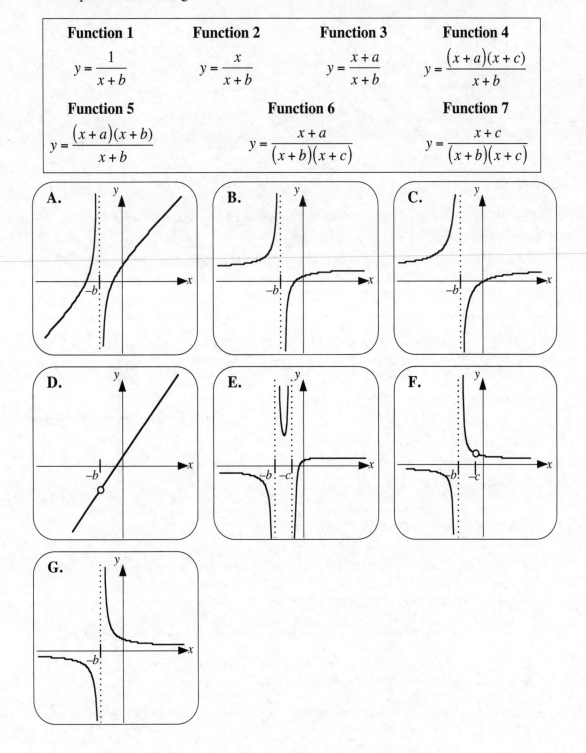

Function 1

$$y = \frac{1}{x+b}$$

Function 2

$$y = \frac{x}{x+b}$$

Function 3

$$y = \frac{x+a}{x+b}$$

Function 4

$$y = \frac{(x+a)(x+c)}{x+b}$$

Function 5

$$y = \frac{(x+a)(x+b)}{x+b}$$

Function 6

$$y = \frac{x+a}{(x+b)(x+c)}$$

Function 7

$$y = \frac{x+c}{(x+b)(x+c)}$$

Multiple Choice **5.** Which of the following functions has a point of discontinuity at (p, q)?

    A. $y = \dfrac{(x - p)(x - q)}{x - p}$

    B. $y = \dfrac{(x - p)(x - q)}{x - q}$

    C. $y = \dfrac{(x - p)(x - p + q)}{x - p}$

    D. $y = \dfrac{(x - q)(x + p - q)}{x - q}$

Answer Key

1. **a)** horizontal asymptote $y = 0$.   **b)** vertical asymptote $x = -1$, horizontal asymptote $y = -4$

    c) horizontal asymptote $y = -\dfrac{1}{3}$

    d) vertical asymptote $x = -1$, horizontal asymptote $y = 0$, point of discontinuity $\left(-4, -\dfrac{1}{3}\right)$.

    e) vertical asymptote $x = -1, x = -\dfrac{1}{3}$, horizontal asymptote $y = 2$.

    f) vertical asymptote $x = \dfrac{2}{3}$, horizontal asymptote $y = 2$, point of discontinuity $\left(-4, \dfrac{13}{7}\right)$.

2. **a)** $f(x) = (x - 3)(x + 3)$, $g(x) = x(3 - x)(3 + x)$

    b) $\left(\dfrac{f}{g}\right)(x) = -\dfrac{1}{x}, x \neq \pm 3$

    c) vertical asymptote $x = 0$, horizontal asymptote $y = 0$,

        points of discontinuity $\left(-3, \dfrac{1}{3}\right), \left(3, -\dfrac{1}{3}\right)$.

    d) See graph at side.

    e) Domain: $\{x \mid x \neq 0, \pm 3, x \in R\}$

        Range: $\left\{y \mid y \neq 0, \pm\dfrac{1}{3}, y \in R\right\}$

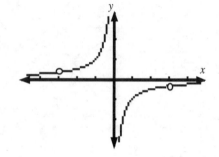

3. **b)** vertical asymptote $x = -2$, horizontal asymptote $y = -2$

    c) Domain: $\{x \mid x \neq -2, x \in R\}$ Range: $\left\{y \mid y \neq -2, y \in R\right\}$

4. Function 1 → G, Function 2 → C, Function 3 → B, Function 4 → A,

    Function 5 → D, Function 6 → E, Function 7 → F.

    • Function 1 has a vertical asymptote $x = -b$ and a horizontal asymptote $y = 0$, so Function 1 → G.

    • Functions 2 and 3 have a vertical asymptote $x = -b$ and a horizontal asymptote $y = 1$. Function 2 passes through the origin and Function 3 does not, so Function 2 → C and Function 3 → B.

    • Functions 4 and 5 have no horizontal asymptotes. Function 4 has a vertical asymptote $x = -b$, and Function 5 has a point of discontinuity at $x = -b$, so Function 4 → A and Function 5 → D.

    • Functions 6 and 7 have two discontinuities. Function 6 has two vertical asymptotes, so Function 6 → E. Function 7 has one vertical asymptote and one point of discontinuity, so Function 7 → F.

5. C

Analyzing Radical and Rational Functions Lesson #6: Solving Radical and Rational Equations

Radical and Rational Equations

A **radical equation** is an equation which contains a radical.

A **rational equation** is an equation in which at least one of the terms is a rational expression with a variable in the denominator.

A value of the variable which satisfies the equation is called a **root** of the equation.

In this lesson we will determine approximate solutions to radical and rational equations using a graphing technique.

Review of Zeros, Roots, and x-intercepts

Fill in the blanks in the following statement regarding the function with equation $y = f(x)$.

" The _____ of the function, the _____ of the graph of the function, and

the _____ of the corresponding equation $y = 0$, are the _____ numbers."

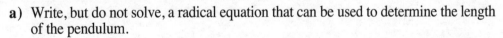

Class Ex. #1

In Physics class, students were given a long piece of string and a weight and asked to create a timing mechanism.

Courtney knew that if they created a simple pendulum, the relationship between the length of the pendulum and the time it takes for the weight to swing back and forth can be approximated by the formula $T = 0.2\sqrt{L}$, where T is in seconds and L is in centimetres.

She decided to create a simple pendulum with a period of one second i.e. it would take one second to swing back and forth.

a) Write, but do not solve, a radical equation that can be used to determine the length of the pendulum.

b) Explain how the length of such a pendulum can be determined by using the x-intercept of the graph of a radical function.

c) Sketch the function in b) on the grid and determine the approximate length of a pendulum with a period of one second.

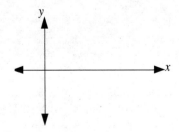

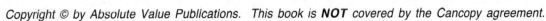

A partial graph of $y = f(x)$, a radical function with an integral zero, is shown.

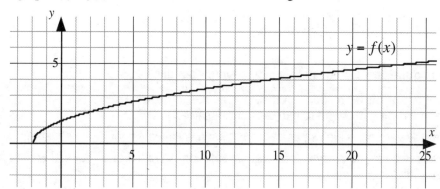

a) State the zero of the function.

b) State the root of the equation $f(x) = 0$.

c) Use the graph to determine, to the nearest whole number,

    i) the solution of the equation $f(x) = 3$ **ii)** the root of the equation $f(x) - 4 = 0$

d) In each case, explain how to use the graph of $y = f(x)$ to determine the approximate solution to the given equation and state the solution to the nearest whole number.

    i) $f(x + 6) = 0$

    ii) $f(x - 3) = 5$

Consider the functions $f(x) = 2x - 3$, $g(x) = x - 1$, and $h(x) = x + 5$.
Determine, graphically, the solutions of the following equations to the nearest hundredth.

a) $\left(\dfrac{f}{g}\right)(x) - 5 = 0$ **b)** $\sqrt{f(x)} = (g \circ h)(x)$ **c)** $\left(\dfrac{f}{g}\right)(x) = \left(\dfrac{g}{h}\right)(x)$

Complete Assignment Questions #1 - #9

Assignment

Use the following information to answer Question #1.

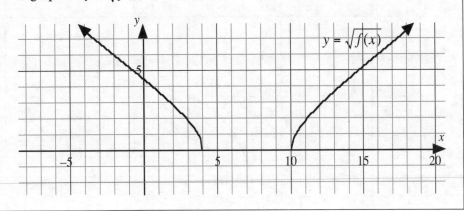

The function $f(x)$ is a quadratic function with integral zeros.
The graph of $y = \sqrt{f(x)}$ is shown.

1. **a)** State the x-intercepts of the graph of the radical function $y = \sqrt{f(x)}$.

    b) State the zeros of the quadratic function $f(x)$.

    c) Estimate, to the nearest tenth, the roots of the following equations.

    i) $\sqrt{f(x)} = 4$ **ii)** $\sqrt{f(x)} - 7 = 0$ **iii)** $1 + \sqrt{f(x)} = 0$ **iv)** $\sqrt{f(x-2)} = 0$

    v) $\sqrt{f(x+4)} - 2 = 0$ **vi)** $f(x+5) - 25 = 0$

    d) The quadratic function, $f(x)$, can be expressed in the factored form $f(x) = a(x - b)(x - c)$.
    If the graph of $y = \sqrt{f(x)}$ passes through the point $(16, 6)$, express $f(x)$ in factored form.

    e) Determine the range of $f(x)$.

    f) Determine the exact value of the y-intercept of the graph of $y = \sqrt{f(x)}$.

2. The partial graph of the rational function $y = g(x)$ is shown. The non-permissible value is an integer, and the horizontal asymptote has equation $y = 3$.

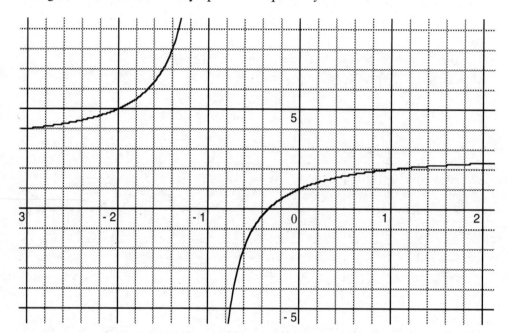

a) State the equation of the horizontal asymptote of the graph of

    i) $y = g(x) + 2$ **ii)** $y = g(x + 2)$ **iii)** $y = g(x + a) - d$

b) State the equation of the vertical asymptote of the graph of

    i) $y = g(x) + 2$ **ii)** $y = g(x + 2)$ **iii)** $y = g(x + a) - d$

c) Estimate, to the nearest tenth, the roots of the following equations.

    i) $g(x) = 1$ **ii)** $g(x) + 1 = 0$ **iii)** $g(x + 1) = 0$ **iv)** $g(x - 5) - 7 = 0$

    v) $g(x) = 3$ **vi)** $g(x + 7) = 3$ **vii)** $g(x) + 7 = 3$

d) The rational function g can be expressed in the form $g(x) = \dfrac{ax + b}{x + c}$.

    If $g(1)$ has an integral value, determine the values of a, b, and c.

3. Solve the following radical equations graphically. Answer to the nearest hundredth where necessary. Sketch and label the displayed graphs on the grid.

a) $\sqrt{3x - 7} = x - 5$

b) $\dfrac{3x + 1}{x - 5} = 8$

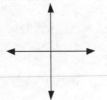

c) $\sqrt{2(5x - 1)} + 3 = 0$

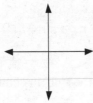

d) $\dfrac{5x^2 - 14x - 3}{x - 3} = \dfrac{3x + 7}{x - 3}$

4. Consider the functions $f(x) = x^2 - x - 30$ and $g(x) = x - 6$.
Determine, graphically, the solutions of the following equations to the nearest tenth.

a) $\left(\dfrac{g}{f}\right)(x) - 3 = 0$

b) $\left(\dfrac{f}{g}\right)(x) - 3 = 0$

c) $\left(\dfrac{f}{g}\right)(x) - 11 = 0$

d) $\sqrt{f(x)} = (g \circ f)(x)$

5. The radius, r, of a baseball is related to the surface area, A, by the formula $r = \dfrac{1}{2}\sqrt{\dfrac{A}{\pi}}$.

a) If the radius of a baseball used in Major League Baseball is 1.45 inches, determine the equation of a radical function which can be graphed so that the x-intercept of the graph would determine the surface area of the baseball.

b) Determine, graphically, the surface area of the baseball to the nearest square inch.

6. A"seconds pendulum" is defined as a pendulum which takes one second to swing from left to right. It has a period of two seconds (http://en.wikipedia.org/wiki/Seconds_ pendulum). Use the information in Class Ex. #1 to determine the length of a "seconds pendulum".

Multiple Choice

7. Consider the function $f(x) = \log (x^2)$.
The complete solution to the equation $2\sqrt{f(x)} - 1 = 0$ is

A.   1.33   B. ± 1.33

C.   3.16   D. ± 3.16

8. A student was asked to determine the root(s) of the radical equation $\sqrt{f(x + p)} = q$, where $p, q > 0$, using the graph of the function $y = \sqrt{f(x)}$.

In order to determine the roots of the radical equation $\sqrt{f(x + p)} = q$, the student could

A.   determine the x-coordinate(s) of the point(s) where $\sqrt{f(x)} = q$
on the graph of $y = \sqrt{f(x)}$, then add p units to the x-coordinate(s)

B.   determine the x-coordinate(s) of the point(s) where $\sqrt{f(x)} = q$
on the graph of $y = \sqrt{f(x)}$, then subtract p units from the x-coordinate(s)

C.   determine the x-coordinate(s) of the point(s) where $\sqrt{f(x)} = p$
on the graph of $y = \sqrt{f(x)}$, then add q units to the x-coordinate(s)

D.   determine the x-coordinate(s) of the point(s) where $\sqrt{f(x)} = p$
on the graph of $y = \sqrt{f(x)}$, then subtract q units from the x-coordinate(s)

Numerical Response

9. Consider the rational function $f(x) = \dfrac{2x^3 - 15x^2 + 36x - 27}{x - 3}$.

To the nearest tenth, the largest solution of the radical equation $\sqrt{f(x)} = 0$ is _____ .

(Record your answer in the numerical response box from left to right.)

Answer Key

1. a) 4 and 10   **b)** 4 and 10

   c) Answers may vary slightly   **i)** 0.6 and 13.4   **ii)** –3.3 and 17.3   **iii)** no solution
                            iv) 6 and 12   **v)** –1.1 and 7.1   **vi)** –5.7 and 9.7

   d) $f(x) = 0.5(x - 4)(x - 10)$ **e)** $\left\{ y \,|\, y \geq -\dfrac{9}{2}, y \in R \right\}$ **f)** $2\sqrt{5}$

2. a) i) $y = 5$ **ii)** $y = 3$ **iii)** $y = 3 - d$ **b) i)** $x = -1$ **ii)** $x = -3$ **iii)** $x = -1 - a$
   c) i) 0   **ii)** –0.5   **iii)**   –1.3   **iv)** 3.5   **v)** no root   **vi)** no root   **vii)** –0.7
   d) $a = 3, b = 1, c = 1$

3. a) 9.70   **b)** 8.2   **c)** no solution   **d)** –0.51, 3.91

4. a) –4.7   **b)** –2.0   **c)** no solution   **d)** –5.8, 6.8   **5. a)** $f(x) = \dfrac{1}{2}\sqrt{\dfrac{x}{\pi}} - 1.45$ **b)** 26 in^2

6. 1 metre   **7.** B   **8.** B   **9.** | 1 | . | 5 | |

Analyzing Radical and Rational Functions Lesson #7: Practice Test

No calculator may be used for this section of the test.

1. The domain and range of the function $y = -\sqrt{-x + 1}$ are, respectively, all real numbers such that

    A. $x \geq 1, y \geq 0$

    B. $x \geq -1, y \leq 0$

    C. $x \leq -1, y \geq 0$

    D. $x \leq 1, y \leq 0$

Use the following information to answer the next two questions.

> A student is analyzing the graph of the function $y = g(x)$. She correctly deduces that the range of the function $y = \sqrt{g(x)}$ is $\{y \mid 0 \leq y \leq 4, y \in R\}$.
>
> She makes four statements about the graph of $y = g(x)$.
>
> **Statement 1:** The point $(1, 2)$ lies on the graph of $y = g(x)$.
>
> **Statement 2:** The graph of $y = g(x)$ has no x-intercepts.
>
> **Statement 3:** The graph of $y = g(x)$ has no points in quadrants three or four.
>
> **Statement 4:** The maximum value of $y = g(x)$ is 2.

2. Which statement(s) **must** be false?

    A.   Statement 2 only

    B.   Statement 4 only

    C.   Statement 2 and 4 only

    D.   Some other statement, or combination of statements, must be false.

3. Which statement(s) **must** be true?

    A.   Statement 1 only

    B.   Statement 3 only

    C.   None of the statements must be true.

    D.   Some other statement, or combination of statements, must be true.

Use the following information to answer the next three questions.

> Consider the graph of the rational function $f(x) = \dfrac{x-7}{x^2 - 9x + 14}$.

4. Which one of the following statements is true regarding the graph of $f(x)$?

   A. The horizontal asymptote has equation $y = 0$.
   B. The horizontal asymptote has equation $y = 1$.
   C. The horizontal asymptote has equation $x = 7$.
   D. There is no horizontal asymptote.

5. Which one of the following statements is true regarding the graph of $f(x)$?

   A. The vertical asymptote has equation $x = 0$.
   B. The vertical asymptote has equation $x = 2$.
   C. The vertical asymptote has equation $x = 7$.
   D. There is no vertical asymptote.

Numerical Response 1. If the point of discontinuity of the graph can be represented by (a, b), then the value of $a + b$, correct to the nearest tenth, is _____.

(Record your answer in the numerical response box from left to right.)

Section B *A graphing calculator may be used for the remainder of the test.*

6. The range of $y = \sqrt{f(x)}$ is $[3, 12]$.
   Which one of the following points could lie on the graph of $y = f(x)$?

   A. $(3, \sqrt{3})$ B. $(9, 2)$

   C. $(8, 5)$ D. $(18, 18)$

7. Which of the following statements concerning the roots of the equation
   $\dfrac{2x^3 - 19x^2 + 56x - 48}{x - 4} = 0$ is correct?

   A. The only root is 1.5.
   B. The only root is 4.0.
   C. There are two roots, 1.5 and 4.0.
   D. There are no roots.

2. To the nearest hundredth, the solution of the equation $\dfrac{x-9}{8-x} = 20$ is _____ .

(Record your answer in the numerical response box from left to right.)

Use the following information to answer the next five questions.

Consider the function $f(x) = 2 - 4\sqrt{5x - 3}$.

8. The range of the function $y = f(x)$ is

A. $\{y \mid y \in R\}$ **B.** $\{y \mid -2 \le y \le 2, y \in R\}$
C. $\{y \mid y \le 2, y \in R\}$ **D.** $\{y \mid y \ge 2, y \in R\}$

3. The domain of the function $y = f(x)$ is $x \ge c$.
The value of c, to the nearest tenth, is _____ .

(Record your answer in the numerical response box from left to right.)

9. If $g(x) = \sqrt{f(x)}$, then the domain of $g(x)$ is

A. $\{x \mid x \ge 0, x \in R\}$
B. $\{x \mid x \ge 0.6, x \in R\}$
C. $\{x \mid x \ge 0.65, x \in R\}$
D. $\{x \mid 0.6 \le x \le 0.65, x \in R\}$

10. The solution of the equation $f(x) = -5$ can be determined from the x-intercepts of the graph of

A. $y = 2 - 4\sqrt{5x - 3}$
B. $y = -3 - 4\sqrt{5x - 3}$
C. $y = -7 - 4\sqrt{5x - 3}$
D. $y = 7 - 4\sqrt{5x - 3}$

4. The solution of the equation $f(x) = -5$, to the nearest hundredth, is _____ .

(Record your answer in the numerical response box from left to right.)

Use the following information to answer the next two questions.

$y = f(x)$ is a continuous function with zeros –5, 1, and 4, and domain $x \in R$

The domain of $y = \sqrt{f(x)}$ is the set of real numbers such that $x \le -5$ or $x \ge 4$.

Zach has been given a code to describe whether the function is positive, negative, zero, or does not exist for particular values of x.

For the function value $f(x_0)$, he used the following code:
- If the function is **negative** at $x = x_0$, use the code number 1.
- If the function is **zero** at $x = x_0$, use the code number 2.
- If the function is **positive** at $x = x_0$, use the code number 3.
- If the function **does not exist** at $x = x_0$, use the code number 4.

---

 5. In the first box, write the code number for $f(-6)$.
In the second box, write the code for $f(-3)$.
In the third box, write the code number for $f(1)$.
In the last box, write the code number for $f(6)$.

(Record your answer in the numerical response box from left to right.)

11. If the function $f(x)$ has the lowest possible degree, then the multiplicity of the zero at 1 is

A. 1   **B.** 2   **C.** 3

D. unable to be determined

Use the following information to answer the next three questions.

Consider the functions

$$f(x) = \frac{x+a}{x^2+a}, \quad g(x) = \frac{(x+a)(x+c)}{x^2+xa+xb+ab}, \quad h(x) = \frac{2x+b}{x^2-b}, \quad k(x) = \frac{x^2+b}{x^2+a}$$

where a, b, and c are natural numbers.

---

12. Which of the following lists all the functions which have no discontinuities and whose graph has a horizontal asymptote at the x-axis?

A. $f(x)$

B. $k(x)$

C. both $f(x)$ and $h(x)$

D. both $h(x)$ and $k(x)$

13. Function $g(x)$ has

   A.   no points of discontinuity
   B.   two points of discontinuity
   C.   one vertical asymptote
   D.   two vertical asymptotes

14. The function(s) whose graph(s) has an x-intercept at $x = -a$ is

   A. $f(x)$ only
   B. $g(x)$ only
   C. $f(x)$ and $g(x)$ only
   D.   some other function or combination of functions

Use the following information to answer the next two questions.

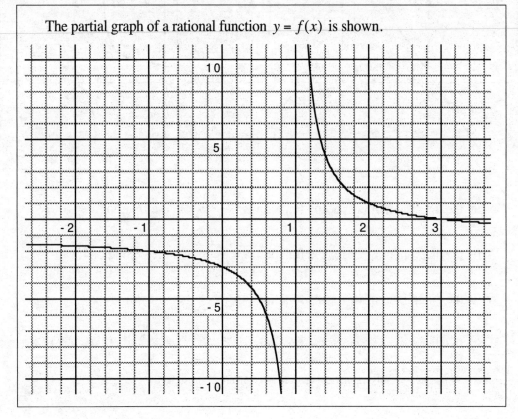

The partial graph of a rational function $y = f(x)$ is shown.

15. The solution of the equation $f(x) - 2.2 = 0$ is

   A. $x = -1.5$ B. $x = -0.9$
   C. $x = 0.8$ D. $x = 1.6$

16. The root of the equation $f(2x) = -6$ is

   A.   0.3   B.   0.6
   C.   1.2   D.   -3.0

Use the following information to answer the next question.

The partial graphs of six rational functions are shown below.

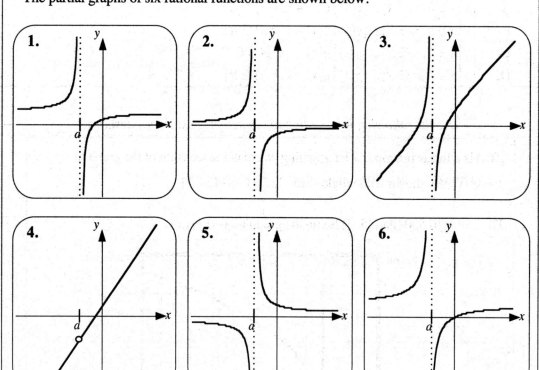

Numerical
Response **6.**   Write the diagram number for the function $y = \dfrac{-2}{x - a}$ in the first box.

Write the diagram number for the function $y = \dfrac{x + 2}{x - a}$ in the second box.

Write the diagram number for the function $y = \dfrac{x}{x - a}$ in the third box.

Write the diagram number for the function $y = \dfrac{x^2 + 2x - ax - 2a}{x - a}$ in the last box.

(Record your answer in the numerical response box from left to right.)

17. The domain and range of $g(x) = a\sqrt{b(x-h)} + k$, $a > 0, b < 0$, are, respectively

    A. $\{x \,|\, x \geq h, x \in R\}$, $\{g(x) \,|\, g(x) \leq k, g(x) \in R\}$

    B. $\{x \,|\, x \geq h, x \in R\}$, $\{g(x) \,|\, g(x) \geq k, g(x) \in R\}$

    C. $\{x \,|\, x \leq h, x \in R\}$, $\{g(x) \,|\, g(x) \geq -k, g(x) \in R\}$

    D. $\{x \,|\, x \leq h, x \in R\}$, $\{g(x) \,|\, g(x) \geq k, g(x) \in R\}$

Use the following information to answer the next three questions.

> $f(x)$ is a linear function. The graphing calculator screenshot of the graph of
> $y = \sqrt{f(x)}$ is shown with window $x:[-2, 7, 1]$, $y:[-1, 4, 1]$.
>
> The points $(0.5, 0)$ and $(5, 3)$ lie on the graph of $y = \sqrt{f(x)}$.

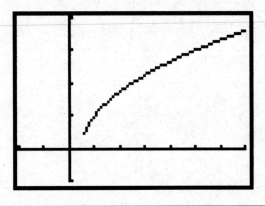

18. $f(5)$ is

    A. 25   **B.** 9   **C.** $\sqrt{3}$

    D. unable to be determined from the given information

19. $f(-5)$ is

    A. -11

    B. -9

    C. -3

    D. unable to be determined
        from the given information

20. The solution of the equation $\sqrt{f(x-1)} - 2 = 0$ is closest to

    A. 1.5   **B.** 2.5

    C. 3.5   **D.** 4.5

Written Response

Consider the function defined by $f(x) = \dfrac{2x^3 + x^2 - 25x + 12}{(x - 3)}$.

- Algebraically determine the coordinates of the point of discontinuity of the graph of the function.

- Describe the relationship between the roots of the equation $\dfrac{2x^3 + x^2 - 25x + 12}{(x - 3)} = 0$ and the x-intercepts of the graph of f.

- Solve the equation $\dfrac{2x^3 + x^2 - 25x + 12}{(x - 3)} = 0$

- Sketch the graph of the function on the grid showing the intercepts and the point of discontinuity.

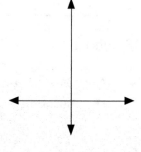

Answer Key

Multiple Choice

1. D	2. C	3. C	4. A	5. B	6. D	7. A	8. C
9. D	10. D	11. B	12. A	13. C	14. A	15. D	16. A
17. D	18. B	19. A	20. C				

Numerical Response

1. | 7 | . | 2 | |

2. | 8 | . | 0 | 5 |

3. | 0 | . | 6 | |

4. | 1 | . | 2 | 1 |

5. | 3 | 1 | 2 | 3 |

6. | 2 | 1 | 6 | 4 |

Written Response

- $(3, 35)$
- The roots of the equation are the same as the x-intercepts of the graph.
- $x = -4, \dfrac{1}{2}$

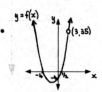

Trigonometry - Functions and Graphs Lesson #1:
Angular Measure - Degrees

Overview

In this unit, we consider angles in standard position expressed in degrees and radians, we develop and apply the equation of the unit circle, we solve problems using trigonometric ratios, and we graph and analyze sine, cosine, and tangent functions.

Note that some of the work in this lesson is a review of work covered in previous courses.

Rotation Angles in Standard Position

Angles can be measured in degrees where 360° is one complete rotation.

A **rotation angle** is formed by rotating an <u>initial arm</u> (or initial side) through an angle $\theta°$ about a fixed point (the vertex).

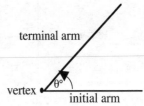

The angle formed between the initial arm and the terminal arm (or terminal side) is the rotation angle.

The angle shown in the diagram is said to be in **standard position**.

On a coordinate grid, standard position means the initial arm is along the positive x-axis and the rotation is about the origin.

A **positive angle** results from a counter clockwise rotation.

The diagram below shows an angle of 235° in standard position.

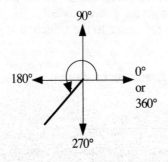

A **negative angle** results from a clockwise rotation.

The diagram below shows an angle of –247° in standard position.

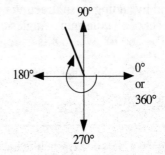

Class Ex. #1

Sketch the rotation angle in standard position and state the quadrant in which the angle terminates.

a) 290°   **b)** –135°   **c)** 750°

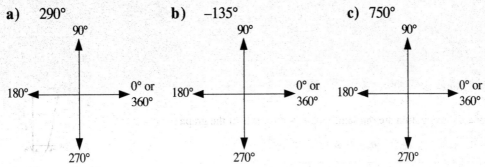

Class Ex. #2

The point *A* lies on the terminal arm of the rotation angle $\theta\,°$.
In each case, draw the angle $\theta\,°$ in standard position.

a) $A(-3, 4)$ **b)** $P(-7, -2)$

Coterminal Angles

a) Draw the rotation angle in standard position.

   i) rotation of 150°   **ii)** rotation of –210°   **iii)** rotation of 510°

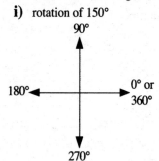 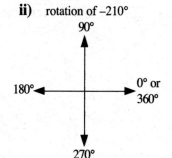 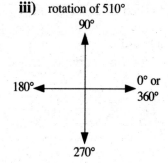

The three rotation angles above have the same terminal arm.
They are called **coterminal angles**.

b) The **principal angle** of a set of coterminal angles is the smallest positive rotation angle
with the same terminal arm. The principal angle is always between 0° and 360°.

In the diagrams above, the principal angle is _____ .

c) There are infinitely many angles that are coterminal with a given angle. They can be
found by adding or subtracting multiples of 360° to/from the given angle.
The set of all coterminal angles can be described with reference to the principal angle $P°$
as $(P + 360\,n)°$ where n is an integer.

The set of angles coterminal with the angles in the diagram can be written

in the form _____ .

Class Ex. #3

In each case   **i)** determine the angle(s), θ , in the domain $-360° \le \theta \le 360°$, which is
                      coterminal with the given angle
        ii) write an expression involving the principal angle that represents <u>all</u> angles
              in the domain $\theta \in R$ that are coterminal with the given angle

a) 285°   **b)** –13°   **c)** 395°

Complete Assignment Question #1 - #3

Reference Angles

A **reference angle** is the acute angle formed between
the terminal arm of the rotation angle and the *x*-axis.

The diagram shows the terminal arm of a rotation angle of 120°
with a reference angle of 60°.

Mark 120° and 60° on the diagram.

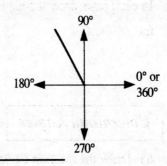

Class Ex. #4 In each case, sketch the rotation angle and state the reference angle.

a) 243°

b) 337°

c) 70°

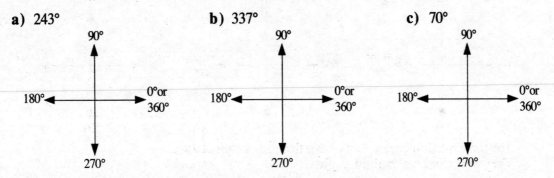

The diagram below describes the relationship between the reference angle and the rotation
angle in each quadrant. If the rotation angle is not between and 0° and 360°, it needs to be
converted to the principal angle for the relationship to be valid.

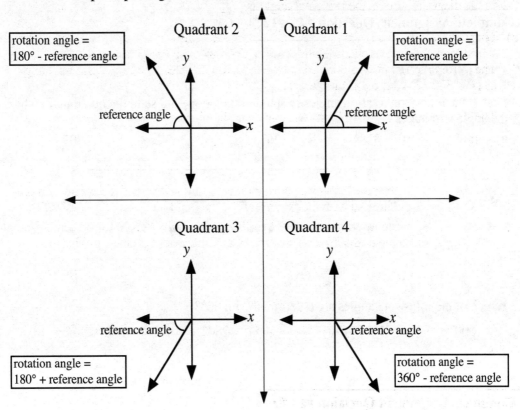

Class Ex. #5 State the reference angle for each of the following rotation angles in standard position.

a) 195° **b)** –258° **c)** –810°

Class Ex. #6 Determine four angles between 0° and 360° which have the same reference angle as a rotation angle of –128°.

Complete Assignment Question #4 - #12

Assignment

1. Sketch the following rotation angles in standard position, and state the quadrant in which the angle terminates.

   a) 160° **b)** 318° **c)** –26° **d)** 569° **e)** –595°

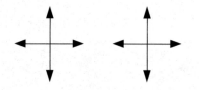

2. Which of the following angles are coterminal with 80°?

   i) 800° **ii)** –100° **iii)** –280° **iv)** 280°

3. In each case   **i)**   determine the angle(s), θ , in the domain $-360° \le \theta \le 360°$, which is coterminal with the given angle

                 ii)   write an expression involving the principal angle that represents <u>all</u> angles in the domain $\theta \in R$ that are coterminal with the given angle

   a)   320°   **b)**   –81°   **c)**   415°

4. Determine the reference angle for the following rotation angles.

   a)   128°   **b)**   285°   **c)**   2°   **d)**   269°

5. In each case, sketch the rotation angle and state the reference angle.

   a)   –300°

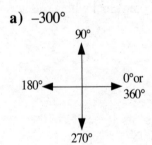

   b)   1100°

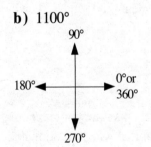

   c)   –109°

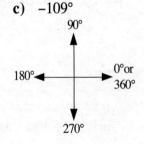

   d)   820°

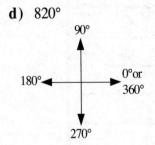

   e)   540°

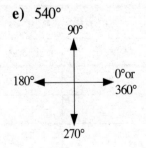

   f)   –270°

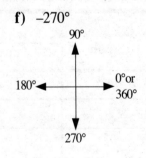

6. a) Sketch a diagram to show a reference angle of 60°
in each of quadrants one to four.

b) State the measure of the rotation angle in each quadrant.

c) Let $P\left(1, \sqrt{3}\right)$ be a point on the terminal arm of the rotation angle in quadrant one.
State the coordinates of points Q, R and S which are on the terminal arms of the rotation
angles in quadrant two, quadrant three, and quadrant four respectively.

7. a) Sketch a rotation angle of –208°
in standard position.

b) Determine four angles between 0° and 360° which have the same reference angle
as a rotation angle of –208°.

c) Determine three angles between –720° and 720° which are coterminal with a rotation
angle of –208°.

d) Write an expression involving the principal angle that represents <u>all</u> angles in the
domain $\theta \in R$ that are coterminal with a rotation angle of –208°.

8. Complete the following table.

Reference Angle	Rotation Angle in:			
	Quad 1	Quad 2	Quad 3	Quad 4
37°				
$\theta°$				
		177°		
			225°	
				299°

9. An angle of –483° in standard position terminates in quadrant

    A. one

    B. two

    C. three

    D. four

10. Which one of these four rotation angles is not coterminal with the other three?

    A. –218°
    B. 158°
    C. 518°
    D. –562°

Use the following information to answer the next question.

A student makes four statements connecting rotation angles and reference angles.

Statement I: In quadrant 1, the rotation angle is equal to the reference angle.

Statement II: In quadrant 2, the rotation angle is equal to 90° plus the reference angle.

Statement III: In quadrant 3, the rotation angle is equal to 180° plus the reference angle.

Statement IV: In quadrant 4, the rotation angle is equal to 270° plus the reference angle.

11. The statements which are true are

    A.   I and III only
    B.   II and IV only
    C.   I, II, and IV only
    D.   I, II, III, and IV

Numerical Response **12.** An angle $x°$ is coterminal with an angle of –163°. If $0 < x < 360$, the value of x is _____ .

(Record your answer in the numerical response box from left to right.)

Answer Key

1. a) **b)** **c)** **d)** **e)**

Quadrant 2   Quadrant 4   Quadrant 4   Quadrant 3   Quadrant 2

2 . i), iii) are coterminal with 80°

3 . a) i) –40°   **ii)** $320° + 360n°, n \in I$ **b) i)** 279°   **ii)** $279° + 360n°, n \in I$
     c) i) 55° and –305   **ii)** $55° + 360n°, n \in I$

4 . a) 52°   **b)** 75°   **c)** 2°   **d)** 89°

5. a) 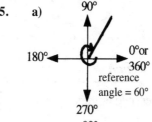   **b)** 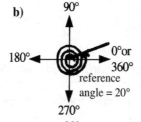   **c)**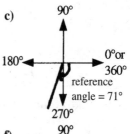

reference angle = 60°   reference angle = 20°   reference angle = 71°

d) 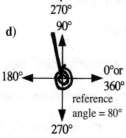   **e)** 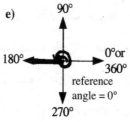   **f)**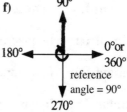

reference angle = 80°   reference angle = 0°   reference angle = 90°

6 . a) See sketch below   **7 . a)** See sketch below

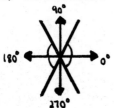   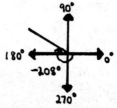

b) 60°, 120°, 240°, 300°   **b)** 28°, 152°, 208°, 332°

c) $Q\left(-1, \sqrt{3}\right), R\left(-1, -\sqrt{3}\right), S\left(1, -\sqrt{3}\right)$ **c)** –568°, 152°, 512°   **d)** $152° + 360n°, n \in I$

8 .

Reference Angle	Rotation Angle in:			
	Quad 1	Quad 2	Quad 3	Quad 4
37°	37°	143°	217°	323°
$\theta°$	$\theta°$	$(180 - \theta)°$	$(180 + \theta)°$	$(360 - \theta)°$
3°	3°	177°	183°	357°
45°	45°	135°	225°	315°
61°	61°	119°	241°	299°

9 . C

10. A

11. A

12.

1	9	7	

Trigonometry - Functions and Graphs Lesson #2:
Angular Measure - Radians

In previous work with angular measure, we have used degrees as the unit of measure. In order to simplify some of the calculations in Calculus, mathematicians developed an alternative angular measure - **radian measure**.

Exploration

The circle has centre O and radius $OP = r$.

a) Measure the length of the radius in cm.

b) Determine the circumference of the circle. Give the answer as an exact value in terms of π.

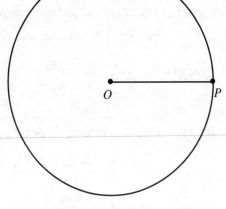

c) • Cut a piece of string or thread equal in length to the radius of the circle.

 • Place the string or thread on the circumference of the circle starting at P.

 • Mark the letter Q on the circumference at the other end of the string or thread.

 • Join OQ; state the length of **i)** OQ, **ii)** arc PQ

 • About how many times will a piece of string or thread equal in length to the radius fit around the circumference of the circle?

The Radian Measure of an Angle

In the diagram above, the measure of angle POQ is defined to be **one radian**.

In general, the **radian measure** of an angle is a <u>ratio</u> that compares the length of an arc of a circle to the radius of the circle, i.e.

$$\text{measure of an angle in radians} = \frac{\text{length of arc forming the angle}}{\text{length of radius}} = \frac{\text{arc length}}{\text{radius}}$$

• In Diagram 1, the radian measure of $\angle AOB$ is given by the ratio $\dfrac{\text{arc } AB}{\text{radius } OA}$. Use the definition to <u>estimate</u> the radian measure of $\angle AOB$.

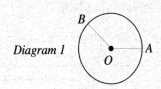

Diagram 1

• As indicated above, <u>one radian</u> is the measure of the angle formed by rotating the radius of a circle through an arc equal in length to the radius of the circle.

In diagram 2, $\angle POQ = 1$ **radian**.

<u>Estimate</u> the degree measure of $\angle POQ$.

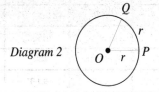

Diagram 2

Converting Between Degrees and Radians

Since an angle can be measured in degrees or radians, it is important to be able to convert from one measure to the other.

Consider a circle with a radius of *r* units. Complete the following:

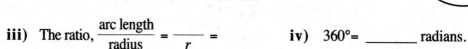

a) i)   One complete rotation in degrees is _____ .

   ii)   The arc length for one complete rotation is _____ ,
which is the _____ of the circle.

   iii)   The ratio, $\dfrac{\text{arc length}}{\text{radius}} = \dfrac{\quad}{r} = $ **iv)** $360° = $ _____ radians.

b) i)   One-half rotation in degrees is _____ .

   ii)   The arc length for one-half rotation is _____ .

   iii)   The ratio, $\dfrac{\text{arc length}}{\text{radius}} = \dfrac{\quad}{\quad} = $ **iv)** $180° = $ _____ radians.

c) i) π radians = 180 degrees   **ii)**   180 degrees = π radians

   so 1 radian = —— degrees   so   1 degree = —— radians

   To convert from radians to degrees,   To convert from degrees to radians,

   multiply by —— .   multiply by —— .

- In mathematics, the symbol " ° " following a number means the unit of angular measure is degrees.

- If there is no unit after the number, or there is the abbreviation "rad", or the word radians, then the unit is radians.

- For example, if you wish to write the sine ratio for a right angle, you must write sin 90°, and NOT sin 90.

Converting Between Degrees and Radians

- π radians = 180°

- Degrees to Radians   multiply by $\dfrac{\pi}{180}$

- Radians to Degrees   multiply by $\dfrac{180}{\pi}$

Class Ex. #1 Convert from degrees to radians (give your answer as an exact value in terms of π).

a) 270°   b) 315°

_____

Class Ex. #2 Convert the following from degrees to radians (to the nearest tenth).

a) 70°   b) 205°

_____

Class Ex. #3 Convert the following from radians to degrees.

a) $\dfrac{\pi}{4}$ b) $\dfrac{-7\pi}{3}$

_____

Class Ex. #4 Convert the following from radians to degrees (to the nearest tenth).

a) 1.57 radians   b) −1.4 rad

Complete Assignment Questions #1 - #4

Coterminal Angles and Reference Angles in Radians

Fill in the blanks in the statements and table below using radian measure.

- **Coterminal angles** are angles with the same terminal arm.
  They are separated by a multiple of 360°, or _____ radians.

- The **principal angle** of a set of coterminal angles is the smallest positive rotation angle with the same terminal arm.
  The principal angle is between 0° and 360°, or between ____ radians and ____ radians.

- A **reference angle** is the acute angle formed between he terminal arm of the rotation angle and the *x*-axis. The relationship between rotation angle and reference angle in each quadrant is given in the table below.

Quadrant	Relationship in Degrees Rotation Angle =	Relationship in Radians Rotation Angle =
One	Reference Angle	
Two	180° − Reference Angle	
Three	180° + Reference Angle	
Four	360° − Reference Angle	

Class Ex. #5

In each of the following

i) draw the angle θ in standard position   **ii)** state the principal angle

iii) determine one positive and one negative coterminal angle for the angle θ

iv) write an expression involving the principal angle that represents all angles in the domain $\theta \in R$ that are coterminal with the given angle

a) $\theta = \dfrac{3\pi}{4}$

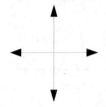

b) $\theta = -\dfrac{\pi}{3}$

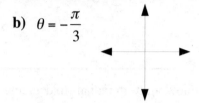

Class Ex. #6

Determine the reference angle for the following rotation angles.

a) $\dfrac{4\pi}{3}$ **b)** $-\dfrac{5\pi}{4}$ **c)** $\dfrac{23\pi}{6}$

Complete Assignment Questions #5 - #7

Arc Length

In this lesson we defined the radian measure of an angle, θ, as

$$\text{radian measure} = \frac{\text{length of arc forming the angle}}{\text{length of radius}} = \frac{\text{arc length}}{\text{radius}}, \quad \text{i.e.} \ \theta = \frac{a}{r} \ .$$

We can rearrange the formula $\theta = \dfrac{a}{r}$ in terms of arc length as

$$a = r\theta$$

where θ = the measure of the angle in **radians**,

a = the length of the arc around the angle, and

r = the length of the radius.

This formula can be used to solve problems involving arc length, radius, and central angle, provided the angle is measured in radians.

Class Ex. #7   A pendulum 30 cm long swings through an arc of 45 cm. Through what angle does the pendulum swing? Answer in degrees and in radians to the nearest tenth.

Class Ex. #8   Calculate the arc length (to the nearest tenth of a metre) of a sector of a circle with diameter 9.2 m if the sector angle is 150°.

Class Ex. #9   A circle with centre *C* and minor arc *AB* measuring 15.2 cm is shown.

If $\angle ABC = \angle BAC = \dfrac{\pi}{6}$ radians, find the length of the radius of the

circle to the nearest tenth of a centimetre.

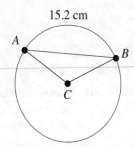

Complete Assignment Questions #8 - #17

Assignment

1. The diagram shows a series of rotation angles in standard position. The lines in the diagram are symmetrical about both the *x*-axis and the *y*-axis. Complete the diagram by determining both the degree measure and the radian measure at the end of each line.

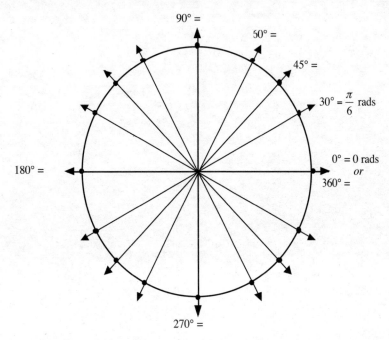

2. Convert from radians to degrees.

   a) $\dfrac{\pi}{2}$ b) $\dfrac{\pi}{6}$ c) $-\dfrac{4\pi}{3}$ d) $\dfrac{3\pi}{4}$ e) $-\dfrac{5\pi}{6}$

3. Convert from degrees to radians. Give the answers to 1 decimal place.

   a) 50°   b) 205°   c) 57.3°   d) 250°

4. Convert from radians to degrees. Give the answers to the nearest tenth.

   a) 0.5 radians   b) 3.1 rad   c) 1.8π radians

5. In each of the following

   i)   draw the angle θ in standard position   ii)   state the principal angle
   iii)   determine one positive and one negative coterminal angle for the angle θ
   iv)   write an expression involving the principal angle that represents all angles in the
         domain $\theta \in R$ that are coterminal with the given angle.

   a) $\theta = \dfrac{5\pi}{4}$ b) $\theta = \dfrac{11\pi}{6}$

   c) $\theta = -\dfrac{2\pi}{3}$ d) $\theta = \dfrac{14\pi}{3}$

6. Determine the reference angle for the following rotation angles.

a) $\dfrac{7\pi}{6}$

b) $\dfrac{3\pi}{4}$

c) $-\dfrac{5\pi}{3}$

d) $-\dfrac{\pi}{6}$

e) $\dfrac{11\pi}{6}$

f) 5π

7. Determine the rotation angle given the reference angle and the quadrant

Reference Angle	Quadrant	Rotation Angle
$\dfrac{\pi}{3}$	3	
$\dfrac{\pi}{8}$	1	
$\dfrac{\pi}{6}$	4	
$\dfrac{\pi}{12}$	2	
$\dfrac{\pi}{2}$	between 3 and 4	

8. A circle has radius 8 cm. Determine (in radians) the measure of the central angle subtended by an arc of length 5.6 cm.

9. Calculate the arc length (to the nearest tenth of a metre) of a sector of a circle with radius 8.4 m if the sector angle is 80°.

10. In the diagram the circle with centre C has radius 6 cm. Determine the length of arc ADB, to the nearest 0.1 cm, if $\angle CAB = \dfrac{\pi}{8}$.

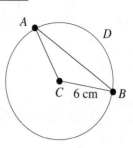

11. A pendulum swings through an angle of 45°. Find the length of the pendulum (to the nearest cm) if the end of the pendulum swings through an arc of length 32 cm.

12. An angle with radian measure 2.36 has degree measure of

    A.   424.80

    B.   135.22

    C.   67.61

    D.   0.04

13. An arc of a circle subtends a central angle of $x°$. If the length of the arc is 1.2 cm and the diameter of the circle is 4 cm, then the value of x to the nearest whole number is

    A. 17

    B. 34

    C. 54

    D. 108

14. Correct to the nearest tenth of a degree, $\dfrac{3\pi}{8}$ rad is equal to _____ °.

(Record your answer in the numerical response box from left to right.)

15. An arc *DE* of a circle, centre *O*, is $\frac{1}{6}$ of the circumference. The size of $\angle DOE$, to the nearest one hundredth of a radian, is _____ .

(Record your answer in the numerical response box from left to right.)

16. A person on a Ferris wheel moves a distance of 5 metres from position *P* to position *Q*. If the diameter of the wheel is 18 metres, the measure of the central angle, to the nearest tenth of a degree, is _____ .

(Record your answer in the numerical response box from left to right.)

17. A satellite makes one complete revolution of the earth in 90 min. Assume that the orbit is circular and that the satellite is situated 280 km above the equator. If the radius of the earth at the equator is 6400 km, then the speed of the satellite, in kilometres per second, to the nearest one hundredth, is _____ .

(Record your answer in the numerical response box from left to right.)

Answer Key

1.

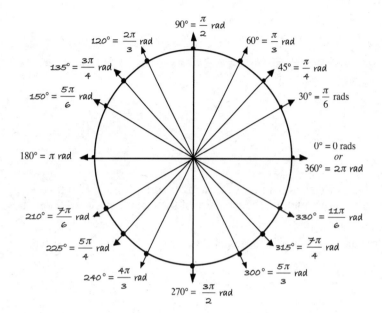

The circle shows:

$90° = \dfrac{\pi}{2}$ rad

$120° = \dfrac{2\pi}{3}$ rad

$135° = \dfrac{3\pi}{4}$ rad

$150° = \dfrac{5\pi}{6}$ rad

$180° = \pi$ rad

$210° = \dfrac{7\pi}{6}$ rad

$225° = \dfrac{5\pi}{4}$ rad

$240° = \dfrac{4\pi}{3}$ rad

$270° = \dfrac{3\pi}{2}$ rad

$60° = \dfrac{\pi}{3}$ rad

$45° = \dfrac{\pi}{4}$ rad

$30° = \dfrac{\pi}{6}$ rads

$0° = 0$ rads
or
$360° = 2\pi$ rad

$330° = \dfrac{11\pi}{6}$ rad

$315° = \dfrac{7\pi}{4}$ rad

$300° = \dfrac{5\pi}{3}$ rad

2. a) 90° **b)** 30° **c)** −240° **d)** 135° **e)** -150°

3. a) 0.9 **b)** 3.6 **c)** 1.0 **d)** 4.4

4. a) 28.6° **b)** 177.6° **c)** 324.0°

5. (i)

a)	**b)**	**c)**	**d)**
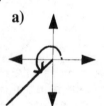	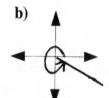	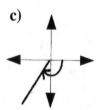	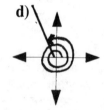

(ii) $\dfrac{5\pi}{4}$ $\dfrac{11\pi}{6}$ $\dfrac{4\pi}{3}$ $\dfrac{2\pi}{3}$

(iii) $\dfrac{13\pi}{4}, \dfrac{-3\pi}{4}$ $\dfrac{23\pi}{6}, \dfrac{-\pi}{6}$ $\dfrac{10\pi}{3}, \dfrac{-8\pi}{3}$ $\dfrac{2\pi}{3}, \dfrac{-4\pi}{3}$ Answers may vary.

(iv) $\dfrac{5\pi}{4} + 2\pi n, n \in I$ $\dfrac{11\pi}{6} + 2\pi n, n \in I$ $\dfrac{4\pi}{3} + 2\pi n, n \in I$ $\dfrac{2\pi}{3} + 2\pi n, n \in I$

6. a) $\dfrac{\pi}{6}$ **b)** $\dfrac{\pi}{4}$ **c)** $\dfrac{\pi}{3}$ **d)** $\dfrac{\pi}{6}$ **e)** $\dfrac{\pi}{6}$ **f)** 0

7. $\dfrac{4\pi}{3}$ $\dfrac{\pi}{8}$ $\dfrac{11\pi}{6}$ $\dfrac{11\pi}{12}$ $\dfrac{3\pi}{2}$

8. 0.7 rad   **9.** 11.7 m   **10.** 14.1 cm   **11.** 41 cm

12. B   **13.** B   **14.**

6	7	.	5

15.

1	.	0	5

16.

3	1	.	8

17.

7	.	7	7

Trigonometry - Functions and Graphs Lesson #3:
Trigonometric Ratios

Trigonometric Ratios

Note that some of the work in this lesson is a review of work covered in previous courses.

Primary Trigonometric Ratios

Complete the following:

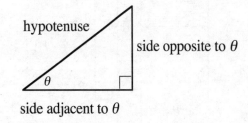

hypotenuse

side opposite to θ

side adjacent to θ

sine ratio $\Rightarrow$ $\sin \theta =$

cosine ratio $\Rightarrow$ $\cos \theta =$

tangent ratio $\Rightarrow$ $\tan \theta =$

These ratios are called the *Primary Trigonometric Ratios* and can be remembered by the acronym **SOHCAHTOA**.

Reciprocal Trigonometric Ratios - the reciprocals of the primary trigonometric ratios.

cosecant ratio $\Rightarrow$ $\csc \theta = \dfrac{1}{\sin \theta}$

secant ratio $\Rightarrow$ $\sec \theta = \dfrac{1}{\cos \theta}$

cotangent ratio $\Rightarrow$ $\cot \theta = \dfrac{1}{\tan \theta}$

- We can remember the reciprocal from each of the primary trigonometric ratios by the fact that each "pair" has only one "*co*" prefix in it.

- The primary and reciprocal trigonometric ratios can be given in terms of x, y and r.

Class Ex. #1

Use the diagram to write all the trigonometric ratios in terms of x, y and r.

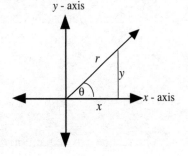

y - axis

x - axis

$\sin \theta =$ $\cos \theta =$ $\tan \theta =$

$\csc \theta =$ $\sec \theta =$ $\cot \theta =$

You should memorize these formulas.

Some students use a phrase like "**s**even **y**ellow **r**abbits" to remember $\sin \theta = \dfrac{y}{r}$.

Determining the Sign of a Trigonometric Ratio

a) In quadrant 1, draw the rotation angle θ in standard position and complete the table.

b) Repeat for quadrants 2 - 4.

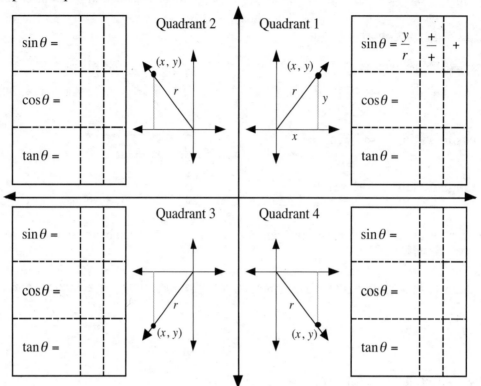

 Note The reciprocal trigonometric ratios follow the same framework as their corresponding primary ratio.

c) Complete the following statements using the information above.

i) Sine ratios and cosecant ratios have **positive** values in quadrants ___ and ___ .

ii) Cosine ratios and secant ratios have **positive** values in quadrants ___ and ___ .

iii) Tangent ratios and cotangent ratios have **positive** values in quadrants ___ and ___ .

iv) Sine ratios and cosecant ratios have **negative** values in quadrants___ and___ .

v) Cosine ratios and secant ratios have **negative** values in quadrants___ and___ .

vi) Tangent ratios and cotangent ratios have **negative** values in quadrants___ and___ .

CAST Rule

The results can be memorized by:

- the **CAST** rule or
- by remembering to "**A**dd **S**ugar **T**o **C**offee"

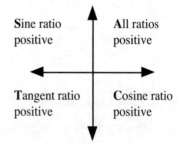

Sine ratio positive | All ratios positive

Tangent ratio positive | Cosine ratio positive

Class Ex. #2

Determine, without using technology, whether the given trigonometric ratios are positive or negative.

a) sin 280°

b) tan $\dfrac{7\pi}{6}$

c) cos $\dfrac{10\pi}{3}$

d) csc (−225°)

e) cot $\left(-\dfrac{13\pi}{6}\right)$

f) sec 1000°

Degree Mode and Radian Mode on a Calculator

Most calculators have the ability to calculate the values of sine ratios, cosine ratios, and tangent ratios, in degrees and in radians. To calculate the values of the reciprocal trigonometric ratios (cosecant ratios, secant ratios, and cotangent ratios), we need to use the reciprocal of the corresponding primary ratios.

For example, to calculate the value of csc $\dfrac{5\pi}{6}$, set the calculator to radian mode, and do either of the following:

$$\csc \frac{5\pi}{6} = \frac{1}{\sin \dfrac{5\pi}{6}} = 2 \qquad \text{or} \qquad \sin \frac{5\pi}{6} = \frac{1}{2}, \ \csc \frac{5\pi}{6} = \frac{1}{\frac{1}{2}} = 2$$

Class Ex. #3

Use a calculator to determine, to four decimal places where necessary, the values of the trigonometric ratios in Class Ex. #2.

a) sin 280°

b) tan $\dfrac{7\pi}{6}$

c) cos $\dfrac{10\pi}{3}$

d) sin 90

e) csc (−225°)

f) cot $\left(-\dfrac{13\pi}{6}\right)$

g) sec 1000°

Expressing Trigonometric Ratios of an Angle in Terms of a Reference Angle

The trigonometric ratios for any angle are either the trigonometric ratios of the reference angle, or the negative of the trigonometric ratios of the reference angle.

Use the following procedure.

i)   Determine the sign of the ratio (positive or negative).
ii)   Determine the measure of the reference angle.
iii)   Combine i) and ii).

To write $\cos \dfrac{11\pi}{8}$ as the cosine of an acute angle using the above procedure, we have

i) the sign is negative, ii) the reference angle $= \dfrac{3\pi}{8}$, and so iii) $\cos \dfrac{11\pi}{8} = -\cos \dfrac{3\pi}{8}$.

The result can be verified on a calculator.

Class Ex. #4

Rewrite as the same trigonometric function of an acute angle.

a) $\cos \dfrac{7\pi}{4}$ 　　　　　　 **b)** $\cot(-100°)$ 　　　　　　 **c)** $\sin \dfrac{11\pi}{2}$

Complete Assignment Questions #1- #4

Determining Trigonometric Ratios from the a Point on the Terminal Arm

Class Ex. #5

The point $P(-15, 8)$ lies on the terminal arm of a rotation angle θ in standard position.

a) Mark the angle θ on the diagram.

b) Calculate the exact length of $OP = r$.

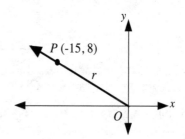

c) Use $x = -15$, $y = 8$ and r from b) to determine the exact values of the primary and reciprocal trigonometric ratios for angle θ.

Using One Trigonometric Ratio to Determine Other Trigonometric Ratios

Class Ex. #6

Cot $A = \dfrac{\sqrt{5}}{2}$ and sin A is negative. Complete the following procedure to determine exact values, with rational denominators, for csc A and sec A.

a) Since the cotangent ratio is positive, and the sin ratio is negative, angle A must terminate in quadrant _____ .

b) Since cot $A = \dfrac{\sqrt{5}}{2} = \dfrac{x}{y}$, we know that the point $\left(-\sqrt{5}, -2\right)$

lies on the terminal arm of angle A in the third quadrant.

Sketch a diagram and draw the reference triangle
illustrating the above information.

c) Use $x^2 + y^2 = r^2$ to determine the value of r, and hence determine the exact values of csc A and sec A.

Complete Assignment Questions #5 - #15

Assignment

1. In which quadrant(s) does the terminal arm of rotation angle θ lie if

   a) sin θ is negative?   **c)** csc θ and tan θ are both negative?

   b) sec θ is positive?   **d)** cot θ is positive and csc θ is negative?

2. Determine, without using technology, whether the given trigonometric ratios are positive or negative.

   a) cos 181°   **b)** csc $\dfrac{11\pi}{6}$ **c)** tan $(-300°)$

   d) sin $\dfrac{14\pi}{3}$ **e)** cot 560°   **f)** sec $\left(-\dfrac{\pi}{4}\right)$

3. Find the value (to 4 decimal places where necessary) of

a) $\tan \dfrac{\pi}{4}$ 　　　　　　　b) $\cos (-382°)$ 　　　　　c) $\sin\left(-\dfrac{2\pi}{3}\right)$

d) $\cot 30°$ 　　　　　　　　e) $\csc 60$ 　　　　　　　f) $\sec\left(-\dfrac{7\pi}{6}\right)$

4. Rewrite as the same trigonometric function of a positive acute angle.

a) $\sin 205° = $ _____ 　　b) $\cot \dfrac{3\pi}{5} = $ _____ 　c) $\csc 107° = $ _____

d) $\sec\left(-\dfrac{19\pi}{9}\right) = $ _____ 　e) $\cos 5\pi = $ _____ 　f) $\tan (-30°) = $ _____

5. The point $(-4, 3)$ lies on the terminal arm of a rotation angle as shown.
Determine the primary and reciprocal trigonometric ratios for the rotation angle.
Express each answer as an exact value.

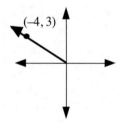

6. The point $(10, -24)$ lies on the terminal arm of an angle θ in standard position. Determine the exact values of $\sec \theta$ and $\csc \theta$.

7. Solve for the required ratios in each of the following. Express each answer as an exact value with a rational denominator.

a) If $\tan \theta = \dfrac{\sqrt{2}}{4}$, and angle θ terminates in the first quadrant, determine $\cot \theta$, $\csc \theta$, and $\sec \theta$.

b) If $\tan \theta = \dfrac{\sqrt{2}}{4}$, and angle θ terminates in the third quadrant, determine $\cot \theta$, $\csc \theta$, and $\sec \theta$.

8. If $\sin X = -\dfrac{1}{3}$ and $\cos X$ is positive, express $\cot X$ as an exact value.

9. $\operatorname{Cos} A = -0.28$, where $\pi \le A \le \dfrac{3\pi}{2}$. Determine the exact value of $\csc A$.

10. The point $\left(\dfrac{1}{5}, -\dfrac{1}{5}\right)$ lies on the terminal arm of an angle A in standard position. The exact value of sec A is

A. $\sqrt{2}$ **B.** $-\sqrt{2}$

C. $\dfrac{\sqrt{2}}{25}$ **D.** $-\dfrac{\sqrt{2}}{25}$

Use the following information to answer the next question.

> Consider the following trigonometric expressions.
>
> **I.** $\cos(2\pi + x)$ **II.** $\cos(2\pi - x)$
>
> **III.** $\cos(\pi - x)$ **IV.** $\cos(-x)$

11. If $\cos x = A$, which of the following is not equal to A?

A. **III** only
B. **IV** only
C. **III** and **IV** only
D. some other combination of **I**, **II**, **III**, and **IV**

12. Without using technology, determine which of the following has a different sign from the others.

A. tan 201°
B. csc (−72°)
C. sec 115°
D. −cot 79°

13. Without using technology, determine which of the following does not have the same value as cot 277°.

A. cot (−83°)
B. cot (−263°)
C. −cot 263°
D. −cot 97°

Use the following information to answer the next question.

Angles A, B, and C are rotation angles with the following properties.

- $\csc A = \csc \dfrac{\pi}{4}$ where $0 \leq A \leq 2\pi$, $A \neq \dfrac{\pi}{4}$

- $\cot B = \cot \dfrac{3\pi}{4}$ where $0 \leq B \leq 2\pi$, $B \neq \dfrac{3\pi}{4}$

- $\sec C = \sec \dfrac{8\pi}{5}$ where $0 \leq C \leq 2\pi$, $A \neq \dfrac{8\pi}{5}$

14. If the value of $A + B + C$ can be expressed in the form $k\pi$, then the value of k, to the nearest hundredth, is _____.

    (Record your answer in the numerical response box from left to right.)

15. The point $(4, -8)$ lies on the terminal arm of an angle θ. If the value of $\sin\theta + \sec\theta$ can be expressed in the form $k\sqrt{5}$, then the value of k, to one decimal place, is _____ .

    (Record your answer in the numerical response box from left to right.)

 The following problems could be used as a lead-in to the next lesson. Use the blank pages at the back of the workbook to answer this group investigation.

a) Sketch an angle of $\dfrac{\pi}{3}$ in standard position with the point $P\left(1, \sqrt{3}\right)$ on the terminal arm. Without using technology, explain and carry out a strategy to determine the exact trigonometric ratios of three different angles greater than $\dfrac{\pi}{2}$ and less than 2π.

b) Consider an angle A in standard position with $\sin A = -\dfrac{5}{13}$ and $0 \leq A \leq 2\pi$. Without using technology, explain and carry out a strategy to determine the exact values of $\cos A$ and $\tan A$.

Answer Key

1. a) quadrant 3 or 4   **b)** quadrant 1 or 4   **c)** quadrant 4   **d)** quadrant 3

2. a) negative   **b)** negative   **c)** positive   **d)** positive   **e)** positive   **f)** positive

3. a) 1   **b)** 0.9272   **c)** –0.8660   **d)** 1.7321   **e)** –3.2807   **f)** –1.1547

4. a) $-\sin 25°$ **b)** $-\cot \dfrac{2\pi}{5}$ **c)** $\csc 73°$ **d)** $\sec \dfrac{\pi}{9}$ **e)** $-\cos 0$ **f)** $-\tan 30°$

5. sine ratio $= \dfrac{3}{5}$,   cosine ratio $= -\dfrac{4}{5}$,   tangent ratio $= -\dfrac{3}{4}$,

cosecant ratio $= \dfrac{5}{3}$,   secant ratio $= -\dfrac{5}{4}$,   cotangent ratio $= -\dfrac{4}{3}$

6. $\sec \theta = \dfrac{13}{5}$, $\csc \theta = -\dfrac{13}{12}$

7. a) $\cot \theta = 2\sqrt{2}$, $\csc \theta = 3$, $\sec \theta = \dfrac{3\sqrt{2}}{4}$ **b)** $\cot \theta = 2\sqrt{2}$, $\csc \theta = -3$, $\sec \theta = -\dfrac{3\sqrt{2}}{4}$

8. $-2\sqrt{2}$ **9.** $-\dfrac{25}{24}$ **10.** A   **11.** A   **12.** A   **13.** D

14. | 2 | . | 9 | 0 |
|---|---|---|---|

15. | 0 | . | 6 | |
|---|---|---|---|

Group Investigation:

a) $\sin \dfrac{2\pi}{3} = \dfrac{\sqrt{3}}{2}$ $\cos \dfrac{2\pi}{3} = -\dfrac{1}{2}$ $\tan \dfrac{2\pi}{3} = -\sqrt{3}$
$\csc \dfrac{2\pi}{3} = \dfrac{2\sqrt{3}}{3}$ $\sec \dfrac{2\pi}{3} = -2$ $\cot \dfrac{2\pi}{3} = -\dfrac{\sqrt{3}}{3}$

$\sin \dfrac{4\pi}{3} = -\dfrac{\sqrt{3}}{2}$ $\cos \dfrac{4\pi}{3} = -\dfrac{1}{2}$ $\tan \dfrac{4\pi}{3} = \sqrt{3}$
$\csc \dfrac{4\pi}{3} = -\dfrac{2\sqrt{3}}{3}$ $\sec \dfrac{4\pi}{3} = -2$ $\cot \dfrac{4\pi}{3} = \dfrac{\sqrt{3}}{3}$

$\sin \dfrac{5\pi}{3} = -\dfrac{\sqrt{3}}{2}$ $\cos \dfrac{5\pi}{3} = \dfrac{1}{2}$ $\tan \dfrac{5\pi}{3} = -\sqrt{3}$
$\csc \dfrac{5\pi}{3} = -\dfrac{2\sqrt{3}}{3}$ $\sec \dfrac{5\pi}{3} = 2$ $\cot \dfrac{5\pi}{3} = -\dfrac{\sqrt{3}}{3}$

b) In quadrant three, $\cos A = -\dfrac{12}{13}$ and $\tan A = \dfrac{5}{12}$.

In quadrant four, $\cos A = \dfrac{12}{13}$ and $\tan A = -\dfrac{5}{12}$.

Trigonometry - Functions and Graphs Lesson #4:
Determining Angle Measure from a Trigonometric Ratio

Review: Angle Measure in Degrees From Primary Trigonometric Ratios

In previous courses, we used the concepts of reference angle and sign of the trigonometric ratio to determine angle measures in degrees given a sine, cosine, or tangent ratio.

Use the following procedure to determine the angle measure between $0°$ and $360°$ given a trigonometric ratio.

Step 1: Determine the quadrant(s) the angle will be in by looking at the sign of the ratio.

Step 2: Determine the reference angle (always between $0°$ and $90°$) and draw a rough sketch in the appropriate quadrant(s). To determine the reference angle, use

2nd	sin	or	2nd	cos	or	2nd	tan

of the **absolute value** of the given quantity.

Step 3: Determine the rotation angle(s) using the reference angle and the quadrant(s).

• Always check the given domain to determine which quadrants are valid in the calculation. Sometimes the domain is restricted to, for example, $0° \le \theta \le 180°$, or $90° \le \theta \le 180°$.

• In the next unit, we will consider domains less than $0°$ or greater than $360°$.

Class Ex. #1 Complete the following to solve $\cos \theta = -0.5$, where $0° \le \theta \le 360°$.

$\cos \theta = -0.5$

quadrants ___ and ___

reference angle = ___ $°$

in quadrant ___, rotation angle =

in quadrant ___, rotation angle =

Class Ex. #2 Given that $(\sin \theta)^2$ can be written as $\sin^2\theta$, solve the equation $\sin^2\theta = 0.5$ on the interval $0° \le \theta \le 360°$.

Angle Measure in Degrees From Reciprocal Trigonometric Ratios

Since there are no calculator keys for cosecant, secant, or cotangent, we must rewrite the reciprocal ratios in their primary form.

For example, to solve $\cot x = \sqrt{3}$, we rewrite this in the primary form $\tan x = \dfrac{1}{\sqrt{3}}$.

Class Ex. #3　Solve $\cot x = \sqrt{3}$, $0° \le x \le 360°$.

Class Ex. #4　Determine the measure of x, to the nearest degree, where $0° \le x \le 360°$.

a) $\sec x = -1.2631$ 　　　　　**b)** $\csc x = 2.45$

Class Ex. #5　Determine the measure of θ, to the nearest whole number, where $0° \le \theta \le 360°$.

a) $\cos \theta = 0$ 　　　　　**b)**　$\csc \theta$ is undefined

Complete Assignment Questions #1 - #4

Angle Measure in Radians From Trigonometric Ratios

A similar procedure can be used to determine angle measure in radians by setting the calculator mode to radian measure.

Step 1:   Determine the quadrant(s) the angle will be in by looking at the sign of the ratio.

Step 2:   Determine the reference angle (always between 0 and $\frac{\pi}{2}$ (approximately 1.57)).

Draw a rough sketch in the appropriate quadrant(s).
To determine the reference angle, use

| 2nd | sin | or | 2nd | cos | or | 2nd | tan |

of the **absolute value** of the given quantity.

Step 3:   Determine the rotation angle(s) using the reference angle and the quadrant(s).

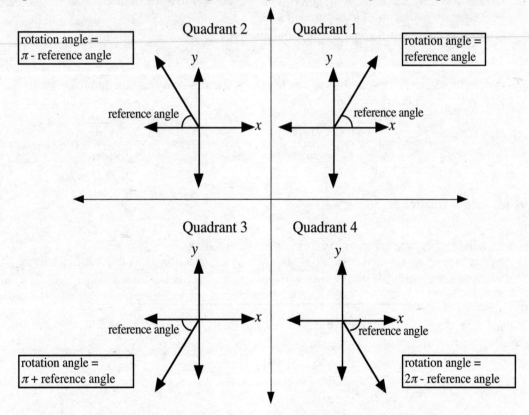

In each case, determine the value(s) of θ to the nearest hundredth of a radian.

Class Ex. #6

a) $\cos \theta = -0.5, 0 \le \theta \le 2\pi$

b) $\cot \theta = -\dfrac{5}{4}, 0 \le \theta \le \pi$

Determining Angle Measure as an Exact Multiple of π Radians

In Class Ex. #1, we solved $\cos \theta = -0.5, 0° \le \theta \le 360°$.
The reference angle is 60° and the solutions are $\theta = 120°, 240°$.

Converting 120° to $\dfrac{2\pi}{3}$ radians and 240° to $\dfrac{4\pi}{3}$ radians, we know that the solution

to $\cos \theta = -0.5, 0 \le \theta \le 2\pi$ is $\theta = \dfrac{2\pi}{3}, \dfrac{4\pi}{3}$.

In Class Ex. #4a), we solved $\cos \theta = -0.5, 0 \le \theta \le 2\pi$ to the nearest hundredth.
The reference angle is 1.047 ... and the solutions are $\theta = 2.09$, and 4.19.

We can determine the solution as an <u>exact multiple of π radians</u> using the procedure below.

1. Divide the reference angle by π, and convert the answer to a fraction.
    This fraction is the multiple of π radians.
2. Determine the rotation angle(s) using the reference angle and the quadrant(s).

So, to determine the exact solutions to $\cos \theta = -0.5, 0 \le \theta \le 2\pi$, complete the following:

$\cos \theta = -0.5$, in quadrants 2 and 3

reference angle $= \dfrac{1}{3}\pi = \dfrac{\pi}{3}$ (see screenshot)

in quadrant 2, rotation angle $= \pi - \dfrac{\pi}{3} =$

in quadrant 3, rotation angle $= \pi + \dfrac{\pi}{3} =$

```
cos⁻¹(0.5)
          1.047197551
Ans/π
          .3333333333
Ans▶Frac
                  1/3
```

 Note Not all solutions can be given as exact multiples of π radians.
If the reference angle divided by π does not convert to a fraction, then the solution cannot be written as an exact multiple of π radians.

Class Ex. #7 In each case, determine the exact values of θ in the interval $0 \le \theta \le 2\pi$, for which

a) $\sin \theta = \dfrac{1}{2}$ **b)** $\sec \theta = -\sqrt{2}$ **c)** $\csc \theta$ is undefined.

Complete Assignment Questions #5 - #11

Assignment

1. Determine the measure(s) of θ, to the nearest degree, where $0° \le \theta \le 360°$.
   a) $\sin \theta = 0.7301$ **b)** $\cos \theta = -0.9580$

   c) $\tan \theta = \dfrac{5}{2}$ **d)** $\sin \theta = -1$

2. Determine the measure of A, to the nearest degree, for the specified domain.
   a) $\sec A = 1.2364, 0° \le A \le 360°$ **b)** $\cot A = -0.4458, 180° \le A \le 360°$

   c) $\csc A = 1.0138, 0° \le A \le 180°$ **d)** $\cot A$ is undefined $0° \le A \le 360°$

3. Solve for θ, to the nearest degree, where $0° \le \theta \le 360°$.
   a) $\tan^2 \theta = 3$ **b)** $\sec^2 \theta = \dfrac{4}{3}$

4. In each case, determine the value(s) of x to the nearest hundredth of a radian.

   a) $\tan x = 0.5371,\ 0 \le x \le 2\pi$ **b)** $\cot x = -1.5,\ 0 \le x \le 2\pi$

   c) $\csc x = 6,\ 0 \le x \le \pi$ **d)** $\cos x = -\dfrac{4}{5},\ \pi \le x \le 2\pi$

5. In each case, determine the exact values of θ in the interval $0 \le \theta \le 2\pi$, for which

   a) $\sin \theta = \dfrac{1}{2}$ **b)** $\cos \theta = -\dfrac{1}{\sqrt{2}}$ **c)** $\tan \theta = -1$

   d) $\cot \theta = \sqrt{3}$ **e)** $\csc \theta = 1$ **f)** $\sec \theta = 2$

6. Find the values of each angle θ if $0 \le \theta \le 2\pi$.

    a) $\cot^2 \theta = 3$ **b)** $\csc^3 \theta = -8$

7. The values of x for which $\sec x = -10.366$ in the interval $0° \le x \le 360°$ are

    A. $84°, 276°$

    B. $96°, 264°$

    C. $96°, 276°$

    D. $264°, 276°$

8. The domain for which $\sec \theta = -3.1$ has two solutions is

    A. $0 \le \theta \le \pi$

    B. $\pi \le \theta \le 2\pi$

    C. $\dfrac{\pi}{2} \le \theta \le \dfrac{3\pi}{2}$

    D. none of the above

9. Which of the following has a solution in the interval $0 \le x \le 2\pi$ which can be expressed as an exact multiple of π radians?

    A. $\tan x = \dfrac{1}{2}$

    B. $\cot x = \sqrt{2}$

    C. $\csc^2 x = -\dfrac{1}{4}$

    D. $\sec^2 x = \dfrac{4}{3}$

10. If $\csc \theta = \dfrac{7}{2}$, then one approximate measure in radians for θ is

    A. 2.852

    B. 2.897

    C. 3.431

    D. 5.993

Numerical Response

11. To the nearest tenth of a radian, the value of x for which $\cot x = -\dfrac{1}{4}$ and $\pi \le x \le 2\pi$

is _____ .

(Record your answer in the numerical response box from left to right.)

Answer Key

1. a) 47°, 133°   **b)** 163°, 197°   **2. a)** 36°, 324°   **b)**   294°
    c) 68°, 248°   **d)** 270°   **c)** 81°, 99°   **d)** 0°, 180°, 360°

3. a)   60°, 120°, 240°, 300°   **4. a)** 0.49, 3.63   **b)** 2.55, 5.70
    b)   30°, 150°, 210°, 330°   **c)** 0.17, 2.97   **d)** 3.79

5. a) $\dfrac{\pi}{6}, \dfrac{5\pi}{6}$ **b)** $\dfrac{3\pi}{4}, \dfrac{5\pi}{4}$ **c)** $\dfrac{3\pi}{4}, \dfrac{7\pi}{4}$ **d)** $\dfrac{\pi}{6}, \dfrac{7\pi}{6}$ **e)** $\dfrac{\pi}{2}$ **f)** $\dfrac{\pi}{3}, \dfrac{5\pi}{3}$

6. a) $\dfrac{\pi}{6}, \dfrac{5\pi}{6}, \dfrac{7\pi}{6}, \dfrac{11\pi}{6}$ **b)** $\dfrac{7\pi}{6}, \dfrac{11\pi}{6}$

7. B   **8.** C   **9.** D   **10.** A   **11.** | 5 | . | 0 | |

Trigonometry - Functions and Graphs Lesson #5:
Special Triangles, Exact Values, and the Unit Circle

In this lesson, we will determine the exact value of the six trigonometric ratios for

- angles expressed in degrees that are multiples of $0°, 30°, 45°, 60°$, and $90°$
- angles expressed in radians that are multiples of $0, \dfrac{\pi}{6}, \dfrac{\pi}{4}, \dfrac{\pi}{3}$, and $\dfrac{\pi}{2}$.

Some of this material may have been covered in earlier courses.

Investigation

a) Diagram 1 shows an angle of $45°$ $\left(\text{or } \dfrac{\pi}{4} \text{ radians}\right)$ in standard position. The terminal arm has a length of 1 unit. An isosceles triangle has been drawn.

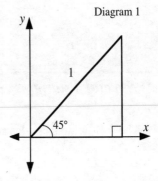

Diagram 1

i) Determine the length of the equal sides of the isosceles triangle. Give your answer as an exact value with a rational denominator.

ii) Use SOHCAHTOA or the x, y, r formulas to complete the following.

$\sin 45° = \qquad \cos 45° = \qquad \tan 45° =$

$\sin \dfrac{\pi}{4} = \qquad \cos \dfrac{\pi}{4} = \qquad \tan \dfrac{\pi}{4} =$

b) Diagram 2 shows an angle of $60°$ $\left(\text{or } \dfrac{\pi}{3} \text{ radians}\right)$ in standard position. The terminal arm has a length of 1 unit.

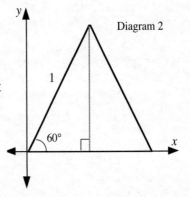

Diagram 2

An equilateral triangle is drawn whose equal sides are 1 unit and a vertical altitude is drawn which divides the equilateral triangle into two congruent triangles.

i) Determine the length of the altitude.

ii) Complete :

$\sin 60° = \qquad \cos 60° = \qquad \tan 60° =$

$\sin \dfrac{\pi}{3} = \qquad \cos \dfrac{\pi}{3} = \qquad \tan \dfrac{\pi}{3} =$

c) Diagram 3 shows an angle of 30° $\left(\text{or } \dfrac{\pi}{6} \text{ radians}\right)$ in standard position. The terminal arm has a length of 1 unit.

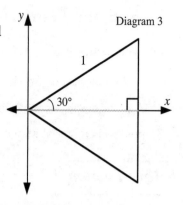

Diagram 3

An equilateral triangle (congruent to the one in b)) is drawn whose equal sides are 1 unit. A horizontal altitude is drawn which divides the equilateral triangle into two congruent triangles.

Complete:

$\sin 30° = \qquad \cos 30° = \qquad \tan 30° =$

$\sin \dfrac{\pi}{6} = \qquad \cos \dfrac{\pi}{6} = \qquad \tan \dfrac{\pi}{6} =$

Special Triangles

The following triangles were developed in the investigation.

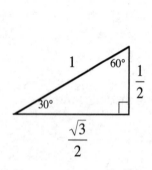

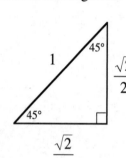

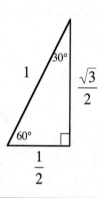

a) Complete the following table.

θ	30°	45°	60°
θ	$\dfrac{\pi}{6}$	$\dfrac{\pi}{4}$	$\dfrac{\pi}{3}$
$\sin \theta$			
$\cos \theta$			
$\tan \theta$			

b) If in each triangle the horizontal distance is x, the vertical distance is y, and the hypotenuse is 1, express the following trigonometric ratios in terms of x and/or y.

i)   sine ratio

ii)   cosine ratio

iii)   tangent ratio

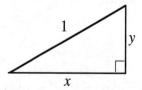

Creating The Unit Circle

The three triangles from the previous page are placed in quadrant one on a Cartesian Plane.

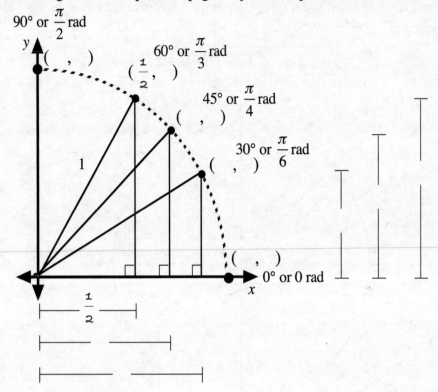

a) Write the lengths of the horizontal and vertical line segments indicated and the coordinates of the five points marked.

b) How do the coordinates of the points relate to the measure of the rotation angles?

c) Complete the chart.

d) Explain why $\tan \dfrac{\pi}{2}$ is undefined.

θ	0°	30°	45°	60°	90°
θ	0	$\dfrac{\pi}{6}$	$\dfrac{\pi}{4}$	$\dfrac{\pi}{3}$	$\dfrac{\pi}{2}$
$\sin\theta$					
$\cos\theta$					
$\tan\theta$					

e) Complete the following:
  • The sine ratios increase from ___ to ___. The cosine ratios decrease from ___ to ___.

  • The tangent ratios are equal to the _____ ratios divided by the _____ ratios.

Complete Assignment Question #1

The Unit Circle

The **unit circle** can be formed by reflecting the above diagram in the *x*-axis, in the *y*-axis, and in both the *x*-axis and the *y*-axis.

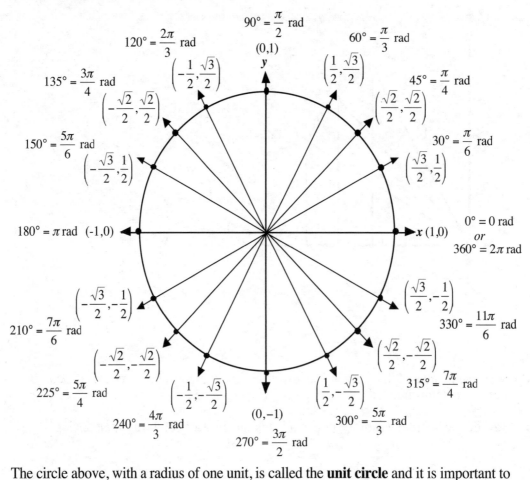

The circle above, with a radius of one unit, is called the **unit circle** and it is important to understand how it works.

Recall the formulas $\sin \theta = \dfrac{y}{r}$, $\cos \theta = \dfrac{x}{r}$, $\tan \theta = \dfrac{y}{x}$, and $\cot \theta = \dfrac{x}{y}$.

- In the unit circle, where $r = 1$, we have:

$$\sin \theta = \underline{\hspace{1cm}} \qquad \text{and} \qquad \cos \theta = \underline{\hspace{1cm}}$$

- Every point on the unit circle has coordinates (x, y) which can be written as $(\cos \theta, \sin \theta)$

- $\tan \theta = \dfrac{\sin \theta}{\cos \theta}$ - $\cot \theta = \dfrac{\cos \theta}{\sin \theta}$

Class Ex. #1

Use the unit circle to find the exact value of all the trigonometric ratios for a rotation angle of 300°. Give each answer with a rational denominator.

sin 300° =   cos 300° =   tan 300° =

csc 300° =   sec 300° =   cot 300° =

Class Ex. #2

Use the unit circle to find the exact value of

a) $\cos \dfrac{3\pi}{4}$ **b)** $\cot \dfrac{5\pi}{3}$ **c)** $\tan 600°$ **d)** $\csc 3\pi$

Class Ex. #3

Use a calculator to determine, to four decimal places, the coordinates of the point on the unit circle that corresponds to a rotation of $\dfrac{2}{5}\pi$.

Class Ex. #4

$P\left(\dfrac{\sqrt{2}}{2}, -\dfrac{\sqrt{2}}{2}\right)$ and $Q\left(-\dfrac{1}{2}, \dfrac{\sqrt{3}}{2}\right)$ are two points on the unit circle. If an object rotates counterclockwise from point P to point Q, through what angle has it rotated? Answer in degrees and in radians.

Class Ex. #5

Without using a graphing calculator, determine the exact value of $\log_2\left(\cos \dfrac{7\pi}{4}\right)$.

Class Ex. #6

The point $A(-0.6157, -0.7880)$ lies on the unit circle. Determine the value of θ, where θ is the angle made by the positive x-axis and the line passing though A.

Alternative Method to the Unit Circle: Using Reference Triangles

We have summarized the exact values of trigonometric ratios for

$0°$ (0 rad), $30°$ $\left(\dfrac{\pi}{6} \text{ rad}\right)$, $45°$ $\left(\dfrac{\pi}{4} \text{ rad}\right)$, $60°$ $\left(\dfrac{\pi}{3} \text{ rad}\right)$ and $90°$ $\left(\dfrac{\pi}{2} \text{ rad}\right)$ in the following chart.

θ	$0°$	$30°$	$45°$	$60°$	$90°$
θ	0	$\dfrac{\pi}{6}$	$\dfrac{\pi}{4}$	$\dfrac{\pi}{3}$	$\dfrac{\pi}{2}$
$\sin\theta$	0	$\dfrac{1}{2}$	$\dfrac{\sqrt{2}}{2}$	$\dfrac{\sqrt{3}}{2}$	1
$\cos\theta$	1	$\dfrac{\sqrt{3}}{2}$	$\dfrac{\sqrt{2}}{2}$	$\dfrac{1}{2}$	0
$\tan\theta$	0	$\dfrac{\sqrt{3}}{3}$	1	$\sqrt{3}$	undefined

This chart should be memorized.

We can use the above table together with the concept of reference angles and the CAST rule to determine the exact values of the trigonometric ratios of multiples of the above angles in quadrants 2, 3, and 4.

Complete the work below to determine the exact values of

a) $\sin 210°$

Solution

A rotation angle of $210°$ has a reference angle of $30°$.

In quadrant 3 the sine ratio is negative.

$\sin 210° = -\sin 30°$

$\sin 210° =$

b) $\cos \dfrac{5\pi}{3}$

Solution

A rotation angle of $\dfrac{5\pi}{3}$ has a reference angle of ____

In quadrant ____ the cosine ratio is _____ .

$\cos \dfrac{5\pi}{3} =$

$\cos \dfrac{5\pi}{3} =$

c) $\tan (-225)°$

Solution

Complete Assignment Questions #2 - #10

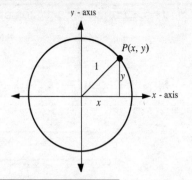

y - axis

P(x, y)

1

y

x

x - axis

The Equation of the Unit Circle

Let $P(x, y)$ be any point on the unit circle as shown in the diagram.

Use the Pythagorean Theorem to determine the equation of the unit circle.

The equation of the unit circle is _____ .

The Equation of a Circle with Centre at the Origin and Radius r

Let (x, y) be any point on the circle with centre $(0, 0)$ and radius r.

Use the Pythagorean Theorem to determine the equation of the circle.

The equation of a circle with centre $(0, 0)$ and radius r is _____ .

Class Ex. #7   Determine which of the following points lie on the unit circle.

a) $\left(\dfrac{1}{2}, \dfrac{1}{2}\right)$ **b)** $\left(\dfrac{16}{65}, -\dfrac{63}{65}\right)$ **c)** $\left(-\dfrac{2}{3}, \dfrac{\sqrt{5}}{3}\right)$

Class Ex. #8   The point $P\left(-\dfrac{1}{5}, y\right)$ lies on the unit circle in quadrant 3.

a) Determine the value of y.

b) The point P lies on the terminal arm of a rotation angle θ. Determine the exact values of $\sec \theta$ and $\cot \theta$.

c) Determine the value of θ to the nearest tenth of a radian if $0 \le \theta \le 2\pi$.

Class Ex. #9

a) Determine the equation of a circle with centre at the origin and radius 8 units.

b) If the point $\left(-4, b\sqrt{3}\right)$ lies on the circle, determine all possible values of b.

Complete Assignment Questions #11 - #16

Assignment

1. The diagram on page 537 has been reflected in the *x*-axis, the *y*-axis, and in both axes to produce the diagram below.

Complete the diagram by writing the coordinates and the rotation angle (in degrees and in radians) for each point on the circumference of the circle.

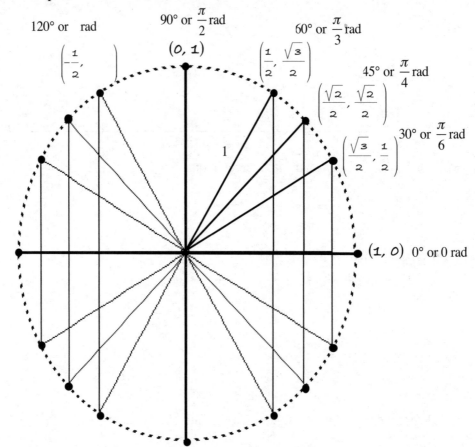

2. Use either the unit circle or a reference triangle to determine the exact value of the following.

    a) $\cos 150°$ **b)** $\sin 315°$ **c)** $\sin (-30)°$

    d) $\tan 240°$ **e)** $\tan 480°$ **f)** $\cos^2 225°$

3. Determine the exact value of the following.

    a) $\sin \dfrac{5\pi}{3}$ **b)** $\tan \dfrac{7\pi}{6}$ **c)** $\cos \left(-\dfrac{2\pi}{3}\right)$

    d) $\sin (-\pi)$ **e)** $\cos \left(-\dfrac{5\pi}{3}\right)$ **f)** $\tan^2 \dfrac{2\pi}{3}$

4. Determine the exact value of the following.

    a) $\sec 300°$ **b)** $\cot \dfrac{5\pi}{6}$ **c)** $\csc \left(-\dfrac{5\pi}{3}\right)$

    d) $\cot 930°$ **e)** $\sec \dfrac{3\pi}{2}$ **f)** $\csc 5\pi$

5. State the exact coordinates of the point on the unit circle that correspond to each rotation.

   a) $\dfrac{3}{2}\pi$ radians

   b) 360°

   c) $\dfrac{7\pi}{6}$

6. Use a calculator to determine, to four decimal places, the coordinates of the point on the unit circle that corresponds to each rotation.

   a) 175°

   b) $\dfrac{13\pi}{10}$ radians

7. The point T (0.4695, –0.8829) lies on the unit circle. Determine the value of θ, in degrees, where θ is the angle made by the positive x-axis and the line passing through T.

 Note **Do not use technology to answer questions #8, #9, and #10.**

8. $P\left(-\dfrac{1}{2}, -\dfrac{\sqrt{3}}{2}\right)$ and $Q\left(\dfrac{\sqrt{3}}{2}, \dfrac{1}{2}\right)$ are two points on the unit circle. If an object rotates counterclockwise from point P to point Q, through what angle has it rotated? Answer in degrees and in radians.

9. Determine the exact value of

   a) $\log_3\left(\cot \dfrac{4\pi}{3}\right)$

   b) $\log_4 (\csc 510°)$

   c) $\sin^2 \dfrac{3\pi}{4} + \cos^2 \dfrac{3\pi}{4}$

10. Find the measure of θ where $0 \le \theta \le 2\pi$.

   a) $\sin \theta = -\dfrac{\sqrt{3}}{2}$

   b) $\tan \theta = 0$

   c) $\tan \theta$ is undefined

11. Write the equation of the following.

    a) the unit circle   **b)** circle with centre $(0,0)$ and radius $\sqrt{10}$

    c) circle with centre $(0,0)$ and passing through the point $(-8,6)$

12. The point $A\left(x, \dfrac{\sqrt{5}}{5}\right)$ lies on the unit circle in quadrant 2.

    a) Determine the value of x. Answer as a radical with a rational denominator.

    b) The point A lies on the terminal arm of a rotation angle θ.
        Determine the exact values of $\tan \theta$ and $\csc \theta$.

    c) Determine the value of θ to the nearest tenth of a radian if $0 \le \theta \le 2\pi$.

13. If the point $\left(-a, a\sqrt{2}\right)$ lies on the circle with centre $(0,0)$ and radius 12, determine all possible values of a.

14. The exact value of $\sec\left(-\dfrac{3\pi}{4}\right)$ can be written in the form $k\sqrt{2}$. The value of k is

    A.   1
    B.   −1
    C.   2
    D.   −2

15. Which one of the following points does not lie on the unit circle?

   A. $(-1, 0)$

   B. $\left(-\dfrac{3}{4}, \dfrac{\sqrt{7}}{4}\right)$

   C. $\left(\dfrac{2}{5}, \dfrac{3}{5}\right)$

   D. $\left(-\dfrac{8}{17}, -\dfrac{15}{17}\right)$

Numerical Response

16. The smallest value of θ for which $\cot\theta$ is undefined in the interval $[90°, 360°]$ is _____ .

(Record your answer in the numerical response box from left to right.)

Answer Key

1. See page 534

2. a) $-\dfrac{\sqrt{3}}{2}$ b) $-\dfrac{\sqrt{2}}{2}$ c) $-\dfrac{1}{2}$ d) $\sqrt{3}$ e) $-\sqrt{3}$ f) $\dfrac{1}{2}$

3. a) $-\dfrac{\sqrt{3}}{2}$ b) $\dfrac{\sqrt{3}}{3}$ c) $-\dfrac{1}{2}$ d) 0 e) $\dfrac{1}{2}$ f) 3

4. a) 2 b) $-\sqrt{3}$ c) $\dfrac{2\sqrt{3}}{3}$ d) $\sqrt{3}$ e) undefined   f) undefined

5. a) $(0, -1)$ b) $(1, 0)$ c) $\left(-\dfrac{\sqrt{3}}{2}, -\dfrac{1}{2}\right)$

6. a) $(-0.9962, 0.0872)$ b) $(-0.5878, -0.8090)$

7. $298°$ **8.** $150°$ or $\dfrac{5\pi}{6}$ radians   **9.** a) $-\dfrac{1}{2}$ b) $\dfrac{1}{2}$ c) 1

10. a) $\dfrac{4\pi}{3}, \dfrac{5\pi}{3}$ b) $0, \pi, 2\pi$ c) $\dfrac{\pi}{2}, \dfrac{3\pi}{2}$

11. a) $x^2 + y^2 = 1$ b) $x^2 + y^2 = 10$ c) $x^2 + y^2 = 100$

12. a) $-\dfrac{2\sqrt{5}}{5}$ b) $\tan\theta = -\dfrac{1}{2}$, $\csc\theta = \sqrt{5}$ c) 2.7

13. $\pm 4\sqrt{3}$ **14.** B   **15.** C   **16.**
1	8	0	

Trigonometry - Functions and Graphs Lesson #6:
Graphing Primary Trigonometric Functions

Periodic Functions

A **periodic function** is a function whose graph repeats regularly over some interval of the domain. The length of this interval is called the **period** of the function.

The **amplitude** of a periodic function is defined as half the distance between the maximum and minimum values of the function.

Class Ex. #1

Determine the period and the amplitude for each of the following periodic functions.

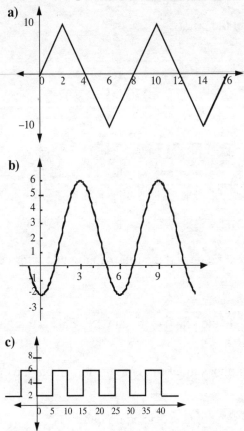

a)

b)

c)

Graphing the Primary Trigonometric Functions

In this lesson we will learn the graphs of $y = \sin x$, $y = \cos x$, and $y = \tan x$.

To investigate the graphs of trigonometric functions we will use the table of values method to graph each function on a domain of $0° \le x \le 360°$ and use the graphing calculator to complete the graph.

We will develop the graph of $y = \sin x$ as a class lesson;
the graphs of $y = \cos x$ and $y = \tan x$ will be assignment questions.

Exploration │ *Graphing y = sin x where x is in Degrees*

a) Complete the following table of values for domain $0° \le x \le 360°$. Give your answers to two decimal places where necessary.

x	0°	30°	60°	90°	120°	150°	180°
$y = \sin x$							

x	210°	240°	270°	300°	330°	360°
$y = \sin x$						

b) Plot the points on the grid below. Do not join the points.

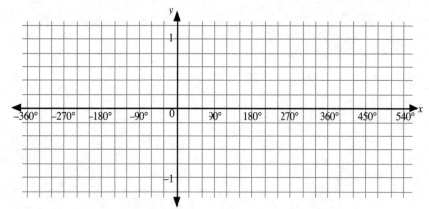

c) Graph $y = \sin x$ on your calculator using degree mode and the following window format.
$$x: [-360, 540, 30]$$
$$y: [-1.2, 1.2, 0.2]$$

d) On the grid, copy the graph from c) to complete the graph of $y = \sin x$, $-360° \le x \le 540°$.

• $y = \sin x$ is a periodic function whose graph continues indefinitely to the left and to the right.

• The graph shown in b) is a partial graph of $y = \sin x$ on a restricted domain.

Class Ex. #2

State the following for the function $y = \sin x$, where x is defined on the set of real numbers and is expressed in degrees.

a) Domain _____

b) Range _____

c) Amplitude _____

d) Period _____

e) x-intercept(s)_____

f) y-intercept(s)_____

Class Ex. #3

A student was asked to reproduce the graph in Exploration b) in radian mode.

a) Write down the graphing calculator window format the student should use.

b) Sketch the graph of $y = \sin x$ for $0 \le x \le 2\pi$ showing the intercepts.

Complete Assignment Questions #1 - #12

Assignment

1. a) Complete the following table of values for domain $0 \le x \le 2\pi$. Give your answers to two decimal places where necessary.

x	0	$\dfrac{\pi}{6}$	$\dfrac{\pi}{3}$	$\dfrac{\pi}{2}$	$\dfrac{2\pi}{3}$	$\dfrac{5\pi}{6}$	π
$y = \cos x$							

x	$\dfrac{7\pi}{6}$	$\dfrac{4\pi}{3}$	$\dfrac{3\pi}{2}$	$\dfrac{5\pi}{3}$	$\dfrac{11\pi}{6}$	2π
$y = \cos x$						

b) Plot the points on the grid below. Do not join the points.

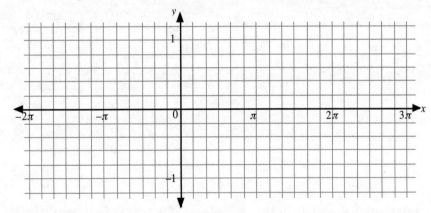

c) Graph $y = \cos x$ on your calculator using radian mode and the following window format.

$$x: [-2\pi, 3\pi, \frac{\pi}{6}]$$
$$y: [-1.2, 1.2, 0.2]$$

d) On the grid, copy the graph from c) to complete the graph of $y = \cos x$, $-2\pi \le x \le 3\pi$.

2. State the following for the function $y = \cos x$, where x is defined on the set of real numbers and is expressed in radians.

   a) Domain _____

   b) Range _____

   c) Amplitude _____

   d) Period _____

   e) x-intercept(s)_____

   f) y-intercept(s)_____

3. A student was asked to reproduce one complete cycle of the graph of $y = \cos x$ starting from zero degrees.

   a) Write down a graphing calculator window format the student could use.

   b) Sketch the graph of $y = \cos x$, $0° \le x \le 360°$, showing the intercepts.

4. Complete the following:

   a) When $\sin x$ has a maximum value, the value of $\cos x$ is _____.

   b) When $\sin x$ has a minimum value, the value of $\cos x$ is _____.

   c) When $\sin x$ has a value of zero, the value of $\cos x$ is _____.

5. **a)** Using the same grid sketch the graph of $y = \sin x$ and $y = \cos x$ for domain $-\pi \le x \le 2\pi$.

   b) For what values of x, in the domain $0 \le x \le 2\pi$, do $\sin x$ and $\cos x$ have the same value?

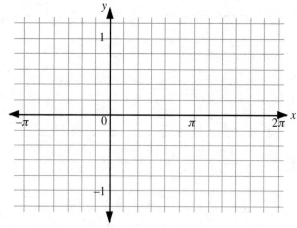

   c) What is the minimum horizontal translation applied to the graph of $y = \cos x$ which would result in the graph of $y = \sin x$?

   d) If $\sin x = \cos(x - c)$ for $x \in R$, find the smallest positive value of c.

   e) If $\cos x = \sin(x - k)$ for $x \in R$, find a value for k.

6. a) Complete the following table of values for domain $0° \le x \le 180°$. Give your answers to two decimal places where necessary.

x	0°	15°	30°	45°	60°	75°	90°
$y = \tan x$							

x	105°	120°	135°	150°	165°	180°
$y = \tan x$						

b) Plot the points on the grid below. Do not join the points.

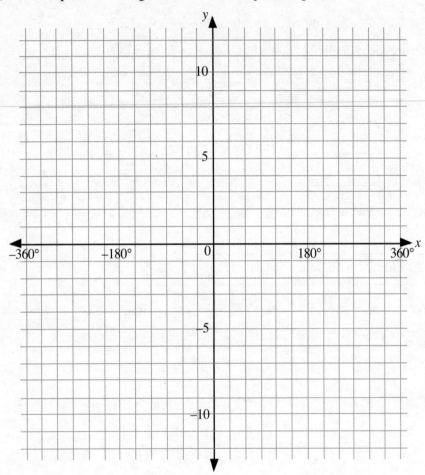

c) To investigate what happens to the graph of $y = \tan x$ as x approaches 90°, complete the following table.

x	80°	85°	89°	89.9°	89.99°	89.999°
$y = \tan x$						

x	100°	95°	91°	90.1°	90.01°	90.001°
$y = \tan x$						

d) To graph $y = \tan x$ on your calculator using degree mode, use the following instructions:

Step 1: Enter $y = \tan x$ using the $\boxed{\text{Y=}}$ key.

Step 2: Press the $\boxed{\text{Zoom}}$ key.

Step 3: Access "ZTrig" and press $\boxed{\text{Enter}}$.

e) Write down the graphing calculator window format for "ZTrig".

f) On the grid in b) complete the graph of $y = \tan x$ for domain $-360° \le x \le 360°$.

g) Is $y = \tan x$ a periodic function? If so, what is the period?

h) Does the concept of amplitude apply to the graph of $y = \tan x$?

7. State the following for the function $y = \tan x$, $0° \le x \le 360°$.

a) Domain _____

b) Range _____

c) Period _____

d) x-intercept(s) _____

e) y-intercept(s)_____

f) Equations of vertical asymptotes _____

Multiple Choice | Questions #8 - #11 refer to the function $f(x) = \tan x$, $x \in R$.

8. The domain of the function is

A. $x \ne n\pi, \ n \in I$

B. $x \ne \dfrac{n\pi}{2}, \ n \in I$

C. $x \ne \dfrac{\pi}{2} + n\pi, \ n \in I$

D. $x \in R$

9. The asymptotes of the graph of the function are

A. $x = n\pi, \ n \in I$

B. $x = \dfrac{n\pi}{2}, \ n \in I$

C. $x = \dfrac{\pi}{2} + n\pi, \ n \in I$

D. $x = 2n\pi, \ n \in I$

10. The range of the function is

A. $x \ne \dfrac{\pi}{2} + n\pi, \ n \in I$

B. $x \in R$

C. $f(x) \ne \dfrac{\pi}{2} + n\pi, \ n \in I$

D. $f(x) \in R$

11. The zeros of the function are

A. $x = n\pi, \ n \in I$

B. $x = \dfrac{n\pi}{2}, \ n \in I$

C. $x = \dfrac{\pi}{2} + n\pi, \ n \in I$

D. $x = 2n\pi, \ n \in I$

12. Which of the following statements is incorrect?

A. The graph of $y = \sin x$ has an x-intercept of π.

B. The graph of $y = \cos x$ has a minimum value when $x = \pi$.

C. The graph of $y = \tan x$ has a an x-intercept of π.

D. The graph of $y = \cos x$ has an x-intercept of π.

Answer Key

1. a)

x	0	$\frac{\pi}{6}$	$\frac{\pi}{3}$	$\frac{\pi}{2}$	$\frac{2\pi}{3}$	$\frac{5\pi}{6}$	π
$y = \cos x$	1	0.87	0.5	0	–0.5	–0.87	–1

x	$\frac{7\pi}{6}$	$\frac{4\pi}{3}$	$\frac{3\pi}{2}$	$\frac{5\pi}{3}$	$\frac{11\pi}{6}$	2π
$y = \cos x$	–0.87	–0.5	0	0.5	0.87	1

d)

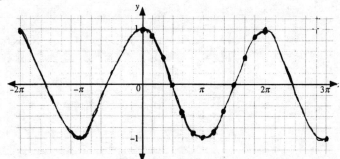

2. a) $x \in R$ **b)** $\{y \,|\, -1 \le y \le 1, y \in R\}$ **c)** 1   **d)** 2π **e)** $\frac{\pi}{2} + n\pi, n \in I$ **f)** 1

3. a) $x:[0, 360, 30]$ $y:[-1.2, 1.2, 0.2]$ answers may vary   **b)**

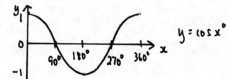

4. a) 0   **b)** 0   **c)** ± 1

5. a) $\to$ $\to$ $\to$ $\to$ $\to$ $\to$

b) $\frac{\pi}{4}$ and $\frac{5\pi}{4}$

c) $\frac{\pi}{2}$ radians to the right

d) $\frac{\pi}{2}$ **e)** $-\frac{\pi}{2}$

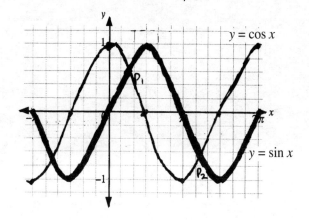

6 . a)

x	0°	15°	30°	45°	60°	75°	90°
$y = \tan x$	0	0.27	0.58	1	1.73	3.73	undefined

x	105°	120°	135°	150°	165°	180°
$y = \tan x$	−3.73	−1.73	−1	−0.58	−0.27	0

c)

x	80°	85°	89°	89.9°	89.99°	89.999°
$y = \tan x$	5.67	11.43	57.29	573	5730	57 296

x	100°	95°	91°	90.1°	90.01°	90.001°
$y = \tan x$	−5.67	−11.43	−57.29	−573	−5730	−57 296

e) x:[−352.5, 352.5, 90] y:[−4, 4, 1] **f)**
g) Yes, the period is 180°
h) no

7 . a) $\{x \mid x \neq 90°, 270° \; x \in R\}$
 b) $y \in R$
 c) 180°
 d) 0°, 180°, 360°
 e) 0
 f) $x = 90°, x = 270°$

8 . C   **9 .** C

10 . D   **11 .** A

12 . D

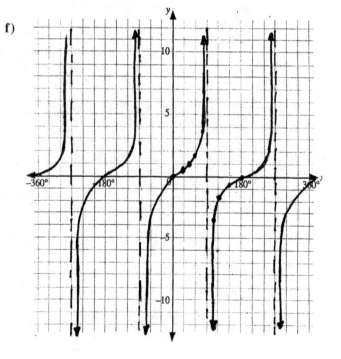

Trigonometry - Functions and Graphs Lesson #7:
Transformations of Trigonometric Functions - Part One

In the next two lessons we will consider the graphs of the functions whose equations are

$$y = a \sin[b(x - c)] + d \quad \text{and} \quad y = a \cos[b(x - c)] + d$$

and relate them to the graphs of the functions whose equations are $y = \sin x$ and $y = \cos x$.

In this lesson we concentrate on the effects of the parameters a and b.

Class Ex. #1

a) Use the knowledge gained from the transformation unit to describe how the graph of the given function compares to the graph of $y = \sin x$, where x is in degrees.

i) $y = 2 \sin x$

ii) $y = \sin 2x$

iii) $y = -3 \sin x$

iv) $y = \sin (-3x)$

b) In which of the above examples is there a change in amplitude compared to the graph of $y = \sin x$?

c) In which of the above examples is there a change in period compared to the graph of $y = \sin x$?

d) Complete the table. Use a graphing calculator if necessary.

e) Describe the effect of the parameter "a" on the graphs of $y = a \sin x$.

f) Describe the effect of the parameter "b" on the graphs of $y = \sin bx$.

Equation	Amplitude	Period
$y = \sin x$		
$y = 2 \sin x$		
$y = \sin 2x$		
$y = -3 \sin x$		
$y = \sin (-3x)$		
$y = 5 \sin 4x$		
$y = \dfrac{1}{3} \sin \dfrac{1}{2}x$		
$y = a \sin bx$		

g) Would you expect similar effects on the graph of $y = a \cos bx$? Investigate if necessary.

Effects of a and b in $y = a \sin bx$, $y = a \cos bx$, and $y = a \tan bx$

Changing the parameter "a" on the graphs of $y = a \sin x$ and $y = a \cos x$ results in a vertical stretch about the x-axis with the following:

- If $a > 0$, the result is a vertical stretch of factor a about the x-axis.

- If $a < 0$, the result is a reflection in the x-axis
  and a vertical stretch of factor $|a|$ about the x-axis.

Changing the parameter "a" on the graph of $y = a \tan x$ also results in a vertical stretch of factor "a" about the x-axis.

Changing the parameter "b" on the graphs of $y = \sin bx$, $y = \cos bx$, and $y = \tan bx$ results in a horizontal stretch about the y-axis with the following:

- If $b > 0$, the result is a horizontal stretch of factor $\dfrac{1}{b}$ about the y-axis.

- If $b < 0$, the result is a reflection in the y-axis
  and a horizontal stretch of factor $\dfrac{1}{|b|}$ about the y-axis.

$y = a \sin bx$ or $y = a \cos bx$

amplitude $= \|a\| = \dfrac{\text{Max} - \text{Min}}{2}$
period $= \dfrac{360°}{\|b\|}$ (for degree measure)
period $= \dfrac{2\pi}{\|b\|}$ (for radian measure)

$y = a \tan bx$

amplitude is not applicable
period $= \dfrac{180°}{\|b\|}$ (for degree measure)
period $= \dfrac{\pi}{\|b\|}$ (for radian measure)

Hints for Graphing a Trigonometric Function Manually

- Sketch the primary trigonometric graph, i.e. $y = \sin x$ or $y = \cos x$.

- Adjust the basic graph for any change in amplitude by considering the max and min points.

- Adjust the new graph for any change in period by dividing the period into four parts using the maximum and minimum points, and the points where the graph intersects the mid-line (the horizontal line running through the centre of the graph).

Class Ex. #2   Consider the graph of $y = 4 \cos 2x$, $0 \le x \le 2\pi$.

a) State the amplitude and period.

b) Sketch the graph on the grid. Use a graphing calculator to verify.

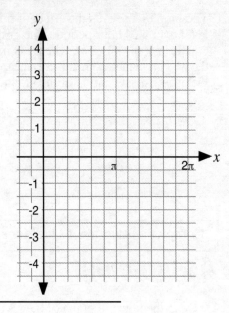

Class Ex. #3   Write the equation of

a) a sine function having an amplitude of $\dfrac{2}{3}$ and a period of $\dfrac{\pi}{6}$

b) a cosine function having an amplitude of 3 and a period of 720°

c) a tangent function having a period of $\dfrac{\pi}{2}$.

Class Ex. #4   Consider the partial graph shown.

a) State the amplitude and period of the graph.

b) Determine the equation of the sine function which the graph represents.

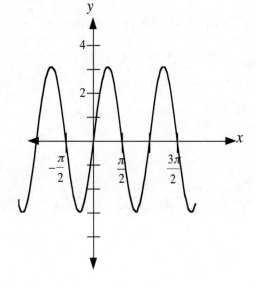

Class Ex. #5

The graph represents the effect of tides on mean sea level over a 24 hour period. The graph has equation $h(t) = a \cos bt$, where t is in hours and h is the height, in metres, relative to mean sea level. Determine the equation of the graph.

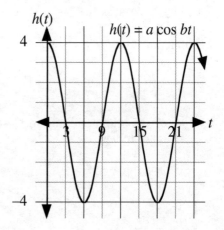

Complete Assignment Questions #1 - #16

Assignment

1. Describe how the graph of the given function compares to the graph of $y = \cos x$.

   a) $y = 5 \cos x$

   b) $y = 2 \cos \frac{1}{2}x$

   c) $y = -\frac{1}{3} \cos 4x$

   d) $y = 0.2 \cos (-6x)$

2. State the amplitude.

   a) $y = 5 \sin x$ **b)** $y = \cos 3x$ **c)** $y = \frac{7}{3} \sin 2x$ **d)** $y = -4 \cos \frac{5}{6}\theta$

3. State the period in degrees.

   a) $y = 6 \sin x$ **b)** $y = \tan 3x$ **c)** $y = \frac{2}{3} \cos \frac{x}{7}$ **d)** $y = -2 \tan \frac{2}{3}\theta$

4. State the period in radians.

   a) $y = 7 \tan x$ **b)** $y = \cos 3x$ **c)** $y = \frac{1}{4} \sin \frac{x}{3}$ **d)** $y = 5 \tan \frac{1}{2}\theta$

5. Write the equation of a **sine** function with the given amplitude and period.

  a) amplitude 2, period 1080°   **b)** amplitude 8, period $\dfrac{\pi}{4}$ **c)** amplitude $\dfrac{3}{2}$, period 6π

6. Write the equation of a **cosine** function with the given amplitude and period.

  a) amplitude 1, period 180°   **b)** amplitude 5, period $\dfrac{4\pi}{3}$ **c)** amplitude $\dfrac{5}{3}$, period 3π

7. Write the equation of a **tangent** function with the given period.

  a) period 45°   **b)** period $\dfrac{4\pi}{3}$

8. Determine the equation of each graph in the form.

  a) $y = a \sin bx$

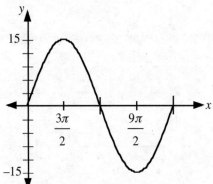

  b) $y = a \cos bx$

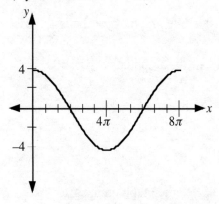

9. The trigonometric graph shown has a maximum value of 3 and a minimum value of −3. Determine the equation of the graph in the form $y = a \sin bx$.

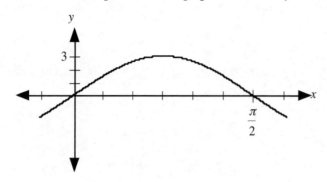

10. The trigonometric graph shown has a maximum value of 5 and a minimum value of −5. Determine the equation of the graph in the form $y = a \cos bx$.

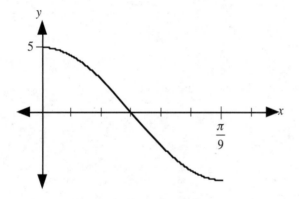

11. Consider the graph of $y = 3 \cos \dfrac{x}{2}$, $0 \le x \le 2\pi$.

a) State the amplitude and period.

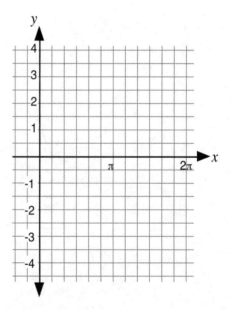

b) Sketch the graph on the grid.
Use a graphing calculator to verify.

12. The graph represents the change in sea level over a 24 hour period. The graph has equation $h(t) = a \sin bt$, where t is in hours and h is the height, in metres, relative to mean sea level.

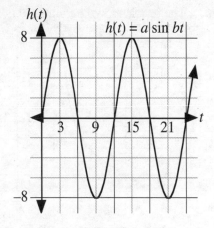

a) Determine the equation of the graph.

b) Calculate the height above mean sea level, to the nearest tenth, when $t = 4$.

13. a) Which transformations applied to the graph of $y = \sin x$ result in the graph shown?

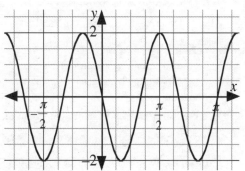

b) Write the equation of the graph in the form $y = a \sin bx$.

14. Which of the following functions does not have a period of π?

    A. $\quad y = \sin 2x$ **B.** $\quad y = \cos 2x$ **C.** $\quad y = \tan 2x$ **D.** $\quad y = \tan x$

15. Which of the following statements is incorrect?

    A.   The maximum value of the graph of $y = 3 \cos 2x$ is 3.

    B.   The graph of $y = 3 \sin 2x$ has a y-intercept of 3.

    C.   The graph of $y = 4 \cos 3x$ has an x-intercept of $\dfrac{\pi}{6}$.

    D.   The graph of $y = 2 \tan 2x$ has an asymptote with equation $x = \dfrac{\pi}{4}$.

16. The graph shown has equation $y = \tan bx$.

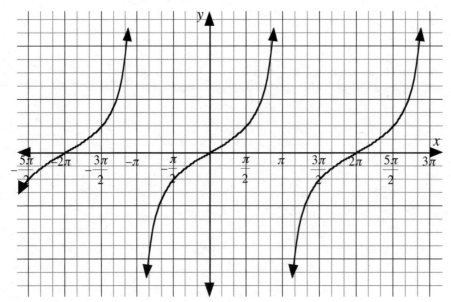

The value of b, to the nearest tenth, is _____ .

(Record your answer in the numerical response box from left to right.)

Answer Key

1. **a)** a vertical stretch by a factor of 5 about the x-axis

    b) a vertical stretch by a factor of 2 about the x-axis and a horizontal stretch by a factor of 2 about the y-axis

    c) a vertical stretch by a factor of $\frac{1}{3}$ about the x-axis, a horizontal stretch

        by a factor of $\frac{1}{4}$ about the y-axis, and a reflection in the x-axis.

    d) a vertical stretch by a factor of 0.2 about the x-axis, a horizontal stretch by a factor of $\frac{1}{6}$

        about the y-axis, and a reflection in the y-axis

2. **a)** 5   **b)** 1   **c)** $\frac{7}{3}$ **d)** 4   **3.** **a)** 360°   **b)** 60°   **c)** 2520°   **d)** 270°

4. **a)** π **b)** $\frac{2\pi}{3}$ **c)** 6π **d)** 2π

5. **a)** $y = 2 \sin \frac{1}{3}x$ **b)** $y = 8 \sin 8x$ **c)** $y = \frac{3}{2} \sin \frac{1}{3}x$

6. **a)** $y = \cos 2x$ **b)** $y = 5 \cos \frac{3}{2}x$ **c)** $y = \frac{5}{3} \cos \frac{2}{3}x$ **7.** **a)** $y = \tan 4x$ **b)** $y = \tan \frac{3}{4}x$

8. **a)** $y = 15 \sin \frac{1}{3}x$ **b)** $y = 4 \cos \frac{1}{4}x$ **9.** $y = 3 \sin 2x$ **10.** $y = 5 \cos 9x$

11. **a)** amp = 3, period = 4π **b)** $\rightarrow$ $\rightarrow$ $\rightarrow$ $\rightarrow$

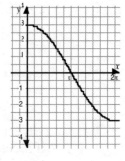

12. **a)** $y = 8 \sin \frac{\pi}{6}t$ **b)** 6.9 metres

13. **a)** a vertical stretch by a factor of 2 about the x-axis, a horizontal stretch by

        a factor of $\frac{1}{3}$ about the y-axis, a reflection in the x-axis

    b) $y = -2 \sin 3x$ or $y = 2 \sin (-3x)$

14. C   **15.** B   **16.** | 0 | . | 5 | |

Trigonometry - Functions and Graphs Lesson #8:
Transformations of Trigonometric Functions - Part Two

In this lesson we will consider the graphs of the functions whose equations are

$$y = a \sin[b(x - c)] + d \quad \text{and} \quad y = a \cos[b(x - c)] + d$$

and relate them to the graphs of the functions whose equations are $y = \sin x$ and $y = \cos x$.

In the first part of the lesson we concentrate on the effects of the parameters c and d.

Class Ex. #1

a) Describe how the graph of the given function compares to the graph of $y = \sin x$, where x is in degrees.

    i) $y = \sin(x - 30°)$

    ii) $y = \sin x + 2$

    iii) $y = \sin(x + 60°) - 1$

    iv) $y - 45 = \sin(x - 45°)$

Note

In trigonometry
- a horizontal translation is called a **horizontal phase shift**, and,
- a vertical translation is called a **vertical displacement**.

Class Ex. #2

Complete the table to describe how the graph of the given function compares to the graph of $y = \sin x$ where x is in radians. Use a graphing calculator if necessary.

Equation	Horizontal Phase Shift	Vertical Displacement
$y = \sin x$		
$y = \sin\left(x - \dfrac{\pi}{4}\right)$		
$y = \sin x + 5$		
$y + \pi = \sin\left(x + \dfrac{3\pi}{2}\right)$		
$y = \sin(x - c) + d$		
$y = a \sin[b(x - c)] + d$		

Would you expect similar effects on the graph of $y = a \cos[b(x - c)] + d$?
Investigate if necessary.

Effects of c and d in y = a sin [b(x − c)] + d and y = a cos [b(x − c)] + d

Changing the parameter "c" on the graphs of
$y = a \sin [b(x − c)] + d$ **and** $y = a \cos [b(x − c)] + d$
results in a horizontal phase shift with the following:

- a horizontal phase shift to the <u>right if $c > 0$</u>
- a horizontal phase shift to the <u>left if $c < 0$</u>

Changing the parameter "d" on the graphs of
$y = a \sin [b(x − c)] + d$ **and** $y = a \cos [b(x − c)] + d$
results in a vertical displacement with the following:

- a vertical displacement <u>up if $d > 0$</u>
- a vertical displacement <u>down if $d < 0$</u>

The vertical displacement is determined from a graph using the formula $d = \dfrac{\text{Max} + \text{Min}}{2}$.

Summary of the Effects of the Parameters a, b, c, and d

For $y = a \sin [b(x − c)] + d$
$y = a \cos [b(x − c)] + d$

amplitude $= |a| = \dfrac{\text{Max} − \text{Min}}{2}$

period $= \dfrac{360°}{|b|}$ (for degree measure)

period $= \dfrac{2\pi}{|b|}$ (for radian measure)

horizontal phase shift $= c$

- to the right if $c > 0$
- to the left if $c < 0$

vertical displacement $= d$

- up if $d > 0$
- down if $d < 0$
- $d = \dfrac{\text{Max} + \text{Min}}{2}$

For $y = a \tan[b(x − c)] + d$

amplitude - not applicable

a value represents a vertical stretch
of factor l*a*l

period $= \dfrac{180°}{|b|}$ (for degree measure)

period $= \dfrac{\pi}{|b|}$ (for radian measure)

horizontal phase shift $= c$

- to the right if $c > 0$
- to the left if $c < 0$

vertical displacement $= d$

- up if $d > 0$
- down if $d < 0$

Class Ex. #3 Consider equations of the form $y = a \sin[b(x - c)] + d$ and $y = a \cos[b(x - c)] + d$, where $a = 1$, and $b = 1$. Write the equation which represents

a) a cosine function having a horizontal phase shift of 75° right

b) a sine function having a horizontal phase shift of $\dfrac{3\pi}{5}$ radians left,
and a vertical displacement 4 units up

Class Ex. #4 Find the amplitude, period, horizontal phase shift, and vertical displacement of the graphs of the following functions defined on $x \in R$.

a) $y = 2 \sin 3(x + \pi) - 4$

b) $y = -\dfrac{2}{3} \cos \dfrac{1}{4}\left(x - \dfrac{\pi}{12}\right) + 3$

Class Ex. #5 Find the amplitude, period, horizontal phase shift, and vertical displacement of the graphs of the following functions defined on $x \in R$.

a) $y = 2 \sin (3x + \pi) - 4$

b) $y = -\cos\left(2x - \dfrac{\pi}{2}\right) + \pi$

c) Compare the answer to Class Ex. #4a and Class Ex. #5a.

Complete Assignment Questions #1 - #2

Class Ex. #6

The graphs from a) - d) represent the same trigonometric function.

a) Write the equation of the graph in the form $y = a \sin (x - c)$ if $a > 0$ and there is a minimum possible horizontal phase shift.

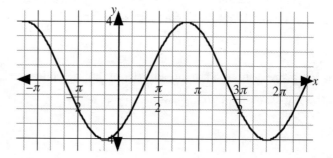

b) Write the equation of the graph in the form $y = a \sin (x - c)$ if $a < 0$ and there is a minimum possible horizontal phase shift.

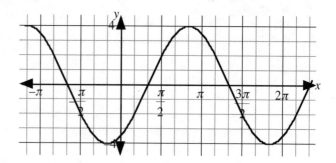

c) Write the equation of the graph in the form $y = a \cos (x - c)$ if $a > 0$ and there is a minimum possible horizontal phase shift.

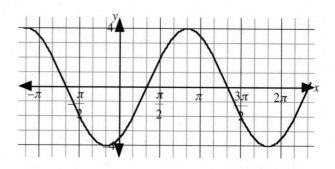

d) Write the equation of the graph in the form $y = a \cos (x - c)$ if $a < 0$ and there is a minimum possible horizontal phase shift.

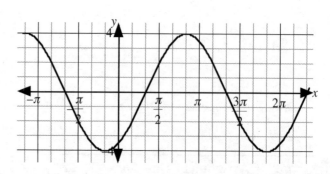

Class Ex. #7

Consider the graph shown.

a) If the graph represents a sine function where $a > 0$, complete the table and write the equation represented by the graph.

Amplitude	
Period	
Min. Horizontal Phase Shift	
Vertical Displacement	

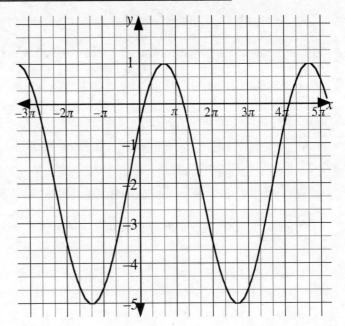

b) Write the equation if the graph in a) represents a sine function where $a < 0$.

c) If the graph represents a cosine function where $a > 0$, complete the table and write the equation represented by the graph.

Amplitude	
Period	
Min. Horizontal Phase Shift	
Vertical Displacement	

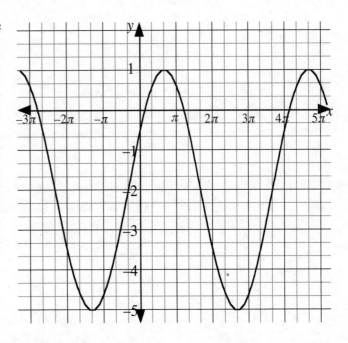

d) Write the equation if the graph in c) represents a cosine function where $a < 0$.

Consider the graphs of the functions $y = a \sin [b(x - c)] + d$ and $y = a \cos [b(x - c)] + d$.

a) Changing which of the parameters a, b, c and d affect the

   i) domain?   **ii)** range?   **iii)** amplitude?   **iv)** period?   **v)** zeros?

b) State the maximum and minimum values of the functions in terms of $a, b, c,$ and d, if $a > 0$.

c) Determine the range of the function $y = 3 \sin 2(x - \pi) - 4$.

> **Complete Assignment Questions #3 - #12**

Assignment

1. Determine the amplitude, period, horizontal phase shift, and the vertical displacement for each function.

   a) $y = \cos \left(x - \dfrac{\pi}{4} \right) + 3$ **b)** $y = 3 \cos \dfrac{1}{2}\left(x - \dfrac{\pi}{2} \right)$ **c)** $y = 3 \cos \dfrac{1}{2}x - \dfrac{\pi}{2}$

   d) $y = \sin \left(4x - \dfrac{\pi}{2} \right)$ **e)** $y = -2 \cos 3(x - 45°) + 4$ **f)** $y = 7 \sin \left(\dfrac{1}{4}x + 20° \right) - 1$

2. a) Determine the equation of a sine function that has a vertical displacement 3 units up, a horizontal phase shift of 60° to the left, a period of 210° and an amplitude of 4.

b) Determine the equation of a cosine function with a vertical displacement 5 units down, a horizontal phase shift of $\dfrac{2\pi}{3}$ radians to the right, a period of $\dfrac{5\pi}{4}$ and an amplitude of 3.

3. Graphs 1 and 2 each represent the graphs of trigonometric functions.

a) Assuming a minimum possible phase shift, write the equation of each graph in the form
$y = a \sin[b(x - c)] + d$ if: **i)** $a > 0$ **ii)** $a < 0$

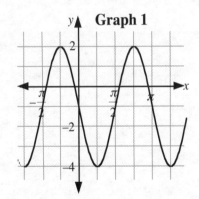

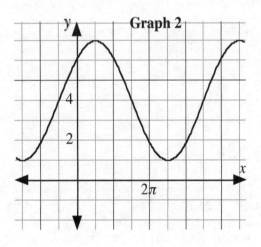

b) Assuming a minimum possible phase shift, write the equation of each graph in the form
$y = a \cos [b(x - c)] + d$ if: **i)** $a > 0$ **ii)** $a < 0$

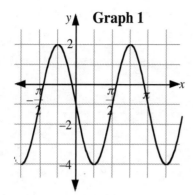

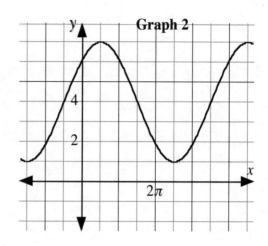

4. The cosine graph shown has a range $-3 \le y \le 9$.
The graph has an equation in the form
$y = a \cos [b(x - c)] + d, a > 0$.

Determine the equation if the graph has a minimum
possible phase shift.

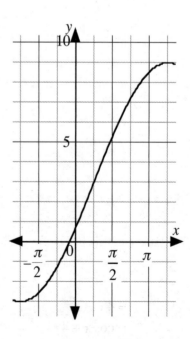

5. The sine graph shown has a maximum value of 20 and
a minimum value of 10. If the graph has a minimum
possible phase shift, determine the equation of the
graph in the form $y = a \sin [b(x - c)] + d$ with $a > 0$.

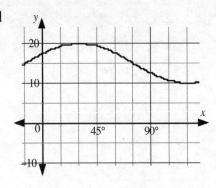

6. Determine the equation of each graph in the form $y = \tan b(x - c)$.

a)

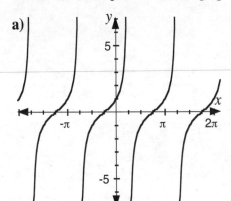

b)

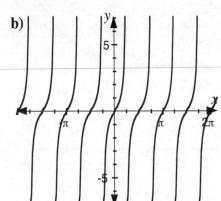

7. Determine the range of the functions represented below.

a) $y = 2 \sin x - 2$

b) $y = 3 \cos \dfrac{1}{2}\left(x - \dfrac{\pi}{2}\right) + 1$

c) $y = -\dfrac{1}{2} \cos 4(x - \pi) - 3$

d) $y = a \sin [b(x - c)] + d$, where $a > 0$

8. Which of the following graphs has the
same x-intercepts as the graph of $y = \cos x$?

   A. $y = \cos 4x$

   B. $y = 4 \cos x$

   C. $y = \cos x + 4$

   D. $y = \cos (x + 4)$

9. Which equation is a tangent function with
period $\dfrac{\pi}{3}$, and a vertical displacement -3?

   A. $y = \tan \dfrac{\pi}{3}x - 3$

   B. $y = \tan 3(x - 3)$

   C. $y = \tan 3x - 3$

   D. $y = \tan 6x - 3$

10. The equation $y = \pi \cos(\pi x - \pi)$ has a period and a horizontal phase shift to the right, respectively, of

   A. π and π
   B. π and 1
   C. 2 and π
   D. 2 and 1

11. Which statement concerning the graph of $y = -4 \cos \dfrac{x}{2} + 2$ is <u>not</u> correct?

   A. The maximum value is 6.
   B. The period is 4π.
   C. The amplitude is -4.
   D. The vertical displacement is 2.

12. The period, to the nearest tenth, of the function $y = \sin 0.25x$, where x is in radians, is _____ .

(Record your answer in the numerical response box from left to right.)

Answer Key

1.

	amplitude	period	phase shift	vertical displacement
a)	1	2π	$\dfrac{\pi}{4}$ right	3 up
b)	3	4π	$\dfrac{\pi}{2}$ right	0
c)	3	4π	0	$\dfrac{\pi}{2}$ down
d)	1	$\dfrac{\pi}{2}$	$\dfrac{\pi}{8}$ right	0
e)	2	120°	45° right	4 up
f)	7	1440°	80° left	1 down

2. **a)** $y = 4 \sin \dfrac{12}{7}(x + 60°) + 3$

   b) $y = 3 \cos \dfrac{8}{5}\left(x - \dfrac{2\pi}{3}\right) - 5$

(Note for **a)** and **b)**: the value of a can also be negative)

3. **a)** **i)**   for $a > 0$, **Graph 1** $y = 3 \sin 2\left(x \pm \dfrac{\pi}{2}\right) - 1$,   **Graph 2** $y = 3 \sin \dfrac{1}{2}\left(x + \dfrac{\pi}{2}\right) + 4$

     ii)   for $a < 0$, **Graph 1** $y = -3 \sin 2x - 1$,   **Graph 2** $y = -3 \sin \dfrac{1}{2}\left(x - \dfrac{3\pi}{2}\right) + 4$

  b) **i)**   for $a > 0$, **Graph 1** $y = 3 \cos 2\left(x + \dfrac{\pi}{4}\right) - 1$,   **Graph 2** $y = 3 \cos \dfrac{1}{2}\left(x - \dfrac{\pi}{2}\right) + 4$

     ii)   for $a < 0$, **Graph 1** $y = -3 \cos 2\left(x - \dfrac{\pi}{4}\right) - 1$,   **Graph 2** $y = -3 \cos \dfrac{1}{2}\left(x + \dfrac{3\pi}{2}\right) + 4$

4. $y = 6 \cos \dfrac{1}{2}\left(x - \dfrac{5\pi}{4}\right) + 3$ **5.** $y = 5 \sin 2(x + 15°) + 15$

6. **a)** $y = \tan\left(x + \dfrac{\pi}{4}\right)$ **b)** $y = \tan 2x$

7. **a)** $\{y \mid -4 \le y \le 0, y \in R\}$ **b)** $\{y \mid -2 \le y \le 4, y \in R\}$

    c) $\left\{y \mid -\dfrac{7}{2} \le y \le -\dfrac{5}{2}, y \in R\right\}$ **d)** $\{y \mid -a + d \le y \le a + d, y \in R\}$

8. B   **9.** C   **10.** D   **11.** C   **12.** | 2 | 5 | . | 1 |

Trigonometry - Functions and Graphs Lesson #9:
Sinusoidal Functions

Sinusoidal Functions

A function whose graph resembles the sine or cosine curve is called a **sinusoidal function**. The graph of a sinusoidal function is called a sinusoidal graph. Many periodic phenomena have sinusoidal graphs, e.g. the time of sunrise as a function of the day of the year, the height of a chair of a ferris wheel as a function of time, the depth of the ocean due to changing tides as a function of time, etc.

In this lesson the equation of the sinusoidal function will be given. In the next lesson we will derive the equation of the sinusoidal function from given information.

Most of the equations used will be functions of time and the variable used will be t. The period of the graph will be in time units. Graphical methods will be used to solve problems and determining a suitable window is an essential feature of the solution.

Class Ex. #1   The depth, d metres, of water in a harbour, t hours after midnight, can be approximated by the function $d(t) = 12 + 5 \cos 0.5t$, where $0 \le t \le 24$.

a) Determine the maximum and minimum depths of water in the harbour.

b) Determine the period of the function.

c) Write a suitable window which can be used to display the graph of the function.

d) What is the depth of water, to the nearest tenth of a metre at 2:00 a.m.?

e) A ship which requires a minimum of 8.5 metres of water is in harbour at midnight. By what time, to the nearest minute, must it leave to prevent grounding?

f) What is the next time, to the nearest necessary minute, that the ship can return to the harbour?

Class Ex. #2

In a certain town in Alberta, the time of sunrise for any day can be found using the formula

$$t = -1.79 \sin\left(2\pi\frac{(d-78)}{365}\right) + 6.3$$

where t is the time in hours after midnight and d is the number of the day in the year.

a) Write a suitable window which can be used to display the graph of the function.

b) Use the formula to determine, to the nearest minute, when the sun rose on May 7, the 127th day of the year.

c) Determine on which days of the year the sun rose at 7 a.m.

Complete Assignment Questions #1 - #7

Assignment

1. The alarm in a noisy factory is a siren whose volume, V decibels, fluctuates so that t seconds after starting, the volume is given by the function $V(t) = 18 \sin \dfrac{\pi}{15} t + 60$.

   a) What are the maximum and minimum volumes of the siren?

   b) Determine the period of the function.

   c) Write a suitable window which can be used to display the graph of the function.

   d) After how many seconds, to the nearest tenth, does the volume first reach 70 decibels?

   e) The background noise level in the factory is 45 decibels. Between which times, to the nearest tenth of a second, in the first cycle is the alarm siren at a lower level than the background noise?

   f) For what percentage, to the nearest per cent, of each cycle is the alarm siren audible over the background factory noise?

2. A top secret satellite is launched into orbit from a remote island not on the equator. When the satellite reaches orbit, it follows a sinusoidal pattern that takes it north and south of the equator (i.e. the equator is used as the horizontal axis). Twelve minutes after it is launched it reaches the farthest point north of the equator. The distance north or south of the equator can be represented by the function $d(t) = 5000 \cos [\frac{\pi}{35}(t-12)]$ where $d(t)$ is the distance, in km, of the satellite north of the equator t minutes after being launched.

a) How far north or south of the equator is the launch site? Answer to the nearest km.

b) Is the satellite north or south of the equator after 20 minutes? What is this distance to the nearest kilometre?

c) When, to the nearest tenth of a minute, will the satellite first be 2500 km south of the equator?

3. The height of a tidal wave approaching the face of the cliff on an island is represented by the equation $h(t) = 7.5 \cos \left(\frac{2\pi}{9.5} t \right)$ where $h(t)$ is the height, in metres, of the wave above normal sea level t minutes after the wave strikes the cliff.

a) What are the maximum and minimum heights of the wave relative to normal sea level?

b) What is the period of the function?

c) How high, to the nearest tenth of a metre, will the wave be, relative to normal sea level, one minute after striking the cliff?

d) Normal sea level is 6 metres at the base of the cliff.
   i) For what values of h would the sea bed be exposed?

   ii) How long, to the nearest tenth of a minute, after the wave strikes the cliff does it take for the sea bed to be exposed?

   iii) For how long, to the nearest tenth of a minute, is the sea bed exposed?

4. The depth of water in a harbour can be modelled by the function $d(t) = -5 \cos \dfrac{\pi}{6}t + 16.4$ where $d(t)$ is the depth in metres and t is the time in hours after low tide.

a) What is the period of the tide?

b) A large cruise ship needs at least 14 metres of water to dock safely. For how many hours per cycle, to the nearest tenth of an hour, can a cruise ship dock safely?

5. A city water authority determined that, under normal conditions, the approximate amount of water, $W(t)$, in millions of litres, stored in a reservoir t months after May 1, 2012, is given by the formula $W(t) = 1.25 - \sin \dfrac{\pi}{6}t$.

a) Sketch the graph of this function over the next three years.

b) In the summer of 2012, the authority decided to carry out the following simulation to determine if they had enough water to cope with a serious fire.

"If, on November 1, 2013, there is a serious fire which requires 300 000 litres of water to be brought under control, will the reservoir run dry if water rationing is not imposed?"

i) Explain how to use the graph in a) to solve the problem.

ii) Will the reservoir run dry if water rationing is not imposed? If so, in what month will this occur?

Use the following information to answer the next two questions

The graph below shows how the number of hours (*h*) of daylight in a European city changes during the year.

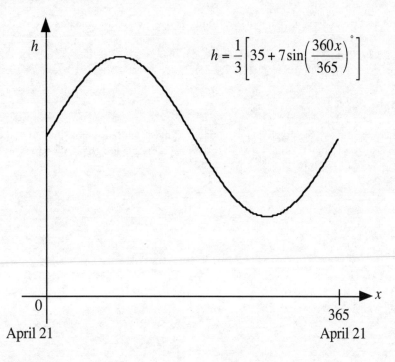

$$h = \frac{1}{3}\left[35 + 7\sin\left(\frac{360x}{365}\right)^{\circ}\right]$$

0   365

April 21   April 21

Numerical Response **6.** Mid-winter is the day with the least hours of daylight. The number of hours of daylight, to the nearest tenth of an hour, that there will be on mid-winter's day is _____ .

(Record your answer in the numerical response box from left to right.)

7. The number of days after April 21 that mid-winter occurs is _____ .

(Record your answer in the numerical response box from left to right.)

Answer Key

1. a) max = 78 dB, min = 42 dB, **b)** 30 s **c)** x: [0, 40, 5] y: [30, 100, 10] answers may vary
 d) 2.8 s **e)** 19.7 s - 25.3 s **f)** 81%

2. a) 2369 km north **b)** 3765 km north **c)** 35.3 minutes

3. a) max = 7.5 m, min = –7.5 m **b)** 9.5 min **c)** 5.9 m
 d) i) $h \leq -6$ **ii)** 3.8 min **iii)** 1.9 min

4. a) 12 h **b)** 7.9 h

5. b) i) After $t = 18$ move the graph down 0.3 units. If the graph falls below the t axis, the reservoir will run dry. *or* Draw the line $y = 0.3$. If the line intersects the graph, the reservoir will run dry.
 ii) in month 26, i.e. July, 2014

6. | 9 | . | 3 | |

7. | 2 | 7 | 4 | |

Trigonometry - Functions and Graphs Lesson #10:
Modelling Sinusoidal Functions

In the previous lesson we were asked to solve problems when we were given the equation of a sinusoidal function.

In this lesson we will derive the equation of the sinusoidal function from a graph.

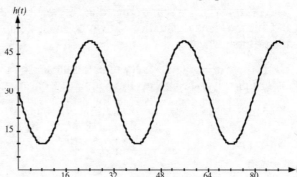

Review

The sinusoidal wave shown has a maximum value of 50 and a minimum value of 10. Write the equation of the sinusoidal wave in the form
$h(t) = a \sin [b(t - c)] + d$, where $a > 0$.

Class Ex. #1

A nail is caught in the tread of a rotating tire at point N in the following sketch.

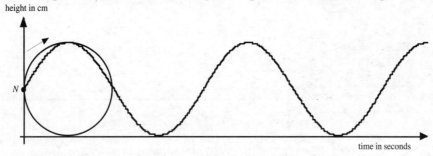

The tire has a diameter of 50 cm and rotates at 10 revolutions per minute. After 4.5 seconds the nail touches the ground.

a) Use the information given to write a scale for each axis.

b) Determine the equation for the height of the nail as a function of time in the form
$h(t) = a \sin bt + d$, where $a > 0$.

c) How far, to the nearest tenth of a centimetre, is the nail above the ground after 6.5 seconds?

Class Ex. #2

The first Ferris Wheel ever built was created by a bridge builder by the name of George W. Ferris in 1893. The diameter of the wheel was approximately 76 metres and the maximum height of the Ferris Wheel was approximately 80 metres. The wheel had 36 wooden carts on the wheel, with each cart able to hold approximately 60 people

The Ferris Wheel was introduced to the world at the 1893 World's Fair in Chicago. The illustration shown below is a copy of a photograph of the original wheel.

Time (t) minutes	Height (h) metres
0	4
2.25	42
4.5	80
6.75	42
9	4

a) If the wheel rotated every nine minutes, use the data in the table to sketch a sinusoidal graph which represents the height of a car in metres, as a function of time in minutes. Assume that the car is at its lowest point at $t = 0$, and draw one complete cycle.

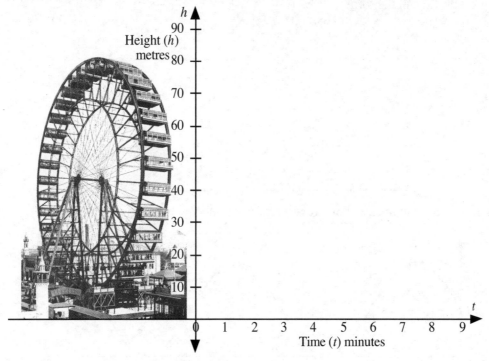

b) Determine the equation of the graph in the form $h(t) = a \cos b(t - c) + d$.

c) How high, to the nearest metre, is the cart 5 minutes after the wheel starts rotating?

d) How many seconds after the wheel starts rotating does the cart first reach 10 metres from the ground? Answer to the nearest second.

Complete Assignment Questions #1 - #5

Assignment

1. The graph shows the height, h metres, above the ground over time, t, in seconds that it takes a person in a chair on a Ferris Wheel to complete two revolutions. The minimum height of the Ferris Wheel is 2 metres and the maximum height is 20 metres.

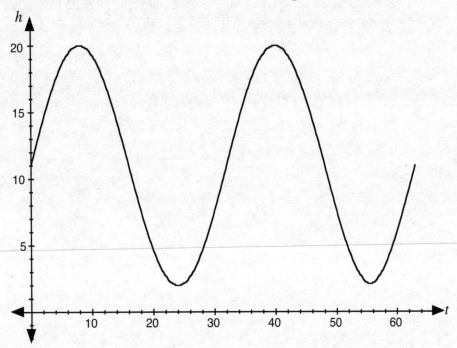

a) How far above the ground is the person as the wheel starts rotating?

b) If it takes 16 seconds for the person to return to the same height, determine the equation of the graph in the form $h(t) = a \sin bt + d$.

c) Determine the distance the person is from the ground, to the nearest tenth of a metre, after 30 seconds.

d) How long from the start of the ride does it take for the person to be at a height of 5 metres? Answer to the nearest tenth of a second.

2. A Ferris Wheel ride can be represented by a sinusoidal function. A Ferris Wheel at Westworld Theme Park has a radius of 15 m and travels at a rate of six revolutions per minute in a clockwise rotation. Ling and Lucy board the ride at the bottom chair from a platform one metre above the ground.

a) Sketch three cycles of a sinusoidal graph to represent the height Ling and Lucy are above the ground, in metres, as a function of time, in seconds.

b) Determine the equation of the graph in the form $h(t) = a \cos [b(t - c)] + d$.

c) If the Ferris Wheel does not stop, determine the height Ling and Lucy are above the ground after 28 seconds. Give answer to the nearest tenth of metre.

d) How long after the wheel starts rotating do Ling and Lucy first reach 12 metres from the ground? Give answer to the nearest tenth of a second.

e) How long does it take from the first time Ling and Lucy reach 12 metres until they next reach 12 metres from the ground? Give answer to the nearest second.

3. Consider the following information for a town in Saskatchewan for a leap year of 366 days:

- The latest sunrise time is at 09:00 on December 21 (day 356).
- The earliest sunrise time is at 03:30 on June 21 (day 173).
- There is NO daylight saving time in Saskatchewan.
- The sunrise times vary sinusoidally with the day of the year.

a) Write a sinusoidal equation which relates the time of sunrise, t, to the day of the year, d.

b) Use the equation to determine what time, to the nearest minute, the sun rises on March 11.

c) Determine the average time the sun rises throughout the year.

d) How many days of the year does the sun rise before 6 a.m.?

Use the following information to answer the next question.

In Inverdeen harbour, the maximum depth of water is 22 metres at 1 a.m. and 1 p.m. as shown on the grid below.

The minimum depth of water is 6 metres at 7 a.m. and 7 p.m.

The depth is 14 metres at 4 a.m., 10 a.m., 4 p.m. and 10 p.m.

Assume that the relation between the depth of water, y metres, and the time, t hours, is a sinusoidal function.

4. a) If $t = 0$ at midnight, sketch the graph of the sinusoidal function on the grid below.

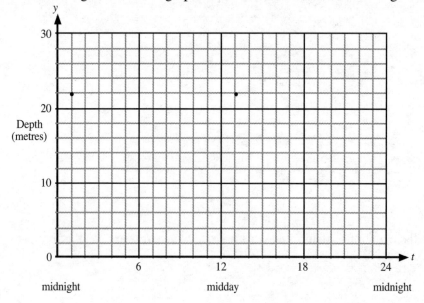

b) State the amplitude and period of the sinusoidal function. (Include units in the answers.)

c) Determine an equation of the sinusoidal function in the form

$y = a \sin [b(t - c)] + d$, where $a > 0$ and $c > 0$.

d) If the equation of the sinusoidal function is written in the form

$$y = a \cos [b(t - c)] + d, \quad \text{where } a > 0 \text{ and } c > 0,$$

only one of the parameters, a, b, c, d will be different from the values in c).
State which parameter will be different and give its value.

e) Calculate the depth of the water, to the nearest tenth of a metre, at 3:30 pm.

5. Andrea, a local gymnast, is doing timed bounces on a trampoline. The trampoline mat
is 1 metre above ground level. When she bounces up, her feet reach a height of 3 metres
above the mat, and when she bounces down her feet depress the mat by 0.5 metres. Once
Andrea is in a rhythm, her coach uses a stopwatch to make the following readings:

- At the highest point the reading is 0.5 seconds.
- At the lowest point the reading is 1.5 seconds.

a) Determine the maximum and minimum heights of Andrea's feet above the ground as
she is bouncing on the trampoline.

b) Sketch two periods of the graph of the sinusoidal function which represents Andrea's
height above the ground, in metres, as a function of time, in seconds.

c) How high was Andrea above the mat when the coach started timing?

d) Determine the equation of the graph in the form $h(t) = a \sin bt + d$.

e) How high, to the nearest tenth of a metre, was Andrea above the ground after 2.7 seconds?

f) Determine Andrea's exact height above the mat after 17 seconds.

g) How long after the timing started did Andrea first touch the mat? Answer to the nearest tenth of a second.

Answer Key

1. a) 11 metres   **b)** $h(t) = 9 \sin\left(\dfrac{\pi}{16}t\right) + 11$ **c)** 7.6 metres   **d)** 19.7 seconds

2. b) $h(t) = 15 \cos \dfrac{\pi}{5}(t - 5) + 16$ **c)** 11.4 metres   **d)** 2.1 seconds   **e)** 6 seconds

3. a) $t = 2.75 \cos\left(\dfrac{\pi}{183}(d + 10)\right) + 6.25$ **b)** 06:45   **c)** 06:15   **d)** 173

4. a) see graph below
   b) amplitude = 8m, period = 12 hours
   c) $y = 8 \sin\left(\dfrac{\pi}{6}(t - 10)\right) + 14$
   d) $c = 1$ **e)** 16.1 m

5. a) max = 4 m, min = 0.5 m
   b) see graph below
   c) 1.25 metres   **d)** $h(t) = 1.75 \sin \pi t + 2.25$
   e) 3.7 metres   **f)** 1.25 metres   **g)** 1.3 seconds

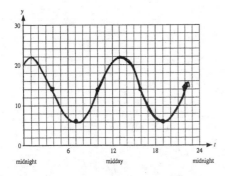

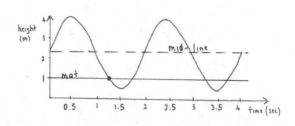

Trigonometry – Functions and Graphs Lesson #11: Practice Test

1. If the value of csc X is positive and the value of cot X is negative, then X must lie in the interval

   A. $\left(0, \dfrac{\pi}{2}\right)$ **B.** $\left(\dfrac{\pi}{2}, \pi\right)$ **C.** $\left(\pi, \dfrac{3\pi}{2}\right)$ **D.** $\left(\dfrac{3\pi}{2}, 2\pi\right)$

2. The exact value of $\sec \dfrac{7\pi}{6}$ is

   A. $\dfrac{2\sqrt{3}}{3}$ **B.** $-\dfrac{2\sqrt{3}}{3}$

   C. 2 **D.** -2

Use the following information to answer the next question.

> As part of a review for an exam, a student makes four statements in which the answers are either quadrant 1, quadrant 2, quadrant 3, or quadrant 4.
>
> **Statement 1:** A rotation angle of $\dfrac{65\pi}{6}$ radians in standard position terminates in quadrant a.
>
> **Statement 2:** If $\tan A < 0$ and $\sec A > 0$, then angle A terminates in quadrant b.
>
> **Statement 3:** Angles in standard position coterminal with an angle of $-\dfrac{7\pi}{4}$ radians are all in quadrant c.
>
> **Statement 4:** For $0 \le x \le 2\pi$, the roots of the equation $\csc x = 1.5$ are in quadrant 1 and quadrant d.

 1. Write the value of a in the first box, the value of b in the second box, the value of c in the third box, and the value of d in the last box.

   (Record your answer in the numerical response box from left to right.)

3. The period of the graph of the function $f(x) = \tan 2\pi x$ is

   A. 0.5 **B.** 1 **C.** π **D.** 2π

4. Compared to the graph of $y = \cos x$, the horizontal phase shift of $y = \cos\left(\dfrac{1}{4}x + \dfrac{\pi}{2}\right)$ is

A. $\dfrac{\pi}{8}$ to the left   B. $\dfrac{\pi}{2}$ to the left

C. 2π to the left   D. 8π to the left

5. The terminal arm of angle x, in standard position, contains the ordered pair $\left(\dfrac{-\sqrt{3}}{2}, \dfrac{1}{2}\right)$.
A possible value for angle x is

A. $\dfrac{4\pi}{3}$ B. $\dfrac{7\pi}{6}$

C. $\dfrac{-4\pi}{3}$ D. $\dfrac{-7\pi}{6}$

Section B   *A graphing calculator may be used for the remainder of the test.*

6. An angle has a degree measure of $2\pi°$. To the nearest tenth of a radian, the angle has a radian measure of

A. 0.1   B. 2

C. 19.7   D. 360

7. The minimum value of the function $f(x) = a \cos bx - d$, where $a > 0$, is

A. $-a - d$ B. $a - d$

C. $a - b - d$ D. $-b - d$

8. A pendulum 12 cm long swings through an arc of length 6 cm. To the nearest degree, the angle through which the pendulum swings is

A. 115°

B. 90°

C. 29°

D. 1°

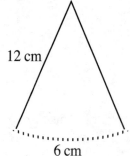
12 cm

6 cm

Use the following information to answer the next question.

The partial graphs of $f(x) = \sin x$ and $g(x) = a\sin[b(x-c)]+d$, where a, b, c and d are whole numbers, are shown below.

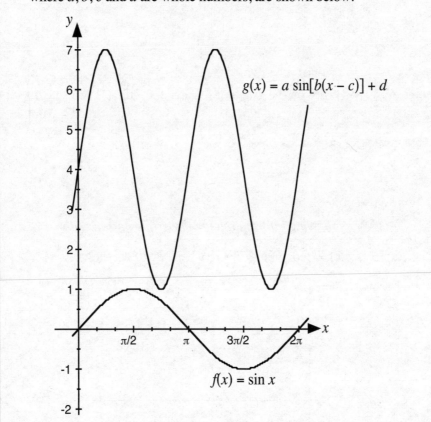

$$g(x) = a\sin[b(x-c)]+d$$

$$f(x) = \sin x$$

Numerical Response **2.** Write the value of a in the first box, the value of b in the second box, the value of c in the third box, and the value of d in the last box.

(Record your answer in the numerical response box from left to right.)

9. If $\tan \theta = \dfrac{7}{24}$ and $\cos \theta < 0$, then the exact value of $\sin \theta$ is

A. -24 **B.** $-\dfrac{24}{25}$

C. $-\dfrac{7}{25}$ **D.** -7

10. The y-intercept of the graph of $y = \cos bx + d$ is

A. b **B.** $b+1$

C. d **D.** $d+1$

3. If $\tan x = -\dfrac{2}{5}$, $\pi < x < 2\pi$, then the measure of x, to the nearest 0.01 radians, is _____.

(Record your answer in the numerical response box from left to right.)

11. The point $A\left(\dfrac{3\pi}{2}, -2\right)$ lies on the graph of $y = k \sin\left(x - \dfrac{\pi}{3}\right)$. The value of k is

A. 4   **B.** $\dfrac{4\sqrt{3}}{3}$

C. −4   **D.** 1

Use the following information to answer the next question.

The partial graph of $f(x) = a\cos[b(x - c)] + d$ where $a > 0$, is shown.

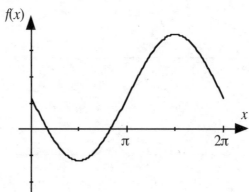

The minimum point on the graph is $S\left(\dfrac{\pi}{2}, -2.4\right)$ and the maximum point is $T\left(\dfrac{3\pi}{2}, 7.2\right)$.

12. The value of a, to the nearest tenth, is

A. 2.4   **B.** 4.8

C. 6.3   **D.** 9.6

13. Which of the following functions have the same period?

$$f(x) = 2\sin[4(x - \pi)] + 1 \qquad g(x) = 2\cos[(x - \pi)] + 5$$

$$h(x) = 3\tan[2(x - \pi)] \qquad k(x) = \sin[2(x - \pi)] + 5$$

A. $f(x)$ and $g(x)$ **B.** $f(x)$ and $h(x)$

C. $h(x)$ and $k(x)$ **D.** $g(x)$ and $k(x)$

14. Which of the following statements is true for all values of x for which the function is defined?

A. $\sin(-x) = \sin x$ **B.** $\cos(-x) = \cos x$ **C.** $\tan(-x) = \tan x$ **D.** $\cot(-x) = \cot x$

15. A fan blade has a diameter of 32 cm. If the blade is rotated 532° about its centre, then a point on the tip of a blade would travel a distance of

A.   1.49 m

B.   2.97 m

C.   85.1 m

D.   170.2 m

16. If $\sin \theta = -0.40$ and $\tan \theta > 0$, then $\sec \theta$, to the nearest hundredth, is

A.   0.92

B.   −0.92

C.   −1.09

D.   1.09

Numerical Response 4. A point on the unit circle is approximated by the ordered pair $(0.80, -0.60)$. To the nearest degree, the angle in standard position between 0° and 360° with a terminal arm passing through this point is _____ .

(Record your answer in the numerical response box from left to right.)

17. The partial graph shown is in the domain $[0, k]$.

A possible equation of the graph is

A. $y = \sin\left(\dfrac{4\pi}{k}\right)x$ **B.** $y = \sin\left(\dfrac{2\pi}{k}\right)x$

C. $y = \sin\left(\dfrac{\pi}{k}\right)x$ **D.** $y = \sin\left(\dfrac{k}{2}\right)x$

5. In the diagram, an arc of length 8 cm subtends an angle of 90° at the centre of the circle. To the nearest tenth of a cm, the diameter of the circle is

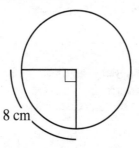

(Record your answer in the numerical response box from left to right.)

---

18. The function $f(\theta) = \tan \theta$ is stretched horizontally by a factor of $\frac{1}{2}$ about the y-axis.

The asymptotes of the graph of the transformed function can be described by which of the following where n is an integer?

A. $\theta = 2n\pi$ B. $\theta = \dfrac{n\pi}{2}$

C. $\theta = \pi + 2n\pi$ D. $\dfrac{\pi}{4} + \dfrac{n\pi}{2}$

---

6. The graph shown is a partial graph of $y = a \sin b(t - c) + d$ where $a, b > 0$.

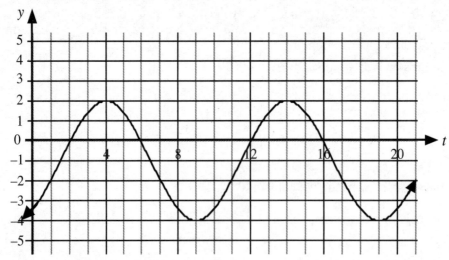

The value of $a + b$, to the nearest tenth, is _____ .

(Record your answer in the numerical response box from left to right.)

Use the following information to answer the next question.

The partial graphs of two trigonometric functions are shown.

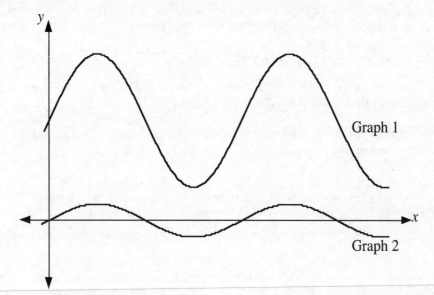

Graph 1 has equation $y = a\cos[b(x - c)] + d$. The equation for graph 2 can be obtained from the equation for graph 1 by changing two of the parameters $a, b, c,$ and d.

19. The two parameters that are changed are

    A. a and d **B.** b and d **C.** a and c **D.** a and b

20. The height, h metres above the ground, at time, t, of a student on the circular Ferris Wheel shown is given by the equation $h(t) = a \cos b(t - c) + d$.

The diameter of the wheel is 12 metres and the student starts at the bottom of the Ferris Wheel at $t = 0$ at a height of 3 metres above the ground.

The value of d in the equation is

    A.   15

    B.   12

    C.   9

    D.   6

Written Response

On one particular day in Kylebane harbour, the equation of the sinusoidal function that represents the relationship between the depth of water, y metres, and the time, t hours after midnight, is $y = 4 \sin\left(\dfrac{\pi}{6}(t + 2)\right) + 15$.

• Calculate the depth of water 4 hours after midnight.

• State the maximum and minimum depths of water in the harbour.

• Calculate, as an **exact value** and as a **decimal** to the nearest tenth of a metre, the depth of water at midnight.

• A large supertanker is in the harbour at midnight. It can remain in the harbour if the depth of water in the harbour is at least 12 metres. Since the minimum depth of water in the harbour is less than 12 metres, the tanker will need to leave the harbour before the depth falls below 12 metres.

Explain clearly how to use a graphical approach to determine the latest time, to the whole hour, that the supertanker can remain in the harbour. State an appropriate graphing calculator window.

• Calculate the latest time, to the whole hour, that the supertanker can remain in the harbour.

Answer Key

Multiple Choice

1. B	**2.** B	**3.** A	**4.** C	**5.** D	**6.** A	**7.** A	**8.** C
9. C	**10.** D	**11.** A	**12.** B	**13.** B	**14.** B	**15.** A	**16.** C
17. A	**18.** D	**19.** A	**20.** C				

Numerical Response

1. | 2 | 4 | 1 | 2 | **2.** | 3 | 2 | 0 | 4 | **3.** | 5 | . | 9 | 0 |

4. | 3 | 2 | 3 | | **5.** | 1 | 0 | . | 2 | **6.** | 3 | . | 6 |

Written Response

• 15 m   • 19 m, 11 m   • $2\sqrt{3} + 15$ m, 18.5 m   • graph $Y_1 = 4 \sin\left(\dfrac{\pi}{6}(x + 2)\right) + 15$,

graph $Y_2 = 12$ and use intersect feature of the calculator to determine the x co-ordinate of the first point of intersection of the two graphs. Window may vary, x:[0, 24, 4] y:[0, 20, 4]   • 5 am

Trigonometry - Equations and Identities Lesson #1:
Solving First Degree Trigonometric Equations

Overview

In this unit, we will

- solve, algebraically and graphically, first and second degree trigonometric equations expressed in degrees and radians, with
    - i) a restricted domain
    - ii) an unrestricted domain leading to a general solution

- prove trigonometric identities using reciprocal identities, quotient identities, Pythagorean identities, sum or difference identities, and double angle identities.

Review

Use an algebraic procedure to solve the following equations on the given domain.

a) $\sin x = -\dfrac{1}{2}, \ 0 \leq x \leq 2\pi.$

b) $3\sec x - 5 = 0, \ 0° \leq x \leq 360°$, to the nearest degree

General Solution

The **general solution** to a trigonometric equation is the solution over the **domain of real numbers**. We will investigate how to determine a general solution graphically and algebraically in this lesson.

Exploring a General Solution Using a Graphical Approach

Consider the equation $\sin x = -\dfrac{1}{2}$ (i.e. $\sin x + \dfrac{1}{2} = 0$).

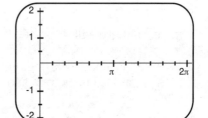

a) Use the following graphical method to estimate the solution to the equation on the domain $0 \le x \le 2\pi$.

- Use window $x\colon [0, 2\pi, \dfrac{\pi}{6}]$ $y\colon[-2, 2, 0.5]$.

- Graph $Y_1 = \sin x + \dfrac{1}{2}$.

- Determine (in terms of π), the x-intercepts of graph Y_1 where $0 \le x \le 2\pi$.

- *Solution is* _____

b) Use the following graphical method to estimate the solution to the equation on the domain $-2\pi \le x \le 4\pi$.

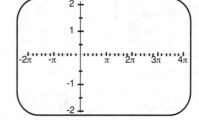

- Use the window $x\colon [-2\pi, , 4\pi, \dfrac{\pi}{6}]$ $y\colon[-2, 2, 0.5]$.

- Graph $Y_1 = \sin x + \dfrac{1}{2}$.

- Determine, as exact values, the x-intercepts of graph Y_1 where $-2\pi \le x \le 4\pi$.

- *Solution is* _____

c) Notice that the solution in b) forms two sets of answers which differ by 2π (or a multiple of 2π) from the answers in a). Complete:

Set 1 $\left(\text{derived from } \dfrac{7\pi}{6}\right)$: _____ are angles which differ by 2π

(or a multiple of 2π).

Set 2 $\left(\text{derived from } \dfrac{11\pi}{6}\right)$: _____ are angles which differ by 2π

(or a multiple of 2π).

d) If the domain is changed to $-4\pi \le x \le 6\pi$, write two more solutions for each set.

e) Use the ideas above to write the <u>general solution</u> to the equation

$\sin x = -\dfrac{1}{2}$ where the domain is unrestricted, i.e. $x \in R$.

- *General Solution is* _____

f) The solution to the equation $\sin x = -\dfrac{1}{2}$ in part b) may also be obtained by using the intersection of two graphs. Show the solution to the equation $\sin x = -\dfrac{1}{2}$ on the given domain by drawing the line with equation $y = -\dfrac{1}{2}$ and marking the points of intersection.

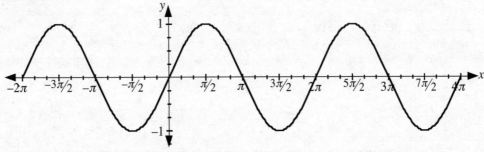

 Note The answers in parts b), c) and d) differ by 2π radians because the graph of $y = \sin x$ has a **period** of 2π radians.

Determining a General Solution Using a Graphical Approach

Use the following procedure to find the general solution.

1. Use a graphing calculator to solve the equation where the domain is **one period** of the graph of the function. Use either the **Intersect Method** or **Zero Method** (see p. 235).

2. Determine the general solution by adding or subtracting **multiples of the period** of the graph of the function to the solutions in 1.

 Class Ex. #1   Solve the equation $\cos x - 0.75 = 0$, $x \in R$, using two different graphical approaches. Give answers to the nearest hundredth of a radian.

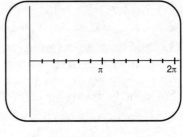

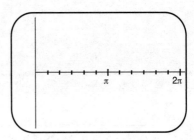

General Solution Using an Algebraic Approach

Use the following procedure to find the general solution using an algebraic approach.

1. Solve the equation where the domain is **one period** of the graph of the function.
2. The general solution can be determined by adding or subtracting **multiples of the period** to the solutions in 1.

Class Ex. #2

Use an algebraic procedure to find the general solution of the equation $2 \cos x - \sqrt{3} = 0, \ x \in R$, where x is in radian measure.

Class Ex. #3

In some cases, the different parts of a general solution can be combined together in one. Determine the general solution, in radians, of the equation

a) $\sin x = 0$ **b)** $\cos x = 0$

Solving on a Restricted Domain

Use the following procedure to solve a trigonometric equation on a restricted domain.

1. Determine the period of the trigonometric function.
2. Solve the equation on the domain $0 \le x \le$ period.
3. Add or subtract **multiples of the period** to the solutions in 1 to solve in **the restricted domain**.

Class Ex. #4

Solve the following equations on the specified domain.

a) $2 \sin x - \sqrt{2} = 0$ for $360° \le x \le 720°$ **b)** $\sqrt{3} \cot x + 1 = 0$ for $-\pi \le x \le 0$

Complete Assignment Questions #1 - #15

Assignment

1. The diagram shows the graph of the equations $y = \cos x$ and $y = 0.5$ in $0 \le x \le 2\pi$.

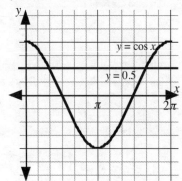

   a) **Explain** how to use the graph to determine the approximate solutions to the equation $\cos x = 0.5$, $0 \le x \le 2\pi$.

   b) Write the solutions to the equation $\cos x = 0.5$, $0 \le x \le 2\pi$. Give solutions as exact values.

   c) Write the general solution to the equation $\cos x = 0.5$.

2. The diagram shows the graph of the equation $y = \tan x - 1$ on the domain $0 \le x \le 2\pi$.

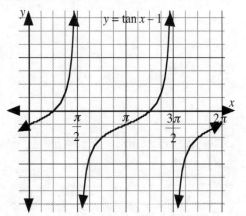

   a) **Explain** how to use the graph to determine the approximate solutions to the equation $\tan x = 1$, $0 \le x \le 2\pi$.

   b) Write the solutions to the equation $\tan x = 1$, $0 \le x \le 2\pi$. Give solutions as exact values.

   c) Write the general solution to the equation $\tan x = 1$.

3. Determine the solution to each of the following equations, defined on the domain $0 \le x \le 2\pi$, using a **graphical** approach. Give solutions as exact values.

   a) $\sin x = \dfrac{\sqrt{3}}{2}$ **b)** $\tan x = -1$ **c)** $2 \sec x - 4 = 0$

4. Use the solutions in #3 to write the general solutions to the equations.

   a) $\sin x = \dfrac{\sqrt{3}}{2}$

   b) $\tan x = -1$

   c) $2 \sec x - 4 = 0$

5. Determine the solution (to the nearest hundredth) to each of the following equations, defined on the domain $0 \le x \le 2\pi$, using a **graphical** approach.

   a) $\cos x = 0.6$ **b)** $\cot x = -\dfrac{1}{3}$ **c)** $\csc x - 3 = 0$

6. Use the solutions in #5 to write the general solutions to the equations.

   a) $\cos x = 0.6$

   b) $\cot x = -\dfrac{1}{3}$

   c) $\csc x - 3 = 0$

7. Determine the solution to each of the following equations, defined on the domain $0 \le x \le 2\pi$, using an **algebraic** approach.

   a) $2 \sin x = -\sqrt{3}$ **b)** $\cot x + \sqrt{3} = 0$ **c)** $3 \sec x + 6 = 0$

8. Use the solutions in #7 to write the general solutions to the equations.

   a) $2 \sin x = -\sqrt{3}$

   b) $\cot x + \sqrt{3} = 0$

   c) $3 \sec x + 6 = 0$

9. Determine the general solution to the following equations where x is in **degree measure**. Answer to the nearest degree.

   a) $\cos x = -0.639$ **b)** $5 \csc x + 6 = 0$

10. Use an algebraic approach to solve the following equations on the specified domain.

   a) $2 \cos x - \sqrt{2} = 0$
   for $-2\pi \le x \le 0$

   b) $\csc x + 2 = 0$
   for $2\pi \le x \le 6\pi$

   c) $\sqrt{3} \tan x = 1$
   for $-\pi \le x \le 3\pi$

11. Determine the general solution, in degrees, of the equation

   a) $\sin x = 0$

   b) $\cos x = 0$

Multiple Choice

12. The general solution to the equation $\csc A + 2 = 0$ is

   A. $A = \dfrac{\pi}{6} + n\pi, \; n \in I$

   B. $A = \dfrac{\pi}{6} + 2n\pi, \; \dfrac{5\pi}{6} + 2n\pi, \; n \in I$

   C. $A = \dfrac{7\pi}{6} + n\pi, \; \dfrac{11\pi}{6} + n\pi, \; n \in I$

   D. $A = \dfrac{7\pi}{6} + 2n\pi, \; \dfrac{11\pi}{6} + 2n\pi, \; n \in I$

13. In simplest form, the general solution to the equation $\sqrt{3} \cot \theta - 1 = 0$ is

   A. $\theta = \dfrac{\pi}{6} + n\pi, \; n \in I$

   B. $\theta = \dfrac{\pi}{6} + 2n\pi, \; \dfrac{7\pi}{6} + 2n\pi, \; n \in I$

   C. $\theta = \dfrac{\pi}{3} + n\pi, \; n \in I$

   D. $\theta = \dfrac{\pi}{3} + 2n\pi, \; \dfrac{4\pi}{3} + 2n\pi, \; n \in I$

14. The only solutions to a trigonometric equation on the domain $0 \le x \le 2\pi$ are $x = \dfrac{2\pi}{3}$ and $x = \dfrac{4\pi}{3}$. An equation that has these solutions is

  A. $2 \sin x + \sqrt{3} = 0$

  B. $2 \cos x + \sqrt{3} = 0$

  C. $2 \sin x + 1 = 0$

  D. $2 \cos x + 1 = 0$

15. To the nearest degree, the solution to the equation $8 \cot \theta = -1$ in the interval $540° \le \theta \le 720°$, is _____ .

(Record your answer in the numerical response box from left to right.)

Answer Key

1. a) Find the x-coordinates of the points of intersection of the two graphs.

  b) $x = \dfrac{\pi}{3}, \dfrac{5\pi}{3}$ 　　**c)** $x = \dfrac{\pi}{3} + 2n\pi, \dfrac{5\pi}{3} + 2n\pi, n \in I$

2. a) Find the x-intercepts of the graph. 　　**b)** $x = \dfrac{\pi}{4}, \dfrac{5\pi}{4}$ 　**c)** $x = \dfrac{\pi}{4} + n\pi, n \in I$

3. a) $x = \dfrac{\pi}{3}, \dfrac{2\pi}{3}$ 　　**4. a)** $x = \dfrac{\pi}{3} + 2n\pi, \dfrac{2\pi}{3} + 2n\pi, n \in I$ 　　**5. a)** $x = 0.93, x = 5.36$

  b) $x = \dfrac{3\pi}{4}, \dfrac{7\pi}{4}$ 　　　　**b)** $x = \dfrac{3\pi}{4} + n\pi, n \in I$ 　　　　　　**b)** $x = 1.89, x = 5.03$

  c) $x = \dfrac{\pi}{3}, \dfrac{5\pi}{3}$ 　　　**c)** $x = \dfrac{\pi}{3} + 2n\pi, \dfrac{5\pi}{3} + 2n\pi, n \in I$ 　　**c)** $x = 0.34, x = 2.80$

6. a) $x = 0.93 + 2n\pi, 5.36 + 2n\pi, n \in I$ 　　　**7. a)** $x = \dfrac{4\pi}{3}, \dfrac{5\pi}{3}$

  b) $x = 1.89 + n\pi, n \in I$ 　　　　　　　　**b)** $x = \dfrac{5\pi}{6}, \dfrac{11\pi}{6}$

  c) $x = 0.34 + 2n\pi, 2.80 + 2n\pi, n \in I$ 　　　**c)** $x = \dfrac{2\pi}{3}, \dfrac{4\pi}{3}$

8. a) $x = \dfrac{4\pi}{3} + 2n\pi, \dfrac{5\pi}{3} + 2n\pi, n \in I$ 　　　**9. a)** $x = 130° + 360n°, 230° + 360n° \ n \in I$

  b) $x = \dfrac{5\pi}{6} + n\pi, n \in I$ 　　　　　　　**b)** $x = 236° + 360n°, 304° + 360n° \ n \in I$

  c) $x = \dfrac{2\pi}{3} + 2n\pi, \dfrac{4\pi}{3} + 2n\pi, n \in I$

10. a) $x = -\dfrac{7\pi}{4}, -\dfrac{\pi}{4}$ 　**b)** $x = \dfrac{19\pi}{6}, \dfrac{23\pi}{6}, \dfrac{31\pi}{6}, \dfrac{35\pi}{6}$ 　**c)** $x = -\dfrac{5\pi}{6}, \dfrac{\pi}{6}, \dfrac{7\pi}{6}, \dfrac{13\pi}{6}$

11. a) $x = 180n°, n \in I$ 　**b)** $x = 90° + 180n°, n \in I$

12. D 　　　**13.** C 　　**14.** D 　　**15.**

6	3	7	

Trigonometry - Equations and Identities Lesson #2:
Solving Second Degree Trigonometric Equations

In this lesson we will be solving **second degree** equations where the power of the trigonometric function is two (e.g. $\sin^2 x - 3 \sin x = 0$).

Trigonometric equations which can be solved by using identities will be covered in lesson 6.

Factoring Trigonometric Expressions

Just as with polynomial expressions, trigonometric expressions can be factored.
The ability to factor trigonometric expressions is a useful skill in two areas:
- solving trigonometric equations (in this lesson)
- proving trigonometric identities (in lesson 6)

In factoring trigonometric expressions we can apply three basic factoring techniques - common factor, difference of two squares, and trinomials of the form $ax^2 + bx + c, a \neq 0$.

Class Ex. #1

Factor the following trigonometric expressions:

a) $8 \tan A + 4$ **b)** $\sin^2 x - 3 \sin x$ **c)** $4 \sin^2 x - 1$

d) $\csc^2 x - 3 \csc x - 28$ **e)** $2 \cos^2 x + 7 \cos x - 4$

Complete Assignment Question #1

Solving a Second Degree Equation Using a Graphical Approach

Class Ex. #2

Consider the equation $2 \sin^2 x = 1 - \sin x$.

a) Use a **graphical** approach to determine the roots of the equation where $0 \leq x \leq 2\pi$. Give solutions as exact multiples of π.

b) State the general solution to the equation.

> ## Solving a Second Degree Equation Using an Algebraic Approach

Class Ex. #3

Consider the equation $2 \sin^2 x = 1 - \sin x$.

a) Use an **algebraic** approach to determine the roots of the equation where $0 \le x \le 2\pi$. Give solutions as exact values.

b) State the general solution to the equation.

Class Ex. #4

Use an algebraic procedure to determine the roots of the equation on the given domain and write the general solution.

a) $4 \sin^2 A - 1 = 0, 0 \le A \le 2\pi$

b) $\tan^2 x + \tan x = 0, \quad 0 \le x \le 2\pi$

Class Ex. #5

Determine the zeros of the following functions on the specified domain.

a) $f(x) = \csc^2 x - 3 \csc x - 28$,

domain $0° \le x \le 180°$

Answer to the nearest degree

b) $g(\theta) = 2 \cos^2 \theta + 5 \cos \theta - 3$,

domain $-\pi \le \theta \le \pi$

Complete Assignment Questions #2 - #13

Assignment

1. Factor the following trigonometric expressions.

   a) $4 \sin^2 \theta - \cos^2 \theta$

   b) $\cot^2 x - \cot x$

   c) $\sin^2 \theta + 3 \sin \theta + 2$

   d) $\sec x \sin^2 x - 0.25 \sec x$

   e) $\cot^2 \theta - 1$

   f) $\sec^4 \theta - 1$

   g) $4 \cos^2 A - 4 \cos A - 3$

   h) $2 \sin^2 x - 7 \sin x + 6$

2. Consider the equation $2 \cos^2 x + 3 \cos x + 1 = 0$.

   a) Use a **graphical** approach to find the solution to the equation where $0 \le x \le 2\pi$. Give solutions as exact values.

   b) Use an **algebraic** approach to find the solution to the equation where $0 \le x \le 2\pi$. Give solutions as exact values.

   c) State the general solution to the equation.

3. Algebraically find the solutions to the following trigonometric equations. Give solutions as exact values.

   a) $2 \sin^2 \theta + \sin \theta = 0$ where $0 \le \theta \le 2\pi$ **b)** $2 \sin^2 x - \sin x = 1$ where $0 \le x \le 2\pi$

Use the following information to answer the next question.

A student is solving the equation $8\cos^2 x + 2\cos x - 3 = 0$ on the interval $0° \le x \le 360°$. The student's work is shown below.

$$8 \cos^2 x + 2 \cos x - 3 = 0$$

$$(2 \cos x - 1)(4 \cos x + 3) = 0$$

$$\cos x = \frac{1}{2} \qquad \text{or} \qquad \cos x = -\frac{3}{4}$$

quadrant 1/4   quadrant 2/3

reference angle = 60°   reference angle = 139°

$$x = 60° \qquad\qquad\qquad x = 180° - 139°$$

$$x = 360° - 60° \qquad\qquad x = 180° + 139°$$

$$x = 60°, 300° \qquad\qquad x = 41°, 319°$$

$$x = 41°, 60°, 300°, 319°$$

4. a) Verify algebraically that $x = 60°$ is a solution to the equation.

b) Show that $x = 41°$ does not satisfy the equation.

c) Explain the error in the student's work and provide a correct solution to the problem.

Use the following information to answer the next question.

Christine is determining the roots of the equation $2\sin x \cos x = 3\sin x$ on the domain $0 \le x \le 2\pi$.

Her work is shown at the side.

$$2\sin x \cos x = 3\sin x$$

$$\frac{2\sin x \cos x}{\sin x} = \frac{3\sin x}{\sin x}$$

$$2\cos x = 3$$

$$\cos x = \frac{3}{2}$$

no solution

5. a) Is Christine correct in stating that $\cos x = \dfrac{3}{2}$ has no solution? Explain.

b) Use a graphical approach to show that the equation $2\sin x \cos x = 3\cos x$ on the domain $0 \le x \le 2\pi$ does have roots. Give solutions as exact values.

c) Identify Christine's error and provide a correct algebraic solution to the problem.

6. A trigonometric function, $f(x)$, has a period of 2π radians.

a) If the roots of the equation $f(x) = 0$ on the domain $0 \le x \le 2\pi$ are $x = a$, $x = b$, and $x = c$, state the general solution to the equation $f(x) = 0$.

b) Use the generalization in 6a) and the solution in 5c) to state the general solution to the equation $2\sin x \cos x = 3\cos x$.

c) The three sets of answers in b) can be simplified to a single set of answers. Write the general solution to the equation $2\sin x \cos x = 3\cos x$ in simplest form.

7. Algebraically find the solutions to the following trigonometric equations. Give solutions as exact values.

   a) $\cot^2 A + \cot A = 0$ where $-\pi \le A \le \pi$ **b)** $2\cos^2 x = \sqrt{3}\,\cos x$ where $-2\pi \le x \le 0$

8. Algebraically find the general solutions to the following trigonometric equations. Give solutions as exact values.

   a) $2\csc^2\theta - 2 = 3\csc\theta$ **b)** $3\sec\theta = 2 + \sec^2\theta$

9. The diagram below shows the graphs of $y = 6 \sin^2 x$ and $y = 6 \sin x - 1$ where $0 \le x \le 2\pi$.

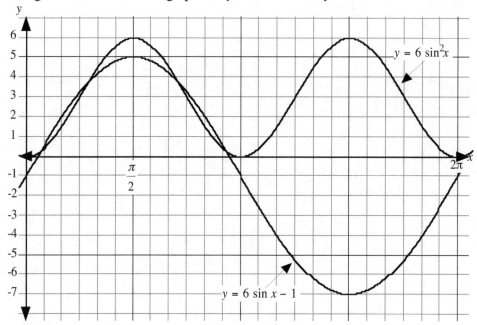

a) **Explain how** you could use this diagram to <u>estimate</u> the solution to the equation
$6 \sin^2 x - 6 \sin x + 1 = 0$, where $0 \le x \le 2\pi$.

b) Algebraically determine the solutions to the equation $6 \sin^2 x - 6 \sin x + 1 = 0$,
where $0 \le x \le 2\pi$. Give the solution correct to the nearest hundredth.

c) **Explain how** you could use this diagram to <u>estimate</u> the solution to the
equation $6 \sin^2 x \, (6 \sin x - 1) = 0$, where $0 \le x \le 2\pi$.

d) Use an algebraic approach to find the solutions to the equation $6 \sin^2 x \, (6 \sin x - 1) = 0$,
where $0 \le x \le 2\pi$. Give the solution correct to the nearest hundredth.

10. The following questions cannot be solved using an algebraic approach. Graphically determine the solution(s) on the set of real numbers to the nearest hundredth of a radian.

a) $3 \sin^2 x = x$ 　　　　　　　　　**b)** $x^2 + \sin 6x - 1 = 0$

Multiple Choice **11.** Which solutions are correct for the equation $12 \sin^2 x - 11 \sin x + 2 = 0$?

　A.　$\sin x = 3, 8$

　B.　$\sin x = \dfrac{11}{12}, -2$

　C.　$\sin x = \dfrac{2}{3}, \dfrac{1}{4}$

　D.　$\sin x = -\dfrac{2}{3}, -\dfrac{1}{4}$

Numerical Response **12.** The number of solutions of the equation $2 \cos^2 x + \cos x - 1 = 0$, where $-8\pi \le x \le 8\pi$ is _____ .

(Record your answer in the numerical response box from left to right.)

13. If angle A is acute and $\log_4 (\sin^2 A) = -1$, then the value of A, to the nearest tenth of a radian, is _____ .

(Record your answer in the numerical response box from left to right.)

Answer Key

1. a) $(2\sin\theta - \cos\theta)(2\sin\theta + \cos\theta)$ **b)** $\cot x(\cot x - 1)$ **c)** $(\sin\theta + 1)(\sin\theta + 2)$

     d) $\sec x(\sin x + 0.5)(\sin x - 0.5)$ **e)** $(\cot\theta - 1)(\cot\theta + 1)$

     f) $(\sec\theta - 1)(\sec\theta + 1)(\sec^2\theta + 1)$ **g)** $(2\cos A - 3)(2\cos A + 1)$ **h)** $(\sin x - 2)(2\sin x - 3)$

2. a) $\dfrac{2\pi}{3}, \pi, \dfrac{4\pi}{3}$ **b)** $\dfrac{2\pi}{3}, \pi, \dfrac{4\pi}{3}$ **c)** $x = \dfrac{2\pi}{3} + 2n\pi, \pi + 2n\pi, \dfrac{4\pi}{3} + 2n\pi, n \in I$

3. a) $0, \pi, \dfrac{7\pi}{6}, \dfrac{11\pi}{6}, 2\pi$ **b)** $\dfrac{\pi}{2}, \dfrac{7\pi}{6}, \dfrac{11\pi}{6}$

4. c) The student has the incorrect reference angle for $\cos x = -\dfrac{3}{4}$. The correct reference angle is $41°$.

     The correct solution to the problem is $x = 60°, 139°, 221°, 300°$.

5. a) Christine is correct because the range of the graph of $y = \cos x$ is $-1 \le x \le 1$, and $\dfrac{3}{2} > 1$.

     b) $x = 0, \pi, 2\pi$

     c) Christine has divided both sides of the equation by $\sin x$. This is only valid provided $\sin x \ne 0$, but in this question $\sin x = 0$ is a solution to the problem. Her division by $\sin x$ is not a valid step because division by zero is not defined. $x = 0, \pi, 2\pi$.

6. a) $x = a + 2n\pi, b + 2n\pi, c + 2n\pi, n \in I$

     b) $x = 2n\pi, \pi + 2n\pi, 2\pi + 2n\pi, n \in I$

     c) $x = n\pi, n \in I$

7. a) $-\dfrac{\pi}{2}, -\dfrac{\pi}{4}, \dfrac{\pi}{2}, \dfrac{3\pi}{4}$ **b)** $-\dfrac{11\pi}{6}, -\dfrac{3\pi}{2}, -\dfrac{\pi}{2}, -\dfrac{\pi}{6}$

8. a) $x = \dfrac{\pi}{6} + 2n\pi, \dfrac{5\pi}{6} + 2n\pi, n \in I$ **b)** $x = 2n\pi, \dfrac{\pi}{3} + 2n\pi, \dfrac{5\pi}{3} + 2n\pi, n \in I$

9. a) Find the x-coordinates of the points of intersection of the two graphs.

     b) $0.21, 0.91, 2.23, 2.93$

     c) Find the x-intercepts of each graph.

     d) $0.00, 0.17, 2.97, 3.14, 6.28$

10. a) $0.00, 0.35, 2.14$ **b)** $-1.38, -1.07, -0.63, 0.21, 0.34, 1.04$

11. C   **12.** | 2 | 4 | | | **13.** | 0 | . | 5 | |

Trigonometry - Equations and Identities Lesson #3:
Solving Equations Involving Multiple Angles

In this lesson we will be solving trigonometric equations involving multiple angles,

such as $\sin 3x = \dfrac{\sqrt{3}}{2}$, $\cos 2x = \dfrac{\sqrt{3}}{2}$, or $\sec \dfrac{1}{2}x = 2$.

Graphically Exploring Solutions to Multiple Angle Equations

Consider the equations $\cos x = -\dfrac{\sqrt{3}}{2}$ and $\cos 2x = -\dfrac{\sqrt{3}}{2}$ where x is in degree measure.

a) Use a graphical approach to determine the solution to the equation

$\cos x = -\dfrac{\sqrt{3}}{2}$ where $0 \le x \le 360°$.

b) Use a graphical approach to determine the solution to the equation

$\cos 2x = -\dfrac{\sqrt{3}}{2}$ where $0 \le x \le 360°$.

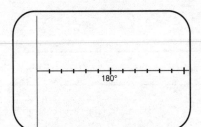

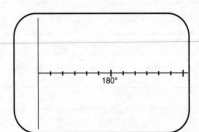

c) Compare the solutions to the two equations in terms of:

  • the number of solutions

  • the values of x.

d) Complete the following.

  i) The general solution to $\cos x = -\dfrac{\sqrt{3}}{2}$ is

  ii) The general solution to $\cos x = -\dfrac{\sqrt{3}}{2}$ consists of two sets of answers which differ by _____ degrees because the graph of $y = \cos x$ has a **period** of _____ degrees.

  iii) The general solution to $\cos 2x = -\dfrac{\sqrt{3}}{2}$ consists of two sets of answers which differ by _____ degrees because the graph of $y = \cos 2x$ has a **period** of _____ degrees.

  iv) The general solution to $\cos 2x = -\dfrac{\sqrt{3}}{2}$ is

---

Solving a Multiple Angle Equation Using a Graphical Approach

Class Ex. #1

a) Given $\tan 2x = \sqrt{3}$, where $0 \leq x \leq 2\pi$, find the exact values of x using a graphical approach.

b) State the general solution to the equation $\tan 2x = \sqrt{3}$.

c) Complete the following statement.

The general solution consists of answers which differ by _____ radians because the graph of $y = \tan 2x$ has a **period** of _____ radians.

Complete Assignment Questions #1 - #3

Algebraically Investigating Solutions to Multiple Angle Equations

Consider the equation $\sin 3x = \dfrac{\sqrt{2}}{2}$.

a) Complete the following to solve the equation $\sin 3x = \dfrac{\sqrt{2}}{2}$, where $0 \leq x \leq 2\pi$.

- If x is defined for domain $0 \leq x \leq 2\pi$, then $3x$ is defined for domain _____ $\leq 3x \leq$ _____ .

  $\sin 3x = \dfrac{\sqrt{2}}{2}$ Quadrants ___ and ___   Reference angle =

  $3x =$ ____ or ____ or $2\pi +$ ____ or $2\pi +$ ____ or $4\pi +$ ____ or $4\pi +$ ____

  $3x =$

  $x =$

b) State the general solution to the equation $\sin 3x = \dfrac{\sqrt{2}}{2}$.

c) Verify the solution using a graphical approach.

- The general solution consists of two sets of answers which differ by $\dfrac{2\pi}{3}$ radians because

  the graph of $y = \sin 3x$ has a **period** of $\dfrac{2\pi}{3}$ radians.

Solving a Multiple Angle Equation Using an Algebraic Approach

Use the following procedure to solve multiple angle equations.

1. Find the domain for the multiple angle.
2. Solve for the multiple angle between 0 and 2π using the CAST rule and reference angle.
3. Add the period of the trigonometric graph of the multiple angle to each of the answers in step 2 until you cover the domain in step 1.

Class Ex. #2

Consider the equation $\sin 2x = -\dfrac{1}{2}$.

a) Find the exact values of x using an algebraic approach where $0 \le x \le 2\pi$. .

b) State the general solution to the equation $\sin 2x = -\dfrac{1}{2}$.

c) Complete the following statement.

The general solution consists of answers which differ by _____ radians

because the graph of $y = \sin 2x$ has a **period** of _____ radians.

d) Verify the solution using a graphical approach.

Use the following information to answer the next question.

The distance above the ground of a student on a circular Ferris wheel is given by the equation

$$h(t) = -4\cos\left[\frac{\pi}{12}t\right] + 5$$

where h is the distance above the ground in metres, and t is the time in seconds, when the student is at the lowest point of the ride for the first time.

Class Ex. #3

a) Determine the time it takes the Ferris wheel to make one complete rotation.

b) Algebraically determine the times, during the first minute of the ride, when the student is 7 metres above the ground.

c) Verify the results graphically.

Complete Assignment Questions #4 - #12

Assignment

1. Use a graphical approach to determine the roots of the equation $\sin 2x = \dfrac{\sqrt{3}}{2}$

   a) on the domain $0 \le x \le 2\pi$ **b)** on the domain of real numbers.

2. Consider the function $f(x) = 1 - \cot 2x$.
   Using a graphical approach, determine the zeros of the function

   a) for $0 \le x \le 2\pi$ **b)** for $x \in R$.

3. Determine the general solution to $\cos \dfrac{1}{2}x = \dfrac{\sqrt{3}}{2}$ using a graphical approach.

4. **a)** Use an algebraic approach to solve the equation $\sin 2x = \dfrac{\sqrt{2}}{2}$, $0 \le x \le 2\pi$.

   b) State the general solution to the equation $\sin 2x = \dfrac{\sqrt{2}}{2}$.

5. **a)** Use an algebraic approach to solve the equation $\sec 3x - \sqrt{2} = 0$, $0° \le x \le 360°$.

   b) State the general solution to the equation $\sec 3x - \sqrt{2} = 0$, where x is expressed in degrees.

6. Use an algebraic approach to determine the general solution to the equations

    a) $\tan 4x = 1$ **b)** $\tan \dfrac{1}{4}x = 1$

7. The graph of $y = 2 \cos 3x + 1$ is displayed on a graphing calculator.

    a) Describe the effects of the parameters $2, 3$, and 1 on the graph of $y = \cos x$.

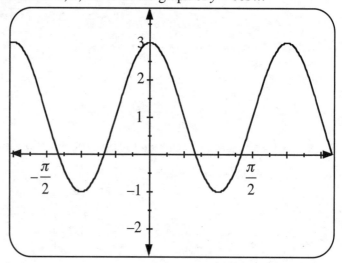

    b) A student was asked to find all the values of θ which satisfy the equation
$\cos 3x = -\dfrac{1}{2}$, $-\dfrac{\pi}{2} \le x \le \dfrac{\pi}{2}$. Explain how the student can find these values from the
graph above and mark these points on the grid.

    c) Show how to find these values by solving algebraically $\cos 3x = -\dfrac{1}{2}$, $-\dfrac{\pi}{2} \le x \le \dfrac{\pi}{2}$.

Use the following information to answer the next question.

In a controlled laboratory experiment, the temperature in
a greenhouse is controlled by an electronic thermostat.
The temperatures vary according to the sinusoidal function

$$C(t) = 28 + 4\sin\frac{\pi}{3}t$$

where C is the temperature in degrees Celsius and
t is the time in hours past midnight.

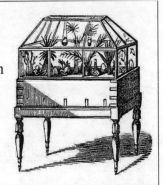

8. **a)** How many temperature cycles are there in one day?

   b) Algebraically determine the temperature at 2:30 pm.

   c) Algebraically determine the times during the day when the temperature is 26°.

9. The roots of the equation $2\sin^2 x - \sin x - 1 = 0$, for $0 \le x \le 2\pi$, are $\dfrac{\pi}{2}, \dfrac{7\pi}{6}$, and $\dfrac{11\pi}{6}$.

   Describe how the roots of the equation $2\sin^2\left(\dfrac{1}{2}x\right) - \sin\left(\dfrac{1}{2}x\right) - 1 = 0$, $0 \le x \le 2\pi$, relate

   to the roots of the equation $2\sin^2 x - \sin x - 1 = 0$, $0 \le x \le 2\pi$. Determine the roots.

Multiple Choice

10. Which of the following is NOT a solution to the equation $2 \sin 3x = 0$?

A. $\dfrac{\pi}{3}$ B. $\dfrac{\pi}{2}$

C. $\dfrac{4\pi}{3}$ D. 2π

11. Which of the following equations does not have a solution in the interval $\pi \le x \le \dfrac{3\pi}{2}$.

A. $\csc x = -2$

B. $\cos 2x = 1$

C. $\tan \dfrac{1}{2}x = 1$

D. $\sin 3x = 1$

Numerical Response

12. The smallest positive solution to the equation $\sin 4x = 0.48$, correct to the nearest hundredth of a radian, is $x =$ _____ .

(Record your answer in the numerical response box from left to right.)

Answer Key

1. a) $\dfrac{\pi}{6}, \dfrac{\pi}{3}, \dfrac{7\pi}{6}, \dfrac{4\pi}{3}$ **b)** $x = \dfrac{\pi}{6} + n\pi, \dfrac{\pi}{3} + n\pi, n \in I$

2. a) $\dfrac{\pi}{8}, \dfrac{5\pi}{8}, \dfrac{9\pi}{8}, \dfrac{13\pi}{8}$ **b)** $x = \dfrac{\pi}{8} + \dfrac{n\pi}{2}, n \in I$ **3.** $x = \dfrac{\pi}{3} + 4n\pi, \dfrac{11\pi}{3} + 4n\pi, n \in I$

4. a) $\dfrac{\pi}{8}, \dfrac{3\pi}{8}, \dfrac{9\pi}{8}, \dfrac{11\pi}{8}$ **b)** $x = \dfrac{\pi}{8} + n\pi, \dfrac{3\pi}{8} + n\pi, n \in I$

5. a) $15°, 105°, 135°, 225°, 255°, 345°$ **b)** $x = 15° + 120n°, 105° + 120n°, n \in I$

6. a) $x = \dfrac{\pi}{16} + \dfrac{n\pi}{4} \ n \in I$ **b)** $x = \pi + 4n\pi, n \in I$

7. a) The amplitude is increased to 2, the period is reduced to $\dfrac{2\pi}{3}$, and the vertical displacement is 1 unit up.

     b) Find the x-intercepts of the graph of $y = 2 \cos 3x + 1$ on the given domain. **c)** $-\dfrac{4\pi}{9}, -\dfrac{2\pi}{9}, \dfrac{2\pi}{9}, \dfrac{4\pi}{9}$

8. a) 4 cycles   **b)** 30° C
     c) 3:30 am, 5:30 am, 9:30 am, 11:30 am, 3:30 pm, 5:30 pm, 9:30 pm, 11:30 pm

9. Since x is replaced by $\frac{1}{2}x$, the roots will be doubled and any value outside the domain $0 \le x \le 2\pi$ will be disregarded. The only root is π.

10. B   **11.** C   **12.**

0	.	1	3

Trigonometry - Equations and Identities Lesson #4:
Trigonometric Identities - Part One

Equations and Identities

In mathematics it is important to understand the difference between an equation
and an identity.

$2x^2 + 3 = 11$ is an **equation**. It is only true for <u>certain values</u> of the variable x.
The solutions to this equation are –2 and 2 which can be verified by substituting these values
into the equation.

$(x + 1)^2 = x^2 + 2x + 1$ is an **identity.** It is true for <u>all values</u> of the variable x.

Reviewing Identities

Recall the basic trigonometric identities:

$$\boxed{\begin{array}{c} \textbf{\textit{Basic Identities}} \\[1em] \sin \theta = \dfrac{y}{r} \qquad \cos \theta = \dfrac{x}{r} \qquad \tan \theta = \dfrac{y}{x} \qquad \text{where } \; x^2 + y^2 = r^2 \end{array}}$$

We have also met the reciprocal trigonometric identities :

$$\boxed{\begin{array}{c} \textbf{\textit{Reciprocal Identities}} \\[1em] \csc x = \dfrac{1}{\sin x} \qquad\qquad \sec x = \dfrac{1}{\cos x} \qquad\qquad \cot x = \dfrac{1}{\tan x} \end{array}}$$

We can use the Basic and Reciprocal trigonometric identities to prove the Quotient and
Pythagorean identities.

Before doing this we will verify some identities using a particular case.

Verifying Identities for a Particular Case

When verifying an identity we must treat the left side (LS) and the right side (RS) **separately** and work until **both sides** represent the same **value**.

This technique **does not prove** that an identity is true for **all** values of the variable - only for the value of the variable being verified.

Class Ex. #1

Verify the following identities for the value given.

a) $\tan x = \dfrac{\sin x}{\cos x}$ for $x = 60°$

b) $\tan^2 x + 1 = \sec^2 x$ for $x = \dfrac{\pi}{6}$

L.S.	R.S.

L.S.	R.S.

Proving the Quotient Identities and the Pythagorean Identities

We can use identities to derive other identities. When proving an identity we must:
- treat the left side (LS) and the right side (RS) **separately**
- work until **both sides** represent the **same expression**.

Remember:
- Do not make the mistake of assuming the answer by writing the LS = RS at the start of a proof and do not move terms from one side to the other.

Class Ex. #2

Use the basic identities to prove the identity $\tan \theta = \dfrac{\sin \theta}{\cos \theta}$, where $\cos \theta \neq 0$. Explain why there is the restriction $\cos \theta \neq 0$.

L.S.	R.S.

Class Ex. #3 Use the basic identities to prove the identity $1 + \tan^2 A = \sec^2 A$.

In the same way the basic identities can be used to prove the following:

Quotient Identities

$$\tan x = \frac{\sin x}{\cos x} \qquad \cot x = \frac{\cos x}{\sin x}$$

and

Pythagorean Identities

$$\sin^2 x + \cos^2 x = 1 \qquad\qquad 1 + \tan^2 x = \sec^2 x \qquad\qquad 1 + \cot^2 x = \csc^2 x$$

• These identities can be written in several ways and this should be remembered in trying to prove more difficult identities in the next lesson. For example

$$\sin^2 x = 1 - \cos^2 x \qquad \cos^2 x = 1 - \sin^2 x$$

$$\tan^2 x = \sec^2 x - 1 \qquad \cot^2 x = \csc^2 x - 1 \qquad \text{etc.}$$

• We use the basic trigonometric identities in terms of x, y and r to prove **only** the Quotient and Pythagorean Identities.

• You will be asked to verify the remaining Quotient and Pythagorean Identities in the Assignment.

• Before considering more complex identities in the next lesson we need to review some skills in simplification and factoring which will help in the proofs.

Complete Assignment Questions #1 - #5

> ## *Using Identities to Simplify Trigonometric Expressions*

Class Ex. #4

Express each as a single trigonometric ratio. Use a graphing calculator to verify.

a) $\dfrac{\sin^2 x}{\cos^2 x} + 1$

b) $\sin x + \cot x \cos x$

Class Ex. #5

Express $\dfrac{2 \tan A}{1 + \tan^2 A}$ in terms of $\sin A$ and $\cos A$ and write in simplest form.

Class Ex. #6

Factor the following trigonometric expressions.

a) $3 \cos^4 \theta - 3\sin^4 \theta$ **b)** $\sin^2 \theta + \sin^2 \theta \cot^2 \theta$

> ### Complete Assignment Questions #6 - #17

Assignment

1. Verify the following identities for the given value of the variable.

a) $\cot x = \dfrac{\cos x}{\sin x}$ for $x = 60°$ **b)** $\sin^2 x + \cos^2 x = 1$ for $x = \dfrac{\pi}{4}$

2. Verify the identity $1 + \cot^2 x = \csc^2 x$ for the given values:

a) $x = \dfrac{\pi}{6}$

b) $120°$

3. Explain why verifying that the two sides of a trigonometric identity are equal for given values (as in #1 and #2 above) is insufficient to conclude that the identity is valid.

4. Use the basic identities to prove the identities in questions #1 and #2.

5. Use the quotient identities or the Pythagorean identities to state whether the following are true or false.

a) $\cos^2 x = 1 + \sin^2 x$

b) $(\sin x)(\csc x) = 1$

c) $\sin x = \pm\sqrt{1 - \cos^2 x}$

d) $(\tan x)(\cot x) = 1$

e) $\tan^2 x - \sec^2 x = 1$

6. Write each expression as a single trigonometric ratio or as the number 1.

a) $\sin^2 x - 1$

b) $\dfrac{\cos t}{\sin t}$

c) $\dfrac{1}{\sec \theta}$

d) $(\sec t)(\sin^2 t)(\csc t)$

e) $\csc^2 x - \cot^2 x$

f) $\sin \theta + (\cot \theta)(\cos \theta)$

7. Factor to write each in a simpler form.

a) $\sec x \sin^2 x - \sec x$

b) $\sin^4 \theta - \cos^4 \theta$

8. Very often in proving identities it is simpler to try to express each side in terms of only $\sin x$, $\cos x$, or both. Express each of the following in terms of only $\sin x$, $\cos x$, or both.

a) $\tan^2 x$

b) $\dfrac{\tan x}{\sin x}$

c) $\dfrac{\tan x}{\csc x}$

d) $\dfrac{1}{1 + \cot^2 x}$

e) $\csc x - \sin x$

f) $1 - \csc^2 x$

g) $\dfrac{1 + \cot^2 x}{\sec^2 x}$

h) $\dfrac{\cos^2 x - 1}{\tan x}$

i) $\dfrac{1 + \cot^2 x}{\cot^2 x}$

In questions #9 - #14 assume the appropriate restrictions.

9. $\dfrac{\cos x}{1 - \sin^2 x}$ is equal to

   A. $\sec x$

   B. $\csc x$

   C. $\sin x$

   D. $\tan x$

10. $\dfrac{\tan^2 x + 1}{\sec x}$ is equal to

   A. $\sec x$

   B. $\csc x$

   C. $\sin x$

   D. $\tan x$

11. $\dfrac{\csc x}{\cot x}$ is equal to

   A. $\cos x$

   B. $\sin x$

   C. $\sec x$

   D. $\tan x$

12. Which is **not** an identity?

   A. $\cos^2 x + \sin^2 x = 1$

   B. $\sin x + \cos x = 1$

   C. $\sec^2 x - \tan^2 x = 1$

   D. $\tan x \cot x = 1$

13. $\sec x - \cos x$ is equal to

   A. $\dfrac{1 - \cos x}{\cos x}$

   B. $\dfrac{1 - 2\cos x}{\cos x}$

   C. $\sin^2 x$

   D. $\sin x \tan x$

14. The expression $\dfrac{\tan A \cos^2 A}{\sec A}$, expressed in terms of $\sin A$, is

   A. $\dfrac{\sin A}{1 - \sin^2 A}$

   B. $\dfrac{1 - \sin^2 A}{\sin A}$

   C. $\sin^2 A$

   D. $\sin A - \sin^3 A$

15. If $\tan x \neq 0, \cos x \neq 0, \cot x \neq 0$, then $\dfrac{1}{\tan x \cos x \cot x}$ is equal to

 A. $\dfrac{1}{\sin x}$

 B. $\sin x$

 C. $\dfrac{1}{\cos x}$

 D. $\cos x$

16. If $\sin x \neq 0, \cos x \neq 0$, then $\dfrac{\tan x \cos x}{3 \sec x \cot x}$ is equal to

 A. $\dfrac{1}{3}$

 B. 3

 C. $\dfrac{1}{3} \sin^2 x$

 D. $\dfrac{1}{3} \csc^2 x$

17. When verifying the identity $\cot^2 x + 1 = \csc^2 x$ for $x = \dfrac{\pi}{7}$, the value on each side of the identity, to the nearest tenth, is _____ .

(Record your answer in the numerical response box from left to right.)

Answer Key

3. The left side and right side may be equal for some values, but may be unequal for other values. An identity is only valid if the left side and the right side are equal for all values for which the identity is defined.

5. b), c) and d) are true. **6. a)** $-\cos^2 x$ **b)** $\cot t$ **c)** $\cos \theta$ **d)** $\tan t$ **e)** 1 **f)** $\csc \theta$

7. a) $-\cos x$ **b)** $(\sin \theta - \cos \theta)(\sin \theta + \cos \theta)$

8. a) $\dfrac{\sin^2 x}{\cos^2 x}$ **b)** $\dfrac{1}{\cos x}$ **c)** $\dfrac{\sin^2 x}{\cos x}$ **d)** $\sin^2 x$ **e)** $\dfrac{\cos^2 x}{\sin x}$

 f) $-\dfrac{\cos^2 x}{\sin^2 x}$ **g)** $\dfrac{\cos^2 x}{\sin^2 x}$ **h)** $-\sin x \cos x$ **i)** $\dfrac{1}{\cos^2 x}$

9. A   **10.** A   **11.** C   **12.** B   **13.** D   **14.** D

15. C   **16.** C   **17.** | 5 | . | 3 | |

Trigonometry - Equations and Identities Lesson #5:
Trigonometric Identities - Part Two

Exploring an Identity

a) Use the quotient identity to show
that $\sin x = \tan x \cos x$.

b) Is this statement true for all values of x? To investigate, sketch the graphs of $f(x) = \sin x$
and $g(x) = \tan x \cos x$ on the grids below, using a window $x:[0, 2\pi, \frac{\pi}{6}]$ $y:[-1.5, 1.5, 1]$.

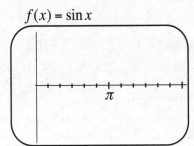

$f(x) = \sin x$

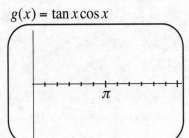

$g(x) = \tan x \cos x$

It appears that the graphs are identical and that $f(x) = g(x)$ for all values of x in
the interval $0 \le x \le 2\pi$. However, this is not the case as shown below.

c) Evaluate. **i)** $f\left(\frac{\pi}{2}\right)$ and $g\left(\frac{\pi}{2}\right)$ **ii)** $f\left(\frac{3\pi}{2}\right)$ and $g\left(\frac{3\pi}{2}\right)$. What do you notice?

d) The graph of $y = g(x)$ has points of discontinuity at $x = \frac{\pi}{2}$ and $x = \frac{3\pi}{2}$.
Explain why, using the results in a).

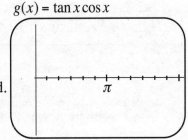

$g(x) = \tan x \cos x$

e) Show the correct graph for $g(x) = \tan x \cos x$ on the grid.

We say that

$\sin x = \tan x \cos x$ is an identity with non permissible values where $\cos x = 0$.

The restrictions on the identity are $x \ne \frac{\pi}{2} + n\pi, n \in I$.

Note The "holes" in the graph may not appear on a calculator graph of a trigonometric function.
However, using the **Zoom Trig** feature in **degree mode** will usually reveal the points of
discontinuity. The graphing calculator may not show the "holes" in radian mode.
The axes will need to be turned off if the points of discontinuity lie on one of the axes.

Non-Permissible Values of an Identitiy

The non-permissible values of an identity are determined by finding the non-permissible values for each side of the identity.

When determining the non-permissible values, there are two areas to focus on.

1. All tangent, cotangent, secant, and cosecant functions have non-permissible values.

    - $\tan x = \dfrac{\sin x}{\cos x}$ and $\sec x = \dfrac{1}{\cos x}$ have non-permissible values when $\cos x = 0$.

    - $\cot x = \dfrac{\cos x}{\sin x}$ and $\csc x = \dfrac{1}{\sin x}$ have non-permissible values when $\sin x = 0$.

2. If the identity has a denominator, then any zero of the denominator will be a non-permissible value of the identity.

- The **non-permissible values** are sometimes called the **restrictions** of the identity.

- In many of the examples, the restrictions are the solutions to $\sin x = 0$ and/or $\cos x = 0$.

- Recall $\sin x = 0 \Rightarrow x = n\pi, n \in I$, and $\cos x = 0 \Rightarrow x = \dfrac{\pi}{2} + n\pi, n \in I$, (see page 594).

In this lesson we will verify and prove more complex trigonometric identities using the skills we learned from the previous lesson.
Some useful steps or hints when trying to prove a trigonometric identity are listed below.

Hints in Proving an Identity

1. Begin with the more complex side.

2. If possible, use the reciprocal, quotient, or Pythagorean identities. For example, use the Pythagorean identities when squares of trigonometric functions are involved.

3. If necessary change all trigonometric ratios to sines and/or cosines.
    For example, replace $\tan x$ by $\dfrac{\sin x}{\cos x}$, and $\sec x$ by $\dfrac{1}{\cos x}$.

4. Look for factoring as a step in trying to prove an identity.

5. If there is a sum or difference of fractions, combine as a single fraction.

Class Ex. #1

Consider the statement $\dfrac{1}{\cos x} - \cos x = \sin x \tan x$.

a) Verify the statement is true for $x = \dfrac{\pi}{3}$.

L.S.	R.S.

b) Use a graphing calculator to show that the statement is probably an identity.

c) Prove the statement is an identity using an algebraic approach.

L.S.	R.S.

d) State the restrictions in terms of x.

Class Ex. #2

Prove the identity $\sin x \cos^2 x + \sin^3 x = \dfrac{1}{\csc x}$ algebraically and determine the non-permissible values

L.S.	R.S.

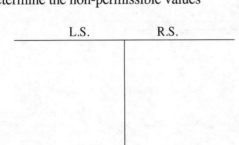

Class Ex. #3

Consider the identity $\dfrac{\sin A + \tan A}{1 + \cos A} = \dfrac{1}{\cot A}$.

a) Prove the identity algebraically.

b) What are the non-permissible values of the identity.

c) Show the non-permissible values on a graph of each side of the identity for the domain $0 \le x \le 2\pi$.

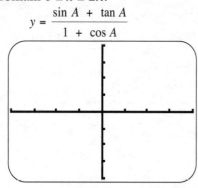

$y = \dfrac{\sin A + \tan A}{1 + \cos A}$

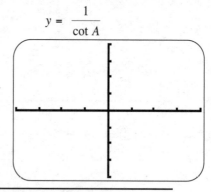

$y = \dfrac{1}{\cot A}$

Class Ex. #4

Prove the identity $\dfrac{\sec^2 x}{\sec^2 x - 1} = \csc^2 x$.

Complete Assignment Questions #1 - #7

Assignment

1. Consider the statement $\dfrac{\cos x - \sin x}{\cos x} = \sin^2 x - \tan x + \cos^2 x$.

    a) Verify the statement is true for $x = \dfrac{\pi}{4}$.

    b) Prove the statement is an identity.

    c) State, and give reasons for, any restrictions.

2. In each of the following
    i)   verify the possibility of an identity using a graphing calculator
    ii) prove the identity using an algebraic approach and state any restrictions.

    a) $\dfrac{\tan \theta \, \cos \theta}{\sin \theta} = 1$

    b) $\sec^2 x - \sin^2 x = \cos^2 x + \tan^2 x$

3. Consider the statement $\dfrac{\cot x - 1}{\tan x - 1} = -\dfrac{1}{\tan x}$.

a) Verify the statement is true for $x = \dfrac{\pi}{3}$

b) Prove the statement is an identity.

c) Determine the non-permissible values of the identity.

d) Show the non-permissible values on a graph of each side of the identity for the domain $0 \le x \le 2\pi$.

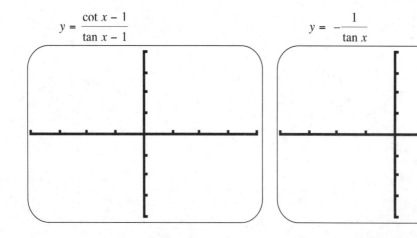

$$y = \dfrac{\cot x - 1}{\tan x - 1}$$

$$y = -\dfrac{1}{\tan x}$$

4. Prove the following identities using an algebraic approach.

a) $(1 - \cos^2 x)(\csc x) = \sin x$

b) $(\sin x + \cos x)^2 = 1 + 2 \sin x \cos x$

c) $\dfrac{1 - \cos x}{\sin x} = \dfrac{\tan x - \sin x}{\tan x \sin x}$

d) $\dfrac{2}{1 - \sin x} + \dfrac{2}{1 + \sin x} = 4 \sec^2 x$

e) $\dfrac{1 + \cos x}{\tan x + \sin x} = \cot x$

f) $\sec x - \cos x = \dfrac{\sin x}{\cot x}$

Multiple Choice **5.** The identity $\dfrac{\sec x + 1}{\sec x - 1} + \dfrac{\cos x + 1}{\cos x - 1} = 0$ has restrictions

A. $x \neq 2n\pi, \dfrac{\pi}{2} + 2n\pi, n \in I$

B. $x \neq 2n\pi, \dfrac{\pi}{2} + n\pi, n \in I$

C. $x \neq \pi + 2n\pi, \dfrac{\pi}{2} + 2n\pi, n \in I$

D. $x \neq 2n\pi, n \in I$

Numerical Response **6.** The value of n, to the nearest tenth, for which the statement below is an identity, is _____ .

$$\dfrac{1 + \sin x}{\cos x} + \dfrac{\cos x}{1 + \sin x} = \dfrac{n}{\cos x}.$$

(Record your answer in the numerical response box from left to right.)

7. If $\dfrac{p}{2} \cos^2 \dfrac{\pi}{5} + \dfrac{p}{2} \sin^2 \dfrac{\pi}{5} = 4$, the value of p, to the nearest tenth, is _____ .

(Record your answer in the numerical response box from left to right.)

Answer Key

1. **a)** both sides equal 0   **c)** $x \neq \dfrac{\pi}{2} + n\pi, n \in I$

2. **a)** $\theta \neq n\pi, \dfrac{\pi}{2} + n\pi, n \in I$ or $\theta \neq n\dfrac{\pi}{2}, n \in I$ **b)** $x \neq \dfrac{\pi}{2} + n\pi, n \in I$

3. **a)** both sides equal $-\dfrac{\sqrt{3}}{3}$ **c)** $x \neq n\pi, \dfrac{\pi}{4} + n\pi, \dfrac{\pi}{2} + n\pi, n \in I$ or $x \neq \dfrac{\pi}{4} + n\pi, n\dfrac{\pi}{2}, n \in I$

d) see graphs below

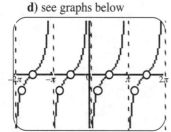

5. B

6. | 2 | . | 0 |

7. | 8 | . | 0 |

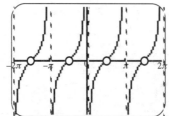

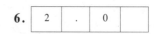

Trigonometry - Equations and Identities Lesson #6:
Sum and Difference Identities

Recall, from the unit circle or the table (opposite), the exact values for the primary trigonometric ratios of special angles.

We will use many of these exact values in this lesson.

θ	0°	30°	45°	60°	90°
θ	0	$\dfrac{\pi}{6}$	$\dfrac{\pi}{4}$	$\dfrac{\pi}{3}$	$\dfrac{\pi}{2}$
$\sin\theta$	0	$\dfrac{1}{2}$	$\dfrac{\sqrt{2}}{2}$	$\dfrac{\sqrt{3}}{2}$	1
$\cos\theta$	1	$\dfrac{\sqrt{3}}{2}$	$\dfrac{\sqrt{2}}{2}$	$\dfrac{1}{2}$	0
$\tan\theta$	0	$\dfrac{\sqrt{3}}{3}$	1	$\sqrt{3}$	undefined

> ### *Investigating Sum and Difference Identities*

a) Consider the statement $\sin(A + B) = \sin A + \sin B$.

   i) Determine whether or not the statement can be verified using $\angle A = 60°$ and $\angle B = 30°$.

   ii) What can we say about the statement $\sin(A + B) = \sin A + \sin B$?

b) Use exact values to verify the following statements.

   i) $\sin(60 + 30)° = \sin 60° \cos 30° + \cos 60° \sin 30°$

   ii) $\sin\left(\dfrac{\pi}{3} - \dfrac{\pi}{6}\right) = \sin\dfrac{\pi}{3} \cos\dfrac{\pi}{6} - \cos\dfrac{\pi}{3} \sin\dfrac{\pi}{6}$

   iii) $\cos(30° + 60°) = \cos 30° \cos 60° - \sin 30° \sin 60°$

   iv) $\cos\left(\dfrac{\pi}{2} - \dfrac{\pi}{4}\right) = \cos\dfrac{\pi}{2} \cos\dfrac{\pi}{4} + \sin\dfrac{\pi}{2} \sin\dfrac{\pi}{4}$

Sum and Difference Identities

The investigation on the previous page is an example of verifying the sum and difference identities for sine and cosine.

$$\sin(A + B) = \sin A \cos B + \cos A \sin B$$
$$\sin(A - B) = \sin A \cos B - \cos A \sin B$$

$$\cos(A + B) = \cos A \cos B - \sin A \sin B$$
$$\cos(A - B) = \cos A \cos B + \sin A \sin B$$

The proof of these identities can be found at
http://pages.pacificcoast.net/~cazelais/173/idns-proof.pdf

The sum and difference identities for sine and cosine can be used to develop the sum and difference identities for tangent.

Complete the work below to show that $\tan(A + B) = \dfrac{\tan A + \tan B}{1 - \tan A \tan B}$.

$$\tan(A + B) = \frac{\sin(A + B)}{\cos(A + B)} = \frac{\sin A \cos B + \cos A \sin B}{\cos A \cos B - \sin A \sin B}$$

Divide numerator and denominator by $\cos A \cos B$, where $\cos A \neq 0$, $\cos B \neq 0$.

$$= \frac{\dfrac{\sin A \cos B + \cos A \sin B}{\cos A \cos B}}{\dfrac{\cos A \cos B - \sin A \sin B}{\cos A \cos B}} =$$

Class Ex. #1

Develop the identity for $\tan(A - B)$ using a similar procedure to the one above.

$$\tan(A + B) = \frac{\tan A + \tan B}{1 - \tan A \tan B} \qquad \tan(A - B) = \frac{\tan A - \tan B}{1 + \tan A \tan B}$$

Class Ex. #2 Express 15° as a difference of two special angles and hence determine the exact value of sin 15° with a rational denominator.

Class Ex. #3 Express $\dfrac{5\pi}{12}$ as a sum of two special angles and hence show that $\cot\dfrac{5\pi}{12} = \dfrac{\sqrt{3}-1}{\sqrt{3}+1}$.

Class Ex. #4 Simplify the following.

a) $\sin 100° \cos 10° - \cos 100° \sin 10°$

b) $\cos\left(\dfrac{1}{4}\pi - \theta\right)\cos\left(\dfrac{1}{4}\pi + \theta\right) - \sin\left(\dfrac{1}{4}\pi - \theta\right)\sin\left(\dfrac{1}{4}\pi + \theta\right)$

Class Ex. #5 Given $\cos A = \dfrac{3}{5}$ and $\cos B = \dfrac{5}{13}$, where $0 \le A \le \dfrac{\pi}{2}$ and $\dfrac{3\pi}{2} \le B \le 2\pi$, find the exact value of $\cos(A + B)$.

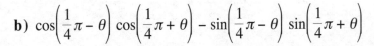

Complete Assignment Questions #1 - #12

Assignment

1. Simplify using the sum and difference identities.

   a) $\cos(180 - B)°$

   b) $\sin\left(\dfrac{\pi}{2} - x\right)$

   c) $\cos(90 + t)°$

   d) $\sin(\pi + x)$

2. Simplify and evaluate the following.

   a) $\sin 70° \cos 20° + \cos 70° \sin 20°$

   b) $\cos 170° \cos 50° + \sin 170° \sin 50°$

   c) $\sin \dfrac{\pi}{3} \cos \dfrac{\pi}{6} - \cos \dfrac{\pi}{3} \sin \dfrac{\pi}{6}$

   d) $\dfrac{\tan \dfrac{15\pi}{8} - \tan \dfrac{3\pi}{8}}{1 + \tan \dfrac{15\pi}{8} \tan \dfrac{3\pi}{8}}$

3. Use exact values to show that

   a) $\sin 75° = \dfrac{\sqrt{6} + \sqrt{2}}{4}$

   b) $\cos \dfrac{\pi}{12} = \dfrac{\sqrt{6} + \sqrt{2}}{4}$

4. Express $\dfrac{7\pi}{12}$ as a sum of two special angles and hence show that $\tan \dfrac{7\pi}{12} = \dfrac{1 + \sqrt{3}}{1 - \sqrt{3}}$.

5. Prove that the exact value of csc 105° is $\sqrt{6} - \sqrt{2}$.

6. Given $\sin x = \dfrac{3}{5}$ and $\sin y = \dfrac{7}{25}$, and x and y are both acute angles, show that

$\tan (x + y) = \dfrac{4}{3}$.

7. Determine exact values for $\cos\left(\theta + \dfrac{\pi}{6}\right)$ and $\sin\left(\theta + \dfrac{\pi}{6}\right)$ if $\tan \theta = \dfrac{4}{3}$, and $\pi \le \theta \le \dfrac{3\pi}{2}$.

8. Prove the following identities.

a) $\tan\left(x + \dfrac{\pi}{4}\right) = \dfrac{1 + \tan x}{1 - \tan x}$

b) $\dfrac{\sin(A - B)}{\cos A \cos B} = \tan A - \tan B$

c) $(\cos A + \cos B)^2 + (\sin A + \sin B)^2 = 2[1 + \cos(A - B)]$

d) $\sin(x + y)\sin(x - y) = \sin^2 x - \sin^2 y$

Multiple Choice

9. If $\cos(A + B) = 0.8320$ and $\cos(A - B) = 0.4358$, then the value of $\cos A \cos B$ is

A. 1.2678

B. 0.6339

C. 0.3962

D. 0.1981

10. The value of $\cos(\pi + y) - \cos(\pi - y)$ is

A. 0

B. 2

C. –2

D. dependent on the value of y

11. Given $\csc x = \dfrac{-17}{15}$, where $\dfrac{3\pi}{2} \le x \le 2\pi$, and $\cot y = -\dfrac{3}{4}$, where $\dfrac{\pi}{2} \le y \le \pi$, the value of $\cos(x - y)$ is

A. $-\dfrac{84}{85}$

B. $-\dfrac{36}{35}$

C. $\dfrac{84}{85}$

D. $\dfrac{36}{35}$

12. If $\sin(A + B) = 0.75$ and $\sin(A - B) = 0.43$, then the value of $\cos A \sin B$, to the nearest hundredth, is _____ .

(Record your answer in the numerical response box from left to right.)

Answer Key

1. a) $-\cos B°$ **b)** $\cos x$ **c)** $-\sin t°$ **d)** $-\sin x$

2. a) 1 **b)** $-\dfrac{1}{2}$ **c)** $\dfrac{1}{2}$ **d)** undefined

7. $\cos\left(\theta + \dfrac{\pi}{6}\right) = \dfrac{4 - 3\sqrt{3}}{10}$, $\sin\left(\theta + \dfrac{\pi}{6}\right) = \dfrac{-4\sqrt{3} - 3}{10}$

9. B   **10.** A   **11.** A   **12.** | 0 | . | 1 | 6 |

Trigonometry - Equations and Identities Lesson #7: Double Angle Identities

Recall the following sum and difference identities from the last lesson.

$$\sin(A + B) = \sin A \cos B + \cos A \sin B$$
$$\sin(A - B) = \sin A \cos B - \cos A \sin B$$

$$\cos(A + B) = \cos A \cos B - \sin A \sin B$$
$$\cos(A - B) = \cos A \cos B + \sin A \sin B$$

$$\tan(A + B) = \frac{\tan A + \tan B}{1 - \tan A \tan B} \qquad \tan(A - B) = \frac{\tan A - \tan B}{1 + \tan A \tan B}$$

Developing the Double Angle Identities

Consider the statement $\sin 2A = 2 \sin A$.

a) Determine whether or not the statement can be verified using $\angle A = \dfrac{\pi}{6}$.

b) What can we say about the statement $\sin 2A = 2 \sin A$?

c) To develop an identity for $\sin 2A$, use the sum identity for $\sin(A + B)$.

  i) Explain how the sum identity for $\sin(A + B)$ can be used to determine an identity for $\sin 2A$.

  ii) Prove that $\sin 2A = 2 \sin A \cos A$.

d) Prove the double angle identity $\cos 2A = \cos^2 A - \sin^2 A$.

e) Prove the double angle identity $\tan 2A = \dfrac{2 \tan A}{1 - \tan^2 A}$.

Note The identity for cos 2A can be expressed in two other forms using the Pythagorean identity
$\sin^2 A + \cos^2 A = 1$.
The proof of the other two forms of the identity is asked for in assignment question #1.

Double Angle Identities

$$\sin 2A = 2\sin A \cos A \qquad \cos 2A = \cos^2 A - \sin^2 A \qquad \tan 2A = \frac{2\tan A}{1 - \tan^2 A}$$

$$\cos 2A = 2\cos^2 A - 1$$

$$\cos 2A = 1 - 2\sin^2 A$$

Class Ex. #1

Prove that the identity $\dfrac{2\tan x}{1 + \tan^2 x} = \sin 2x$ is valid and state the non-permissible values.

Class Ex. #2

a) Use the identity $\sin 2A = 2\sin A \cos A$ with A replaced by $3x$ to determine a double angle identity for $\sin 6x$.

b) Write double angle identities for

    i) $\cos 10A$ **ii)** $\tan x$

Class Ex. #3

Express each of the following in terms of a single trigonometric function.

a) $2\sin 4x \cos 4x$ **b)** $\cos^2 \frac{1}{2}A - \sin^2 \frac{1}{2}A$ **c)** $\sin \frac{5}{2}x \cos \frac{5}{2}x$

Complete Assignment Questions #1 - #9

Assignment

1. Use the sum identity for cosine to prove the following double angle identities.

   a) $\cos 2x = 2\cos^2 x - 1$ **b)** $\cos 2x = 1 - 2\sin^2 x$.

2. Write double angle identities for

   a) $\tan 6x$ **b)** $\cos 3\theta$ **c)** $\sin \dfrac{1}{2}A$

3. Express each of the following in terms of a single trigonometric function.

   a) $2\sin \dfrac{1}{2}x \cos \dfrac{1}{2}x$ **b)** $\cos^2 2A - \sin^2 2A$ **c)** $1 - 2\sin^2 3x$

4. Use a double angle identity to simplify and evaluate

   a) $\dfrac{2\tan \dfrac{\pi}{8}}{1 - \tan^2 \dfrac{\pi}{8}}$ **b)** $\cos^2 \dfrac{\pi}{12} - \sin^2 \dfrac{\pi}{12}$ **c)** $\sin \dfrac{5\pi}{12} \cos \dfrac{5\pi}{12}$

5. Prove the identity $\dfrac{\sin 2x}{1 - \cos 2x} = \cot x$ and state the restrictions on x.

6. Prove the identities   **a)** $\dfrac{1 - \tan^2 x}{1 + \tan^2 x} = \cos 2x$ **b)** $\sin 4x = 4 \sin x \cos^3 x - 4 \sin^3 x \cos x$

Multiple
Choice

7. The expression $\dfrac{\cos^2 \frac{3}{2}x - \sin^2 \frac{3}{2}x}{\sin \frac{3}{2}x \, \cos \frac{3}{2}x}$ is equivalent to

A. $\cos \dfrac{3}{2}x - \sin \dfrac{3}{2}x$ **B.** $\cot 3x$

C. $2 \cot 3x$ **D.** $2 \csc 3x$

8. If $a \cos^2 \dfrac{\pi}{8} - a \sin^2 \dfrac{\pi}{8} = 4\sqrt{2}$, the value of a, to the nearest tenth, is _____ .

(Record your answer in the numerical response box from left to right.)

9. If $\sin 6\theta \cos 2\theta - \cos 6\theta \sin 2\theta = 2 \sin a\theta \cos a\theta$, then the value of a is _____ .

(Record your answer in the numerical response box from left to right.)

Answer Key

2 . a) $\dfrac{2 \tan 3x}{1 - \tan^2 3x}$ **b)** $\cos^2 \dfrac{3\theta}{2} - \sin^2 \dfrac{3\theta}{2}$ **c)** $2 \sin\dfrac{1}{4}A \cos\dfrac{1}{4}$

3 . a) $\sin x$ **b)** $\cos 4A$ **c)** $\cos 6x$ **4 . a)** $\tan\dfrac{\pi}{4} = 1$ **b)** $\cos \dfrac{\pi}{6} = \dfrac{\sqrt{3}}{2}$ **c)** $\dfrac{1}{2} \sin \dfrac{5\pi}{6} = \dfrac{1}{4}$

5 . $x \ne n\pi, n \in I$ **7 . C**   **8 .** | 8 | . | 0 | | **9 .** | 2 | | |

Trigonometry - Equations and Identities Lesson #8: Using Identities to Solve Equations

We have already learned how to solve simple trigonometric equations.

More complex trigonometric equations may require making substitutions using the trigonometric identities we have learned in this unit. This will usually involve expressing the equation in terms of one of the three primary trigonometric functions.

Using Identities to Solve Equations

Class Ex. #1

Solve the following equations where $0 \leq x \leq 2\pi$.

a) $2\cos^2 x + 3\sin x = 0$

b) $\cos\left(x + \dfrac{\pi}{6}\right) - \cos\left(x - \dfrac{\pi}{6}\right) = 1$

Class Ex. #2

Consider the equation $4 - 7\sin x = \cos 2x$.

a) Which of the three identities for $\cos 2x$ would be the most efficient replacement for solving this equation?

b) Determine the general solution to the equation $4 - 7\sin x = \cos 2x$.

Complete Assignment Questions #1 - #5

> ## *Investigating the Validity of Dividing by a Variable Expression*

Consider the two trigonometric equations, **i)** $\sin x = \cos x$, and **ii)** $\sin 2x = \cos x$, where the domain is $0 \le x \le 2\pi$.

a) Part of a student's attempt to solve the equations is shown below. Complete the work.

i) $\sin x = \cos x$

$$\frac{\sin x}{\cos x} = \frac{\cos x}{\cos x}$$

$$\tan x =$$

ii) $\sin 2x = \cos x$

$$2 \sin x \cos x = \cos x$$

$$\frac{2 \sin x \cos x}{\cos x} = \frac{\cos x}{\cos x}$$

b) In order to check her work, she used the intersect feature of a graphing calculator to determine the solution to each equation. The grids below are screen shots of the graphing calculator displays using the window x:$[0, 2\pi, \frac{\pi}{6}]$ y: $[-2, 2, 1]$. Label the graphs shown on each grid and write the solution to the equations below the grid.

i)
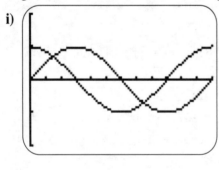

ii)
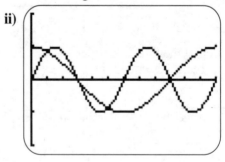

$\sin x = \cos x \Rightarrow x =$ _____ $\sin 2x = \cos x \Rightarrow x =$ _____

c) • Does the algebraic solution in **a) i)** agree with the graphical solution in **b) i)**?

• Does the algebraic solution in **a) ii)** agree with the graphical solution in **b) ii)**?

• The algebraic solution in **a) i)** is correct, but the algebraic solution in **a) ii)** is not complete. This is because the division by $\cos x$ is valid in **a) i)** where $\sin x = \cos x$, but not valid in **a) ii)** where $2 \sin x \cos x = \cos x$.

Under what circumstances in general is division by $\cos x$ not valid?

d) Since **division by a variable expression is not valid if the variable expression can be equal to zero**, we need to determine whether cos x can equal zero in solving the equations sin x = cos x or sin $2x$ = cos x.

Consider a solution to cos x = 0, for example $x = \dfrac{\pi}{2}$.

- If $x = \dfrac{\pi}{2}$ is a solution to either equation, then the step in which the student divides by cos x is **not** valid because she is dividing by zero.

- If $x = \dfrac{\pi}{2}$ is not a solution to either equation, then the step in which the student divides by cos x **is** valid because she is dividing by a non-zero value.

Is $x = \dfrac{\pi}{2}$ a solution to either sin x = cos x or sin $2x$ = cos x?

e) The work in this investigation shows that the student's approach to solving sin $2x$ = cos x is not valid. To determine the correct solution use the double-angle identity for sin $2x$, set the equation equal to zero, and then factor. Show this approach below.

Complete Assignment Questions #6 - #9

Solving Equations Using Double Angle Identities

Class Ex. #3

The diagram shows the graph of two functions, $y = f(x)$ and $y = g(x)$ on domain $0 \le x \le 2\pi$.

a) Write an equation which has a solution provided by the x-intercepts of the graphs.

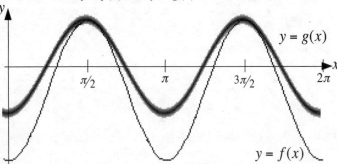

b) Write an equation which has a solution provided by the x-coordinates of the intersection points of the two graphs.

c) The graphs on the previous page represent the functions
$f(x) = 3\sin^2 x - 2$ and $g(x) = -\cos 2x$.

i) Use a graphing calculator to determine the exact roots of the equation
$3\sin^2 x + \cos 2x - 2 = 0,\ 0 \le x \le 2\pi$.

ii) Use a graphing calculator to determine the roots of the equation
$-\cos 2x\,(3\sin^2 x - 2) = 0$, where $0 \le x \le 2\pi$.
Use exact values where possible; otherwise round the answers to the nearest tenth.

d) Verify the roots in c) algebraically.

Complete Assignment Question #10

Assignment

1. Solve for x as an exact value where $0° \le x \le 360°$.

   a) $3 - 3 \sin x - 2 \cos^2 x = 0$

   b) $\tan^2 x - 1 = \sec x$

2. Determine the roots of the equation $7 \sec^2 x + 2 \tan x - 6 = 2 \sec^2 x + 2$, $0 \le x \le 2\pi$. Use exact values where possible; otherwise round the answers to the nearest tenth.

3. Consider the function $f(x) = 2 \cos^2 \dfrac{1}{2}x - 1$. Express the function in terms of $\cos x$, and hence determine the zeros of the function where the domain is the set of real numbers.

4. Consider the function $f(x) = \sin\left(\frac{\pi}{4} + x\right) - \sin\left(\frac{\pi}{4} - x\right)$.

   a) Simplify $f(x)$.

   b) Use the result in a) to solve the equation $f(x) = -1$, where $-2\pi \le x \le 2\pi$.

   c) Verify the solutions in b) graphically.

5. Solve the following equations for $0 \le x \le 2\pi$.

   a) $\cos 2x + \cos x = 0$ b) $\cos 2x = 1 - 2\sin x$ c) $\cos 2x - \sin x = 0$

6. Consider the equations **i)** $\sin 2\theta = \sqrt{3}\sin\theta$ and **ii)** $\cos\theta = \sqrt{3}\sin\theta$.

   a) In which of these equations is division by $\sin\theta$ a valid step?

6. b) Determine the solution to each equation in a) on the domain $0° \leq \theta \leq 360°$.

7. Consider the equation $\sin^2 x - \cos^2 x = 0$, $0 \leq x \leq 2\pi$.

   a) Solve the equation using a trigonometric identity.

   b) Solve the equation by dividing by $\cos^2 x$.

   c) Provide a third algebraic method which can be used to solve the equation.

8. Determine the roots of the following equations for $-180° \leq x \leq 180°$.

   a) $\sin 2x + \cos x = 0$

   b) $\sin 2x - \cos 2x = 0$

Use the following information to answer the next question.

Consider the equation $2\cos^2 x + \sin x = 1$, $0 \le x \le 2\pi$. Olive and Jacob both incorrectly determined that the equation had only one root. Their work is shown below.

Olive's Solution	Jacob's Solution
Line 1 $\quad 2cos^2x + sinx = 1$	Line 1 $\quad 2cos^2x + sinx = 1$
Line 2 $\quad 2(sin^2x - 1) + sinx = 1$	Line 2 $\quad 2(1 - sin^2x) + sinx = 1$
Line 3 $\quad 2sin^2x - 2 + sinx = 1$	Line 3 $\quad 2 - 2sin^2x + sinx = 1$
Line 4 $\quad 2sinx^2x + sinx - 3 = 0$	Line 4 $\quad 2 - 1 = 2sinx^2x - sinx$
Line 5 $\quad (2sinx + 3)(sinx - 1) = 0$	Line 5 $\quad 1 = sinx(2sinx - 1)$

	Olive		Jacob	
Line 6	$2sinx + 3 = 0$	$sinx - 1 = 0$	$sinx = 1$	$2sinx - 1 = 1$
Line 7	$sinx = -\dfrac{3}{2}$	$sinx = 1$	$sinx = 1$	$sinx = 1$
Line 8	$no\ solution$	$x = \dfrac{\pi}{2}$	$x = \dfrac{\pi}{2}$	$x = \dfrac{\pi}{2}$

Olive: Solution $x = \dfrac{\pi}{2}$ Jacob: Solution $x = \dfrac{\pi}{2}$

9. a) Olive made one error in her work which led to the incorrect answer. In which line did the error occur? Describe the error she made.

b) Jacob adopted the wrong method in trying to solve the problem, but in which line did he first write a statement which does not follow mathematically from the previous statement. Describe the mathematical error.

c) Algebraically determine the roots of the equation $2\cos^2 x + \sin x = 1$, $0 \le x \le 2\pi$.

10. The diagram shows the graphs of two trigonometric functions
$y = 2 \cos 2x$ and $y = \sin x - 1$ for $0 \le x \le 2\pi$.

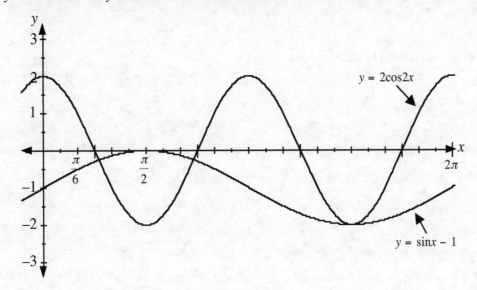

a) Describe how to use the graphs to solve the equation

$2 \cos 2x - \sin x + 1 = 0$, where $0 \le x \le 2\pi$.   Mark these points with **DOTS** on the grid.

b) Use a graphing calculator to determine the roots of the equation in a).
Use exact values where possible; otherwise round the answers to the nearest tenth.

c) Verify the roots in b) algebraically.

d) Describe how to use the graphs to solve the equation $2 \cos 2x (\sin x - 1) = 0$,
where $0 \le x \le 2\pi$. Mark these points with a **SQUARE** on the grid.

e) Use a graphing calculator to determine the exact roots of the equation in d).

f) Verify the roots in e) algebraically.

Answer Key

1. a) $30°, 90°, 150°$ **b)** $60°, 180°, 300°$ **2.** $\dfrac{3\pi}{4}, \dfrac{7\pi}{4}, 0.5, 3.7$ **3.** $x = \dfrac{\pi}{2} + n\pi$

4. a) $\sqrt{2}\sin x$ **b)** $-\dfrac{7\pi}{4}, -\dfrac{5\pi}{4}, \dfrac{5\pi}{4}, \dfrac{7\pi}{4}$

5. a) $x = \dfrac{\pi}{3}, \pi, \dfrac{5\pi}{3}$ **b)** $x = 0, \dfrac{\pi}{2}, \pi, 2\pi$ **c)** $x = \dfrac{\pi}{6}, \dfrac{5\pi}{6}, \dfrac{3\pi}{2}$

6. a) in ii)   **b) i)** $0°, 30°, 180°, 330°, 360°$ **ii)** $30°, 210°$

7. a), b) $\dfrac{\pi}{4}, \dfrac{3\pi}{4}, \dfrac{5\pi}{4}, \dfrac{7\pi}{4}$ **c)** Factor using a difference of squares, and solve each factor equal to zero.

8. a) $x = -150, -90°, -30°, 90°$ **b)** $-157.5°, -67.5°, 22.5°, 112.5°$

9. a) In Line 2, $\cos^2 x = 1 - \sin^2 x$, not $\sin^2 x - 1$.
   b) In Line 6. If the product of two quantities is equal to 1, it does not follow that each of the quantities has to equal 1.
   c) $\dfrac{\pi}{2}, \dfrac{7\pi}{6}, \dfrac{11\pi}{6}$

10. a) Find the x-coordinates of the points of intersection of the two graphs.
   b), c) $0.85, 2.29, \dfrac{3\pi}{2}$ **d)** Find the x-intercepts of each graph.   **e), f)** $\dfrac{\pi}{4}, \dfrac{\pi}{2}, \dfrac{3\pi}{4}, \dfrac{5\pi}{4}, \dfrac{7\pi}{4}$

Trigonometry - Equations and Identities Lesson #9:
Practice Test

Section A *No calculator may be used for this section of the test.*

1. The expression $\csc\left(\dfrac{\pi}{2} + x\right)$ is equivalent to

    A. $\sec x$

    B. $\csc x$

    C. $-\csc x$

    D. $-\sec x$

2. The partial graph of $y = 2\cos 2x - 1$, as represented on a graphing calculator screen, is shown.

The solution to the equation $2\cos 2x = 1$, $0 \le x \le 2\pi$, is

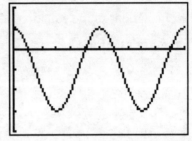

Window

$x: [0, 2\pi, \pi/6]$

$y: [-4, 2, 1]$

    A. $0,\ \pi,\ 2\pi$ **B.** $\dfrac{\pi}{6}, \dfrac{5\pi}{6}, \dfrac{7\pi}{6}, \dfrac{11\pi}{6}$ **C.** $\dfrac{\pi}{3}, \dfrac{2\pi}{3}, \dfrac{4\pi}{3}, \dfrac{5\pi}{3}$ **D.** $\dfrac{\pi}{2}, \dfrac{3\pi}{2}$

3. The expression $3\cos^2 8A - 3\sin^2 8A$ is equal to

    A. $\cos 64A$

    B. $3\cos 16A$

    C. $\cos 16A^3$

    D. $3\cos 4A$

4. Assuming the appropriate restrictions on the value of a, the expression $\dfrac{\tan a + \cot a}{\sec a}$ is equivalent to

    A. $\csc a$

    B. $\sec a$

    C. $\sin a$

    D. $\cos a$

Use the following information to answer the next question.

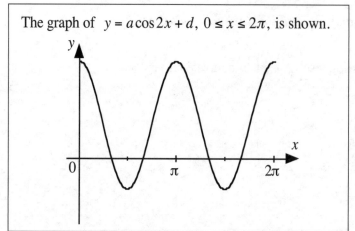

The graph of $y = a\cos 2x + d$, $0 \le x \le 2\pi$, is shown.

1. The number of solutions of the equation $a \cos x + d = 0$, $0 \le x \le 2\pi$, is _____.

(Record your answer in the numerical response box from left to right.)

5. The exact value of $\cos\dfrac{\pi}{12}$ is

A. $\dfrac{\sqrt{2} - \sqrt{3}}{2}$

B. $\dfrac{\sqrt{2} - \sqrt{6}}{4}$

C. $\dfrac{\sqrt{6} - \sqrt{2}}{4}$

D. $\dfrac{\sqrt{6} + \sqrt{2}}{4}$

Section B   *A graphing calculator may be used for the remainder of the test.*

6. $1 - (\sin A + \cos A)^2$ is equivalent to

A. $\sin 2A + 2\cos^2 A$

B. $\sin 2A$

C. $-\sin 2A$

D. 0

2. To the nearest degree, the smallest positive solution of
the equation $\sin 5x = 0.75$ is $x =$ _____ .

(Record your answer in the numerical response box from left to right.)

Use the following information to answer the next question.

The partial graph of $y = 6\sin^2 x$ and $y = 3 + 5\sin x$ intersect at points A and B.

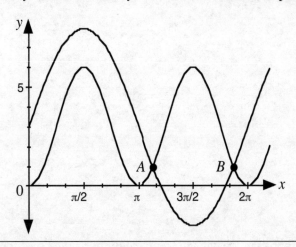

7. The x-coordinates of points A and B are solutions of

    A. $6\sin^2 x\,(3 + 5\sin x) = 0$ **B.** $6\sin^2 x + 5\sin x + 3 = 0$

    C. $6\sin^2 x - 5\sin x - 3 = 0$ **D.** $5\sin x + 3 = 0$

8. The smallest positive solution of $\tan kx = c$ is $x = \dfrac{\pi}{8}$.
The general solution of the equation $\tan kx = c$ is

    A. $x = \dfrac{\pi}{8} + 2nk\pi,\ n \in I$ **B.** $x = \dfrac{\pi}{8} + 2n\pi,\ n \in I$

    C. $x = \dfrac{\pi}{8} + \dfrac{2n\pi}{k},\ n \in I$ **D.** $x = \dfrac{\pi}{8} + \dfrac{n\pi}{k},\ n \in I$

9. With the appropriate restrictions on the value of θ, the expression $\dfrac{\csc 2\theta}{\sec 2\theta}$ can be simplified to

    A. $\sin 2\theta$

    B. $\cos 2\theta$

    C. $\tan 2\theta$

    D. $\cot 2\theta$

10. The complete solution to the equation $\sin x = \log x^2$, where x is in radian measure, is

    A. 2.32   **B.** −0.55, 2.32

    C. −0.52, 0.73   **D.** 0.73

11. If angle A is acute such that $\sin A = \dfrac{4}{5}$, then $\cos\left(\dfrac{\pi}{2} + A\right)$ is equal to

    A. $-\dfrac{4}{5}$

    B. $-\dfrac{3}{5}$

    C. $\dfrac{4}{5}$

    D. $\dfrac{3}{5}$

12. The equation $\sin x = \sin 2x$ has the same solutions as which of the following equations?

    A. $2\cos x - 1 = 0$

    B. $\sin x\,(2\cos x - 1) = 0$

    C. $\sin x = 0$

    D. $2\sin x\,(\cos x - 1) = 0$

13. If b is a positive integer greater than 1, then the number of solutions in the interval $0 \le x \le 2\pi$ to the equation $\sin bx = \dfrac{3}{4}$ is

    A. 2   B. $2b$

    C. b D. $\dfrac{1}{2}b$

14. If $\theta \ne n\pi, n \in I$, then $\cot\theta - \dfrac{\cos\theta + 1}{\sin\theta}$ is equal to

    A. $\csc\theta$

    B. $\sec\theta$

    C. $-\sec\theta$

    D. $-\csc\theta$

3. If $4\cos^2\theta - 11\cos\theta - 3 = 0,\ 0° < \theta < 180°$, then the measure of θ, to the nearest degree, is _____ .

(Record your answer in the numerical response box from left to right.)

15. If $\tan P = \dfrac{5}{12},\ 0 \le P \le \dfrac{\pi}{2}$, and $\tan Q = \dfrac{4}{3},\ \dfrac{\pi}{2} \le Q \le \dfrac{3\pi}{2}$, then the exact value of $\sin(P - Q)$ is

A. -33

B. $-\dfrac{33}{65}$

C. $\dfrac{33}{65}$

D. $-\dfrac{63}{65}$

 4. To the nearest tenth of a radian, the solution

to the equation $\cos\left(x - \dfrac{\pi}{4}\right) = 2x - 5$ is _____ .

(Record your answer in the numerical response box from left to right.)

16. The general solution to the equation $\sin 3x = 1,\ x \in R$ is $x =$

A. $\dfrac{\pi}{2} + 2n\pi,\ n \in I$ B. $\dfrac{\pi}{2} + \dfrac{2}{3}n\pi,\ n \in I$

C. $\dfrac{\pi}{6} + \dfrac{2}{3}n\pi,\ n \in I$ D. $\dfrac{\pi}{6} + 2n\pi,\ n \in I$

Use the following information to answer the next question.

In triangle ABC shown, the exact value of $\sin(a + b)$ can be written in the form $k\sqrt{5}$.

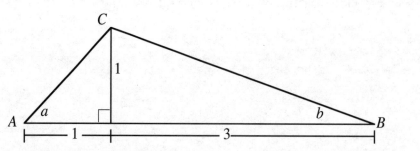

5. To the nearest tenth, the value of k is _____.

(Record your answer in the numerical response box from left to right.)

17. The expression $\dfrac{1 - \cos^2 A}{1 + \tan^2 A}$ is equivalent to

A. $\sin^2 A \cos^2 A$

B. $\sin^4 A$

C. $-\dfrac{\cos^4 A}{\sin^2 A}$

D. $\sin^2 A$

18. A student uses the angle $x = \dfrac{\pi}{6}$ to verify the identity $\dfrac{\sin^2 x}{\sec x + 1} = \dfrac{1 - \cos x}{\sec x}$.

Using $x = \dfrac{\pi}{6}$, the exact value of each side of the identity is

A. $\dfrac{1}{4}$

B. 1

C. $\dfrac{2\sqrt{3} - 3}{3}$

D. $\dfrac{2\sqrt{3} - 3}{4}$

19. The expression $\dfrac{\cos^2 x - \cos^4 x}{\sin^4 x}$, with $\sin x \neq 0$, simplifies to

    A. $\tan^2 x$

    B. $\cot^2 x$

    C. $\cos^2 x \sin^2 x$

    D. $-\cot^2 x \csc^2 x$

20. The expression $\dfrac{\sin A}{\cos A + \sin A \cot A}$ is equivalent to

    A. $2 \tan A$

    B. $\tan A + \cot A$

    C. $\tan A \ \sec A$

    D. $\dfrac{1}{2} \tan A$

 6. The smallest positive solution to the equation $\sec x - 5 = 0$, correct to the nearest tenth of a radian, is $x =$ _____.

(Record your answer in the numerical response box from left to right.)

Written Response

Use the following information to answer this question.

A student graphs the trigonometric function

$f(x) = \cos(2x) - 3\cos x - 1$ on a graphing

calculator, with window $x{:}[0, 2\pi, \pi]$ $y{:}[-4, 4, 1]$.

The graphing calculator screenshot is shown.

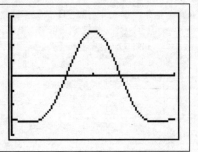

- How can the student use the calculator graph to determine the roots of the equation
  $0 = \cos(2x) - 3\cos x - 1$ in the domain $0 \leq x \leq 2\pi$?

- Use a calculator graph to determine the roots to the equation $0 = \cos(2x) - 3\cos x - 1$ correct to the nearest hundredth of a radian, in the domain $0 \le x \le 2\pi$.

- Use an addition identity to prove the identity $\cos(2x) = 2\cos^2 x - 1$.

- By using the identity in bullet 3, **algebraically** determine the roots of the equation $0 = \cos(2x) - 3\cos x - 1$ in the domain $0 \le x \le 2\pi$. Give the answer in radians as exact values in terms of π.

Answer Key

Multiple Choice

1. A	**2.** B	**3.** B	**4.** A	**5.** D	**6.** C	**7.** C	**8.** D
9. D	**10.** B	**11.** A	**12.** B	**13.** B	**14.** D	**15.** C	**16.** C
17. A	**18.** D	**19.** B	**20.** D				

Numerical Response

1. | 2 | | | |

2. | 1 | 0 | | |

3. | 1 | 0 | 4 | |

4. | 2 | . | 5 | |

5. | 0 | . | 4 | |

6. | 1 | . | 4 | |

Written Response

- The roots of the equation are the x-intercepts of the graph which are found using the zero feature of the calculator.
- 2.09, 4.19
- Use the identity for $\cos(x + x)$.
- $\dfrac{2\pi}{3}, \dfrac{4\pi}{3}$